295

Land,
Climate,
and Man

by
C. J. McCaffray
Nepean High School, Ottawa

C. J. Hunt
Glebe Collegiate Institute, Ottawa

HOLT, RINEHART AND WINSTON OF CANADA, LIMITED
TORONTO

ACKNOWLEDGEMENTS

The authors are indebted to many persons and organizations for constructive suggestions and illustrative material. The following were particularly helpful: Miss Joan Bostock, The Association of Agriculture, Great Britain; Mr. R. H. Faurschou—Prairie Grain Farm; Ernestine Friedl—Vasilika; Crown Zellerbach Canada Limited—Mr. Lyall A. Dagg; Dominion Coal and Steel Company; Mr. N. L. Nicholson, Director, Geographical Branch, Department of Mines and Technical Surveys; Marine Research Division, Department of Mines and Technical Surveys—Mr. F. Barber; National Air Photo Library, Department of Mines and Technical Surveys.

The Macmillan Company has kindly given permission to reproduce a stanza of "Cargoes" from Masefield's *Salt-Water Ballads and Poems*.

Mr. E. D. Baldock, Surveys and Mapping Branch, Department of Mines and Technical Surveys provided material for reproduction of the topographical maps.

Copyright, © 1963, by

HOLT, RINEHART AND WINSTON OF CANADA, LIMITED

Printed in Canada

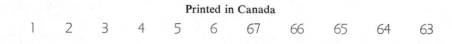

PREFACE

There are few courses in the high-school programme with such variety of topics as this course in the fundamentals of Geography. In one year the student will be introduced to simple map work, oceanography, meteorology, physical geography, and a variety of other subjects in which many students are already keenly interested. Here lies both the attraction and the challenge in the course. Throughout this work we have attempted to make use of the most recent findings in each field. Every effort has been made to relate each of these diverse fields to the others and all of them to man. In maintaining the unity, which is so important at this stage, the teacher should help the student see each field as one integrated part of a vaster reality.

Topographical maps play a prominent part in the early section of the text, but it is hoped that reference will be made back to these maps when the students are examining physical geography and when they are studying the chapters on economic and settlement patterns. The inclusion of the maps at the beginning is designed to facilitate the student's learning at the very outset, the basic language of maps. When he can **read** a map, can **visualize** the scene, and can **describe** it from the map, then it is time for him to begin to analyze the ways in which the land acquired its present form. The difficulties many students experience with topographical maps have led us to concentrate first on description and only later to proceed to analysis and explanation.

Maps and photographs form an essential part of the text and, in many cases, are accompanied by questions useful for launching a fruitful discussion. While each unit is followed by exercises, it should be clear that these are not designed as a substitute for the spontaneous and challenging questions and assignments that teachers will wish to set their classes.

A good globe is essential equipment for the early part of this course. Throughout the year, too, every student should have a good world atlas because it is an indispensable reference work on a course such as this. In addition, it is expected that the teacher will often guide the students to use the school or classroom library in pursuing a fuller knowledge on the many subjects forming part of this course.

CONTENTS

LOOKING AT THE ATLAS

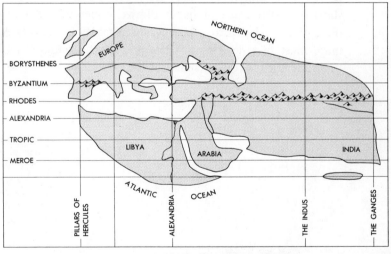

This is a simplification of Erastothenes' map. Here we see the first parallels and meridians —in this case unevenly spaced and named after places. The river on the far east of the map is the Ganges. Name the river in Europe, the one in Africa, and the two in Arabia.

THE BEGINNINGS OF LATITUDE AND LONGITUDE

A good atlas is both a summary of many of man's greatest achievements and a challenge to further endeavours. When we look at an atlas we are observing the work of generations of great men—work that we now take for granted. Erastothenes, in the second century before Christ, must rank as the earliest scientific geographer. He it was who calculated the circumference of the earth to a degree

1

of accuracy which remained unchallenged till quite recent times. Another of his claims to the title, the *Father of Geography*, is that he was the first to superimpose a grid of intersecting lines upon a map. Hipparchus, a scholar working in Alexandria more than 100 years before Christ, took this idea of a grid a step further and developed a regular mathematical series of lines based on his division of a circle into 360 degrees. These mathematical lines—called the *meridians* of longitude and the *parallels* of latitude—make it possible to establish accurately the exact position of any place on the face of the globe. The meridians divide the earth by a series of lines from pole to pole and are measured in degrees from a base line drawn through Greenwich, a famous observatory near London (England). This line is the line of 0° and is called the *prime meridian*. The equator is the base line for the parallels of latitude and these lines are graduated into 90° to the north and to the south respectively.

Open your atlas at any map and you will find the lines of latitude and longitude marked quite clearly. These lines form the background against which every map is drawn. However, you may find that some maps show longitude by straight lines whereas others use curved lines; yet there is only one globe. You may have noticed, too, that the shape of North America, for example, may differ on subsequent pages of the same atlas. How can this be when the maps all presume to represent accurately the same globe? The answer is that the atlas maps do not, and cannot, represent the world accurately because they are attempting to show on a flat piece of paper of two dimensions a real object which has three dimensions. The cartographer (a map maker) who sits down to prepare an atlas map, must first determine what qualities he requires in his map. The chief of these qualities is correct shape of the continents and correct areas.

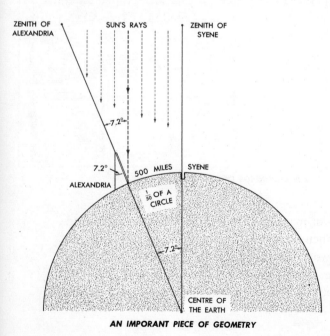

AN IMPORANT PIECE OF GEOMETRY

Erastothenes found that the sun shone directly down a deep well at Syene (near Aswan) on June 21. The sun was, therefore, directly overhead. He had a post set up at Alexandria at noon on the same day and its angle with the sun's rays was 7.2°. This angle, he showed, was equal to the angle at the centre of the earth between Alexandria and Syene. This angle is 1/50 of a circle; and the distance between Alexandria and Syene was 500 miles. Erastothenes determined the circumference of the earth as between 24,000 and 28,000 miles. It is actually 24,860.

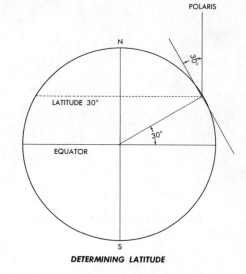

The latitude of any place can be established by taking the angle between Polaris and the horizon. This angle is the same as that at the centre of the earth produced from the same point and the equator. Sextant readings of the sun make similar calculations possible during the day.

DETERMINING LATITUDE

The sailor or airman who is constantly travelling great distances on the surface of the earth, is interested in more than just lines of latitude and longitude when he plots a course. He is interested in finding the shortest route for his journey and the lines which give these short routes are called *great circles*. To understand the significance of great circles you should use a globe and an atlas. If you use an ordinary atlas world map and draw a straight line from the southern tip of Florida through Europe to Formosa, you will notice that this is almost a line of latitude. Now take a piece of string and place one end on southern Florida and, keeping the string pulled taut, the other end on Formosa. You will find that the shortest route between these two places is not the straight line you drew on the map, but is a great circle across the polar regions.

Meridians of longitude are shown here at intervals of 15°. Paired meridians are all of equal length as they form great circles.

Parallels of latitude are shown here at intervals of 15°. Note that each parallel forms a complete circle around the earth, but that the parallels are of differing lengths.

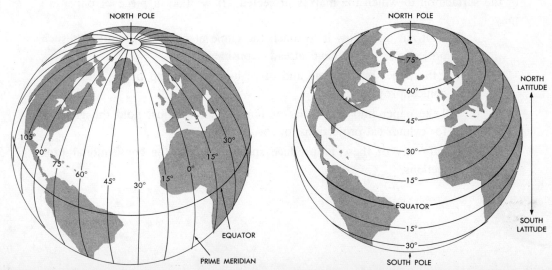

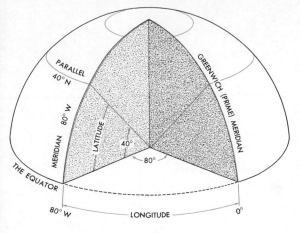

Latitude is expressed as the angle at the centre of the earth between any point and the equator. Longitude is the angle between any point and the prime meridian. Latitude is described as north or south; longitude as east or west. Why can we only have 90° N or S in latitude and 180° E or W in longitude?

THE MEANING OF LATITUDE AND LONGITUDE

Projections

Hipparchus realized that some distortion or cutting would be necessary in order to map the land regions of the earth on a flat surface. If the point of projection is the end of the globe opposite the paper, we have a *stereographic* projection which is generally quite accurate near the centre but which becomes distorted near the edge of the map. If the centre of projection is imagined to be infinity (that is, if the projection lines are parallel), the resulting projection is *orthographic*. In the case of a polar orthographic projection, or one which has a pole at its centre, the equatorial latitudes are compressed beyond recognition. A third type of projection can be drawn with the centre of the earth as a starting point. Again, this *gnomonic* projection is accurate only at the centre. Each of these projections is described as a polar zenithal projection if the paper is thought of as touching the globe at a pole and as an oblique zenithal projection if it touches the globe at any other point except the equator, where we have an equatorial zenithal.

Of these projections the *zenithal gnomonic* is probably the most widely used owing to the fact that great circles appear as straight lines on this map. Aerial navigation is greatly simplified by the use of maps of this type.

A further basis for the classification of projections is the position and shape of the surface on to which the map is projected. If we take a piece of paper we may

> keep it flat and allow it to touch the globe at only one point—for such projections as we have already considered,
>
> roll the paper into a cone and place it over one end of the globe—for conical projections,
>
> roll the paper into a cylinder or tube which will just hold the globe— for cylindrical projections, or
>
> modify any of these to produce special effects—for conventional projections.

4

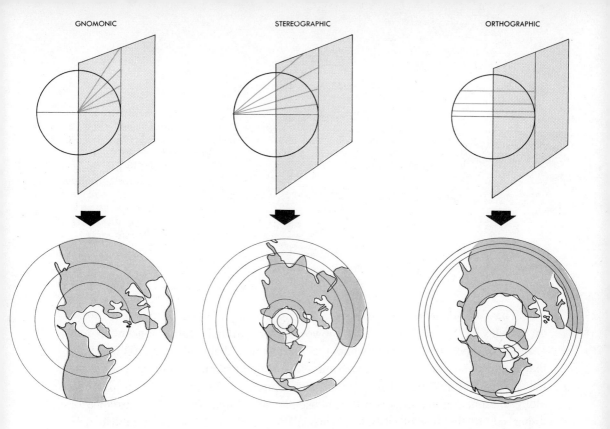

GNOMONIC STEREOGRAPHIC ORTHOGRAPHIC

Three polar projections are shown here. From the diagram work out the major handicap of each method; then find evidence of this on the map.

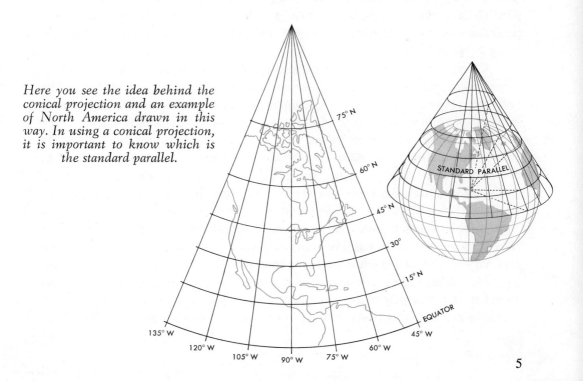

Here you see the idea behind the conical projection and an example of North America drawn in this way. In using a conical projection, it is important to know which is the standard parallel.

75° N
60° N
45° N
30°
15° N
EQUATOR

135° W
120° W
105° W
90° W
75° W
60° W
45° W

STANDARD PARALLEL

5

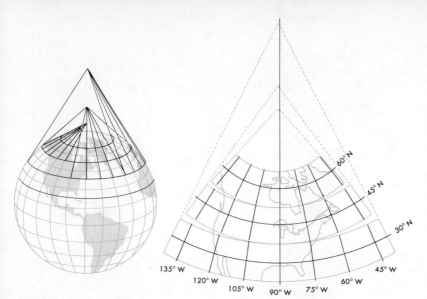

The *conical projections* are used extensively in atlas maps of small areas; on a map of a very large area, however, the parallels form concentric arcs around the apex of the cone while the meridians radiate as straight lines from that apical point. A cone will touch the globe only at points along one continuous line and, therefore, conical projections are accurate in distance and bearings only along this line. However, distortion is usually quite slight for a short distance on either side of this line of latitude. Scale in the meridians is usually established by selecting a central meridian and mapping it in true proportions. To obtain greater accuracy a mathematical equation is often used to produce a simple conic map with two standard parallels, that is, two parallels which are accurate. This map is particularly useful in areas which have a wide range from east to west. Many government maps of Canada are drawn on such a map, the selected parallels being 49° N and 77° N.

A further modification of the conic projection is based on the idea of several cones being placed over the globe and the resulting maps combined. This *polyconic* projection is rather more complicated and has the disadvantage that it splits, or interrupts, the map in several places. However, it does result in a high degree of accuracy in a selected area.

In the case of the *cylindrical projections*, the globe is pictured as wrapped in a cylinder which usually touches the globe at the equator, although it can be arranged to touch on the sphere elsewhere. Projections of this type are conspicuous for the fact that all meridians and parallels are straight lines intersecting at right angles. This makes it much easier to tell compass directions than it is with a conical projection, and, more important, it means that a navigator can obtain the necessary bearing of his destination and then plot his course as a straight line on the map. Sailing a great circle route demands a constant changing of the compass direction and this procedure can become involved, whereas following a fixed bearing is much simpler. Such a straight-line route is known as a *rhumb line*.

Although directions are true on a cylindrical projection, actual accuracy of shape and arc is found only in a 40- to 60-degree belt along the equator. Distortion becomes considerable in polar latitudes. The most famous of these projections is one which is probably still the most widely used in world maps, although it was the work of a great sixteenth-century geographer. Mercator prepared a projection in which he uniformly spaced the lines more widely apart as they progressed from the equator. This procedure preserved the proportion between the degrees of latitude and longitude and also maintained rhumb lines as straight lines. This famous map has probably resulted in more misconceptions than any other owing to its polar exaggeration, but it was for long a very valuable aid to navigators.

The sun dial is a practical device based on simple earth-sun relationships. How does it tell time? How would you construct one for use in your own area?

To understand the cylindrical projection, picture a cylinder encircling the globe on which the features of the globe are projected.

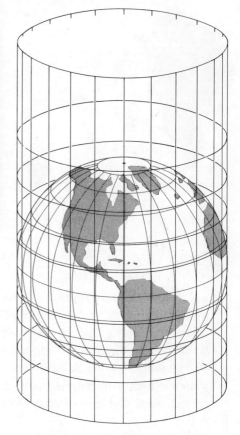

In your atlas you will probably find several projections which, instead of using the word conical or cylindrical, are identified by a man's name. These are the *conventional projections* drawn for a special purpose and according to a special formula. One projection which corrects the defects of Mercator's and shows the landmasses of the world in more or less true proportions is Mollweide's. This is an elliptical projection in which only the central meridian is a straight line; all the others are curves and those of 90° E and 90° W form perfect circles. The parallels are correctly spaced straight lines. Distortion occurs on this map at both ends of the equatorial line. Another projection aimed primarily at representing correct area or size is the very distinctive *Sanson-Flamsteed*, in which the length of the central meridian is half that of the equator. At points farther away from the equator and the central meridian, shapes are distorted in this projection; it is, therefore, widely used only for Africa and South America. For North America those who want a map showing true areas usually employ Bonn's, which is a modified conical projection in which both parallels and meridians are represented by curves.

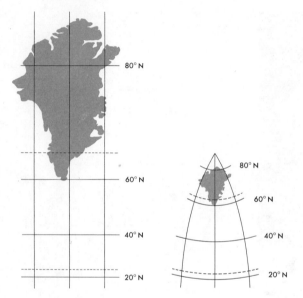

On the far left you see an example of the distortion in northern latitudes which occurs in Mercator's projection.

The word *interrupted* is used to describe a large group of projections in which the map is broken at several points around the edges in an effort to give greater accuracy. One of the most interesting interrupted projections is *Goode's homolosine* projection, which resembles the Mollweide's between the poles and 40° latitude, and the Sanson-Flamsteed between 40° and the equator. The projection, which is interrupted in each of the great oceans, gives a good idea of the correct shape and area of each of the major landmasses.

Time Zones and the Date Line

The world traveller is constantly reminded of his changing longitude by the fact that he will often have to move the hands of his watch forward or back, and may even have to change his calendar and diary. These changes are the results of a number of variable factors: the position of the earth relative to the sun, the inclination of the earth's axis, the side of the earth facing the sun, etc.

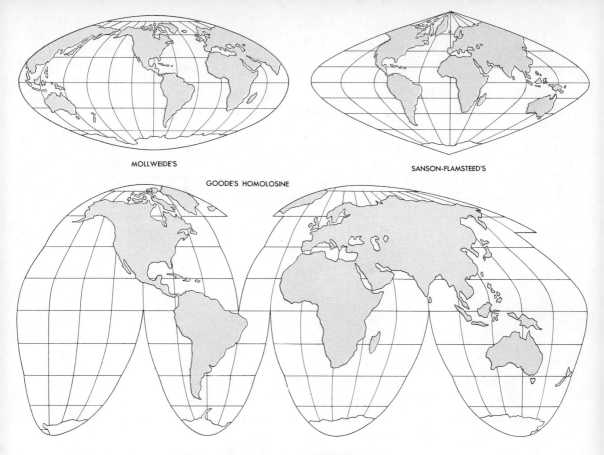

MOLLWEIDE'S

SANSON-FLAMSTEED'S

GOODE'S HOMOLOSINE

THREE COMMON CONVENTIONAL PROJECTIONS

Mollweide's projection is called a "homolographic" because it is an "equal-area" projection. Sanson-Flamsteed's is basically similar, but a special "sine curve" is used, the result of which is a "sinusoidal" projection. Goode's combination of both is a "homolosine" projection.

Centuries ago man began to divide time into twenty-four hours per day; certain groups of these hours were given special names, such as morning and evening. Noon was selected as the time when the sun was almost directly overhead and in most countries time was calculated from noon. Of course, the sun could not be overhead everywhere at the same time and so thousands of places were working on completely different time calculations. No great problem existed while man remained fairly stationary in one locality or only moved seldom and slowly; but as travel became easier, faster, and more common, discrepancies and problems developed. Accordingly, in 1883 the numerous railroads of the United States established four time zones and agreed that within each zone time should be uniform—the same as that of the chief city in the zone. In each case the time became known as the *standard time* of the zone. Sir Sandford Fleming, a Canadian, was one of the leaders at the International Prime Meridian Conference in Washington in 1884. This conference set up the time zones which are still used throughout the world.

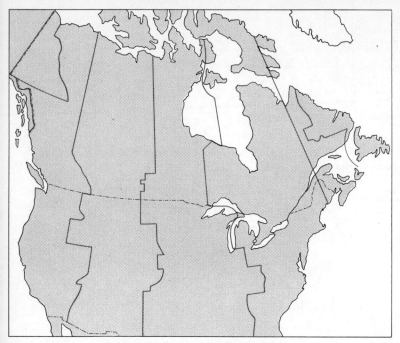

Draw this map in your notebook including the correct name with each time zone. Then add what would be the time in each zone when it is noon in New York.

THE TIME ZONES OF NORTH AMERICA

In summer many areas gain an extra hour of daylight by the expedient of setting clocks one hour ahead of standard time. This is known as daylight-saving time and it means that you are actually getting up an hour earlier when this scheme is in operation.

Whenever you cross from one time zone to another, it is necessary that you alter your watch if you wish to avoid considerable inconvenience. In these days of rapid travel, however, this practice can produce a very curious situation. It is possible for a jet aircraft to leave Vancouver at dawn and travel west at a speed equal to that of the earth's rotation at a particular latitude. In such a case a passenger who continued round the world on this flight would be repeatedly putting his watch back one hour until he arrived again at Vancouver—on the same day and at the same time as he left. Unfortunately, this procedure would be of no advantage, as the people who remained in Vancouver would now be on the following day. What glorious confusion could result from this!

To avert confusion and yet at the same time standardize the solution, the countries of the world have established an International Date Line, which more or less corresponds to the 180° Meridian in the Pacific. People crossing this imaginary line from east to west immediately advance their calendar by one day without altering their watches; they go instantly from one o'clock Monday, for example, to one o'clock Tuesday. A simple reminder of this is, "If you travel to the west, a day goes west." Conversely, a person travelling eastwards across the Pacific will repeat or gain one day.

Care has been taken in determining this line to ensure that it does not cut through any settled communities. For this reason it does not follow the meridian exactly but veers off at certain places to by-pass various island groups.

10

PART ONE

LANDFORMS AND TOPOGRAPHICAL SHEETS

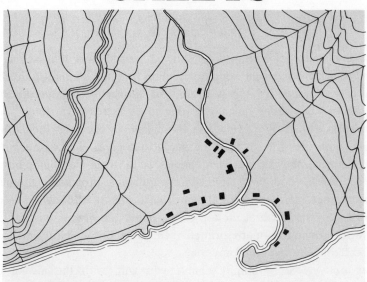

Smoky River and Rocky Mtns.
Guelph
Yamaska Mountain
Vancouver
St. Catharines-Niagara Escarpment
Moose Jaw
Summerside
Gabarouse Bay-Cape Breton Coast

MAPS

There are maps of many different types. These include the map of the school buildings and adjacent streets, as well as many others, from maps such as one uses in junior grades to the road maps published by the oil companies, and from the world maps found in any atlas to the detailed topographical maps which appear in this book. There are almost as many kinds of maps as there are languages in the world. Just as each language is a means of communicating its own rich literature, so each map uses its own symbols to communicate a varying wealth of information. The motorist, the sailor, the airman, the geologist, the farmer, the soldier, the historian, the archaeologist, all use maps in their work. Consequently, skill in the reading of maps can enable one to steal a glimpse at the treasures of many diverse fields of knowledge.

The Road Map

The first purpose of a map is to show a person how to reach a particular destination. This is what most people use maps for, the service-station road map being especially designed for this purpose. To help us reach our destination, the map must show us two things: what direction to go and how far to go.

Direction is shown by a symbol in the legend of the map indicating the line of north and south; direction is then measured in degrees clockwise from that line. Crossing the north-south line at right angles is the east-west line; but for more precise directions beyond these four, one requires a protractor to measure the angle of divergence from either of the two basic lines. Although it is customary to print maps with the north at the top of the map, it is always wise to check this, especially when consulting maps printed in a guide book. North will usually be clearly indicated in the legend of any map.

During this year's geography course you will, with the aid of official or home-drawn maps, probably undertake some field trips in your local areas. When using a map and a compass on such an outing, bear in mind that the north indicated by the compass and that indicated by the map may not be the same. Magnetic declination is stated on any good topographical map. This is a measurement in degrees, which enables you to make the necessary adjustments to compass readings. The reason for the divergence lies in the fact that the magnetic north to which a compass needle points is not quite the same as the true north indicative of the position of the North Pole. The difference in location between the two norths results in a difference in their direction from any other place on earth.

Road maps can also provide many useful examples of *scale*—the means by which the cartographer produces an accurate and valuable representation of any part of the earth's surface. You have all seen, or perhaps constructed, model airplanes, ships, or automobiles. That they should be precisely like the original, but smaller, is the ideal all model makers aim at in their work. Such accurate models are no mere toys, but serve a useful purpose in the designing and planning of the full-scale machine. Changing the scale to make a useful model is precisely the same technique as the one used in mapping. In your atlas you will find a wide variety of scales. Usually being drawn in small scales, atlas maps do not permit the inclusion of great detail. As road maps require greater detail, they are described as large-scale maps.

The Topographical Map

The standard road map is an excellent instrument for planning an automobile journey as it provides the essential information—direction and distance. Very often, however, you may want to know the location of hills and valleys, buildings and open spaces, and other features of the landscape. The map used to give us a detailed picture of an area is called a topographical map, of which there are several examples in this text.

The topographical maps produced by the Canadian Department of Mines and Technical Surveys and by the U.S. Geological Survey are excellent examples of the finest mapping of the present day. As soon as you look at one of these topographical maps, you will notice a wide border around the map with a great amount of apparently extra information. It is essential that some of this material be examined before studying the map itself.

Underneath the name of the area mapped there is the scale expressed in four or five different ways. One of these tells how many inches on the map will represent one mile on the ground. Maps used to be known by this scale, and we, therefore, spoke of the one-inch or four-miles-to-the-inch maps. Close to this miles-to-the-inch scale there are two or three other linear scales; often one is divided into metres and another into yards. These linear scales are of particular value when using dividers to obtain an exact measurement. Finally, there is a scale expressed in a form such as 1:50,000 (one to fifty thousand). This is known as the representative fraction and could be written 1/50,000; obviously, it means that one unit on the map represents 50,000 of these same units on the ground. Thus the old scale of one inch to one mile could be written 1:63,360, since there are 63,360 inches to the mile.

The last-mentioned type of scale is being more and more widely used, and maps are now known by it instead of by the older scale in inches. One great advantage of the use of a fraction scale is that it can be used easily by people who are not familiar with our standards of miles and inches. Thus we look at 1:50,000 and realize that this is 1¼ inches to a mile; a person used to the metric system would see this as one centimetre equalling .5 kilometres. Examine some of the maps in your atlas to see which types of scale are used there.

13

Around the frame of the map, too, you will notice these:

> the contour interval in feet
>
> the magnetic declination
>
> an index to adjoining sheets
>
> the date of the survey on which the map is based
>
> a detailed key explaining all the symbols used on the sheet
>
> the latitude and longitude of the area shown.

Describing a Setting

In the following pages there are several maps of different areas in Canada by means of which you will be able to develop some skill in map reading. It is hoped that this skill will reach the point where you will be able to visualize and describe an area entirely from the map. To this end, it is useful to know the accepted terminology used by geographers to describe landscapes and to understand the natural processes which contribute to their formation. In the following chapters we shall examine the maps and pick out their characteristic features. Later, we shall consider the physical explanation of each of these features.

Many students find map work more interesting and more enjoyable when they buy a detailed 1:50,000 map of their own area. They can then compare what they see around them with what the map reveals. Should you try this you will be surprised at how much the map has to tell you—regardless of how well you already know your district. These maps are obtainable for 25c. each from the Department of Mines and Technical Surveys, Ottawa.

REFERENCE

Roads:
hard surface, heavy duty — 3 or more lanes, part.completed

hard surface, heavy duty — 2 lanes, Route No. 12

hard surface, medium duty — 3 or more lanes, 2 lanes

loose surface, graded and drained — 3 or more lanes, not less than 14 ft. wide

Other Roads — poor condition

Private Road

Trail

Railway: double track — station

single track — stop, siding

abandoned

narrow gauge or electric

Bridge, underpass or overpass

Boundaries: international

provincial

country

reservation, Indian, military, nat. or prov. parks, etc.

Electric Power Line — on steel towers, on wood poles

Telephone, trunk route

Triangulation Station — △

Boundary or Survey Monument — ⊙

Bench Mark — ▲ BM 679.1

14 Spot Elevation (in feet) — .548

House, Barn — ▪ ▪

Buildings — ▪ ▪

Mill or Factory, small Saw Mill, etc. — ♦ SM

School — ▪ S

Church — +

Church with conspicuous Tower or Spire — ♱

Post Office — P

Telephone Exchange — T

Mine or Open Cut — ⚒

Cemetery or Churchyard — C Cⁱ

Quarry

Sand or Gravel Pit

Cliff

Cutting

Embankment, Dump, etc.

Lighthouse — ☀

Wharf or Pier

Foreshore Flats — Sand Mud

Swamp or Marsh

Lake or Slough, nonpermanent

Glacier or Snowfield — or

Stream, intermittent

Contours, elevation — 200 175

Contours, depression — 200 175

Wooded Areas, heavy

Wooded Areas, light

A map—even a simple road map—is a treasure chest of information to those who know how to use it. This map shows the confluence of the Ottawa and St. Lawrence rivers.

1. Find on this map the following features: an airfield, a ferry, a tollbridge, a religious centre, a historical site, three types of boundary (county, provincial, international).

2. Plot two routes from Hawkesbury to Fort Covington and work out the length of each.

3. Describe by means of direction and distance (e.g. Go five miles north along highway 27, then turn east for a further two miles, etc.) a road journey from Cornwall to Lachute.

It must be emphasized, however, that there is always a little more you can learn from a good topographical map; you will never exhaust the map's power to tell a story. In the later chapters, when you are studying landforms and their formations, come back to these maps and try to apply your new knowledge to the map you already know. Thus you might well follow the chapter on glaciation by a half hour examining the Smoky River sheet. Likewise, when you are studying transportation and settlement, towards the end of the year, you should refer again to these maps and apply the principles you have just learned.

Contours and Relief

Perhaps the most numerous lines on a topographical map are the many brown lines called *contour lines*. These lines, which join places with an equal elevation above sea level, are the most widely used representations of relief. In examining contours the terms *vertical interval* and *horizontal equivalent* are used. Vertical interval means the difference in altitude between any two contours; this difference can be calculated by deducting the elevation of the lower contour from that of the upper one. The horizontal equivalent is the horizontal distance between any two contours—a distance which it may not be possible to measure on the ground but which can be measured easily on the map.

Relief can also be shown on a topographical map by means of hachuring, hillshading, and colouring. *Hachuring* is often seen on old atlas maps. Hachures are lines drawn on a map in the direction in which water would flow on that area. More of these lines are drawn on steep slopes than on more gradual inclines with the result that hachures look like a model of the area represented. In spite of this advantage of hachures, they are not employed on Canadian maps because they do not give the actual elevation of land, they obscure other details on the map, and they do not indicate any real difference between high, flat uplands and level, low-lying plains.

A different principle is used in the technique known as *hillshading* in which the cartographer imagines that a light is shining over the area. He then uses dots to give the impression of light and shade to achieve the same effect as in hachuring. In addition to all the defects of hachures, hillshading has the drawback that it does not indicate whether an area slopes uphill or downhill.

In some topographical maps colour is used together with contours to depict relief. Many Canadian maps use green shading to represent forest cover; this has the disadvantage that it prohibits the use of colour for relief. Colouring, however, is used extensively on atlas maps to indicate different elevations. The precise elevation of selected points is shown on every topographical map by detailed spot heights which are usually high points on mountains or hills.

Slope and Gradient

Besides being classified according to their steepness, slopes are also described in terms of their shape; in this context we speak of an even, concave, or convex slope. When you walk or drive up a hill which has a convex slope, you find that the hill is not very steep near the top—this is shown by closely packed lower contours and then a wider spacing at higher elevations. In the case of the concave slope the incline becomes steeper towards the top of the hill.

When you take a long journey on a train, you may sometimes notice little signposts indicating the gradient of the track. There are several occasions when it is of value to know the gradient of a particular slope, especially as it affects drainage, water supply, etc. Some very simple mathematical calculations are needed in measuring a gradient. The following example should be studied closely.

Drawing a Profile

The ultimate skill in map reading is to be able to study a good map and, by doing so, to build up an accurate mental picture of an area. This skill comes only from long practice and from having done many exercises aimed at acquiring a close familiarity with the shapes that contours may take and the types of terrain these shapes represent. The simplest step towards visualizing a scene is the drawing of profiles from contours—a simple mechanical process which can become very easy with a little practice. The procedure is as follows:

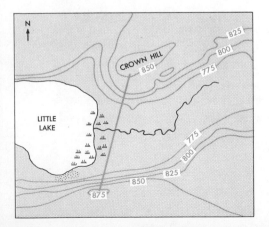

Follow each of the steps outlined on the opposite page to draw a profile along the line from Crown Hill.

On your map draw a line across the area whose profile is to be drawn; then, having examined the scale, draw a line of the same length on the sheet of paper you are using for the profile. Next find the vertical interval between the highest and lowest points along your section—in this case 125 feet. Using a vertical scale of 1/10 inch to every 25 feet draw another six lines parallel to the one you have already drawn on your sheet and number these: in this case from 750 feet up to 875 feet. Now place the top edge of your sheet along the line drawn on the map and drop a perpendicular from each contour to the appropriate line. When you join these points with a flowing line (do not use a ruler) you will have a profile or side-view of the area shown on your map.

One problem in drawing sections or profiles is connected with the fact that you will normally be using a different scale for the vertical interval from that for the horizontal equivalent. In the example used here the horizontal scale is 1:50,000. Express the vertical scale of 1/10 inch to 25 feet as a similar fraction and you will find that it is quite different. It is customary in profiles to state that the vertical scale is six times, eight times, or whatever the figure is, greater than the horizontal. This is known as the *vertical exaggeration*.

Intervisibility

There are several ways of following a predetermined route across country when you have no compass but do have a map. One of the most interesting methods is to plan your walk on the basis of selected landmarks which you will follow in much the same way as ships use lighthouses and lightships as an aid in setting a course. To use this technique it is essential that you be able to determine the visibility of one point from another, and here again a study of contours can often provide the answer.

The following tests can be applied in determining the intervisibility of two points. On a hill with a concave slope the top and bottom of the slope will normally be intervisible. When there is a convex slope, however, we find that the top of the hill cannot be seen from the bottom and vice versa. If between the two points, there is land higher than either of them, they are not intervisible.

The final test of visibility consists in the drawing of a generalized, but accurate, profile along the line adjoining the two points. It should be borne in mind, however, that even the detailed topographical map does not indicate the height of trees or buildings and that when all other calculations have been made, we may still have to make allowance for the obstruction of a view by trees, buildings, or other objects not shown in detail on the map.

SMOKY RIVER AND ROCKY MOUNTAINS

This famous vacation land on the Alberta-B.C. border is clearly an area of many high mountains and deep, forested valleys. You will immediately notice the many glaciers shown by the distinctive blue lines. In places you will notice a glacier with a tributary glacier, but more often icefields flow out in several directions in the form of such valley glaciers as the Coleman and Steppe glaciers. Many tiny, roughly circular, glaciers can be seen high on the slopes of mountains and ridges; these are cirque glaciers. All of these glaciers are particularly significant in that they are mere relics of the great ice sheets that once covered practically the whole of this part of Canada. Of even greater importance is the fact that these glaciers carved, scraped, and built this land into its present shape.

The small area shown here includes a number (how many?) of mountains over 10,000 feet high. Many of these are pointed and steep-sided with almost pyramidal peaks, which, because of their resemblance to a mountain in the Alps, are called *matterhorn peaks*. Using their names as clues, pick out four of these sharp-topped mountains. Often in glaciated uplands two high mountains will be connected by a narrow ridge that has precipitous slopes on either side. When covered with snow, these ridges or arêtes can be extremely dangerous to mountaineers. The closely packed contours between Lynx Mountain and Resplendent Mountain and joining Snake Indian Mountain and Monte Cristo Mountain indicate that these are joined by an arête.

At times the narrow central part of an arête will crumble under the attacks of erosion and a narrow pass will develop. Such a pass is known as a *col*, and among the many on this map you will notice a very clear one at Upright Pass on the provincial border and another at Colonel Pass south of the mountain of that name.

Locate Tatei Ridge, Berg Lake, Robson Glacier. Find on the photograph examples of matterhorn peaks and the other features described on this page.

R.C.A.F.

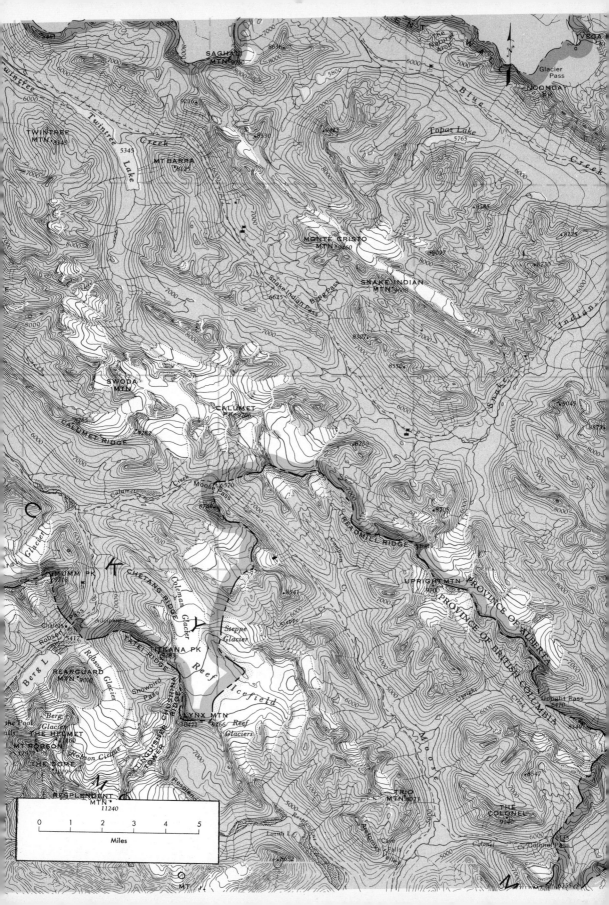

Perhaps the most remarkable feature of this or any similar glaciated mountain area is a bowl-shaped depression high on the mountainside and closely connected with peaks, arêtes, and cols. The steep sides of this depression are indicated by contours that are crescent or even circular in shape and are widely spaced in the centre to indicate the relative flatness of the bottom of the depression. Such depressions are called *cirques*. Several of these cirques are to be seen in the mountain block between Blue Creek and Snake Indian River, and in many other places on this map. Near the 9,045-foot peak east of the Snake Indian River there is a similar depression that spills over suddenly into the valley below. Here and in several other places lakes, called *tarns*, occupy these depressions.

On a journey up the Moose River or the Snake Indian you would be impressed by the fact that the slopes on either side of the valley are steepest higher up towards the rim of the mountains. Cross-sections or profiles drawn across such valleys are described as U-shaped; each of these forms a trough. You should draw several of these sections. Falls are numerous on these rivers; particularly impressive are the falls on the stream flowing south from Berg Lake. Where the velocity of mountain streams has been greatly reduced on the flat valley floor, sand and gravel deltas have formed and streams such as the Smoky River have *braided* channels at many points.

The story of this map is not complete when we have observed and described the physical features of the natural landscape. Magnificent dark green forests cover most of the valley floors and extend far up the mountain sides. On the upper slopes are hundreds of tiny rivulets, many of which dry up and leave empty channels during the summer months. Inaccessibility is shown by the absence of roads and railways; consequently, there is no human settlement here, although the busy tourist centre of Jasper is within 3 miles of the southern edge of this region. Tourists who do penetrate to this area and follow its winding trails will be well rewarded by the breath-taking views from these proud, high mountains.

Map Exercises

1. Express the scale shown on this map (a) as a fraction, and (b) in miles to the inch.

2. In which direction is the Mural Glacier flowing?

3. Which has the steeper gradient, Blue Creek or Moose River?

4. What is the difference in miles between the route from Emperor Falls near Berg Lake to Colonel Pass (a) by air, and (b) by trail?

5. Find at least two examples other than those quoted of (a) a cirque, (b) an arête, (c) a col, (d) a tarn.

6. Calumet Peak is 53°15′ North and 119° West. Find the exact location of this area on an atlas map of Canada. How far is it from your town or district?

GUELPH

Guelph is a town in southern Ontario—a region where there were once many glaciers and where these glaciers dumped great masses of sand, gravel, clay, rock, and other debris. Geographically, we term it a region of *glacial deposition*.

The contours on this map seem to present a very confused picture, but they do at least show us that this is a very hilly area. More detailed examination will reveal a large number of almost cigar-shaped hills running in a northwest-to-southeast direction and reaching elevations of 1,100 to 1,200 feet. In most cases these hills stand only fifty to a hundred feet above the surrounding land. Such cigar-shaped glacial hills are known as *drumlins*. Another curious feature is the long, narrow, winding ridge near Fox Farm to the northeast of Guelph. Such a ridge is known as an *esker*. The origin of both eskers and drumlins is explained elsewhere in this text.

If you draw a profile across the Eramosa River in the vicinity of Eden Mills, you will notice that this river flows in a fairly wide, steep-sided valley. Its width and steep sides indicate that this valley was probably carved by a much larger river than the present Eramosa. Rivers which now flow in the valleys of much larger ancestors are called *misfit streams*. When enormous glaciers melt they release great quantities of water, which then form large, fast-flowing rivers. These rivers often carve deep depressions in the surface of the land—depressions which later rivers may or may not follow. Such depressions are called *spillways*; on this map the Eramosa River is following such a spillway.

Forest vegetation is quite widespread in this area near Guelph. You will notice that in many places the forests remain standing on the low-lying land and in the river valleys, but that the higher land has been cleared of trees or else is only lightly wooded. Several patches of marshland appear on the map. Marshes can occur in monotonously flat country, but such is not the case here. Instead, we can account for these marshes by pointing out the numerous drumlins and explaining that the mounds have interfered with the normal flow of water.

The pattern of settlement shown here should be carefully compared with that in the Yamaska region. This is an area where farms are scattered widely, many of them even standing at some distance from the road. Here we see a farming district of *dispersed* settlement. Most of the farmsteads stand on slightly elevated ground above the threat of flooding. Apart from the dispersed farm units, there are also other population centres of different sizes and types. Guelph is a city only a part of which appears on the map. As the meeting place of highways 6, 7, and 24, and also of two railways, it is clearly of more than purely local importance. The Agricultural College (which stands on a drumlin), the Guelph Reformatory, a golf course, and many bridges also serve to indicate that this is more than a mere meeting place for local farmers. It can also be seen that this city is at the meeting place of two rivers and is thus a *confluence* town.

Eramosa

Grove Inn

24

CANADIAN

Woolen Mill

Eden Mills

G U E L P H

VII

VI

V

IV

III

II

I

7

Fox

Reformatory Reservoir

Boundary

Speedwell Sta

GUELPH

Pump House

Golf Course

College View

W.T. Trans.

Agriculture College

Arkell

IX

VIII

Eramosa

P U S L

Scale 1:50,000

1.25 Inches to 1 Mile Approximately

1   ½   0   1

Eden Mills is a small community which has grown up at a bridging point of the Eramosa River. Most of the buildings in Eden Mills are located on the west banks of the river, which are steeper and so provide greater elevation above the possible flood levels. A few miles south of Eden Mills stands Arkell which is in many ways a typical little farming community. Here we find a little hamlet of a few buildings including the essential church, school, and post office, all standing at a crossroads and, therefore, easily accessible from the surrounding countryside.

Several interesting observations can be made regarding the communications network revealed by this map. Notice that highway 7 from Guelph does not follow the winding Eramosa but instead flanks a small more direct valley and then cuts between two prominent drumlins as it approaches Rockwood. This direct route is followed by both road and railway and it has the advantage of being well above possible flood levels. That gradient is of greater concern to railways than to highway engineers is apparent from the numerous cuttings and embankments on this stretch of line. In several places we see the influence of relief on routes. Near Eramosa the two-lane highway bends abruptly to go around, instead of over, a rather steepsided drumlin. Highway 6 east of the Agricultural College runs along a ridge overlooking a marshy depression.

Map Exercises

1. On a sheet of transparent paper trace and shade in all the drumlins shown on the northern half of this map.

2. Is the Reformatory inside the city of Guelph?

3. Mark off an area of 4 square miles north of Guelph. Trace each building and habitation in this area. Estimate the number of farmsteads in the area you have delimited. How far apart are they? Compare this distribution of settlement carefully with the settlement pattern shown on the Yamaska map.

4. Why do the buildings in Guelph not approach more closely to the Eramosa River?

YAMASKA MOUNTAIN

This map shows a small area in Quebec Province which forms a sharp contrast with the region we have just studied. Notice that the vertical interval used here is only 25 feet; yet even so, over most of the area the contours are much more widely spaced than they are on the Smoky River sheet. This indicates that most of the area is fairly level land. Yamaska Mountain, however, is a remarkable exception to the general evenness of relief.

The circular outline and the steep slopes of Yamaska Mountain are striking features of this area. The shape of this mountain is curious, for a steep, high edge forms its outer fringe or rim and there is a central area composed of several hills and depressions, and two of the latter contain lakes. It looks almost like a cake that has had many small pieces cut from its centre. Below 300 feet we find the contours quite widely spaced; this wide spacing indicates fairly flat, or at most undulating, land. The general picture of this area is one of a wide plain with a sudden, steep-sided mountain jutting upwards. When such a hill is left standing after the erosion of the surrounding land, it is called an *erosional* or *residual* hill.

You can notice several large sand or gravel pits to the southeast of Yamaska Mountain. Such gravel pits play an important part in the building of main highways through an area; indeed, the fact that these lie close to highway 1 in this area should remind you of this truth. The existence of such pits in an area furnishes clues respecting the history of the surrounding landscape. Sand and gravel may be found in sedimentary rocks. In southern Ontario, southern Quebec, and several other Canadian regions, masses of sand and gravel were dumped by melting glaciers. Finally, in certain areas where ancient lakes and seas once existed, their sandy beaches now remain and these, too, may be marked by modern sand pits. To determine definitely which of these three methods of sand-and-gravel formation explains these pits, we must examine other landforms shown on the map and also study the geography of the area in more detail.

We can often learn much about the topography of an area just by examining its rivers or its drainage pattern. The flatness of this terrain is indicated by the numerous meanders on the Rivière Noire and on the smaller Rivière à la Barbue. The fact that much of the land is badly drained and inclined to be marshy can be seen from the geometrically straight upper courses of the Ruisseau Derrill. A river artificially straightened like this is described as a *canalized* river. The few streams on the Yamaska Mountain all flow outwards from the centre. In fact, in some regions of the world we may find dozens of rivers flowing in this manner from a central point or dome. Such a peculiar drainage arrangement is known as a *radial drainage pattern*.

As one studies the rivers on a small portion of a topographical map, it may sometimes appear difficult to determine in which direction they are flowing. A simple solution to this problem is to be found in the shape of the contours. These will always converge at the river in such a way that they point upstream. Of course, the simplest method of all is to read the height of successive contours and just remember that rivers always flow downhill.

The many black, house symbols on this map are in marked contrast with their lack on the previous map. They indicate, of course, that there is a fairly large population living in the Yamaska area. The absence, however, of a close grouping of houses indicates that a farming population is located here. Émileville and St. Paul are the chief population centres, although they are only villages. Émileville has grown up at the place where routes along the river join with those skirting the western edge of the mountain; it is a centre of some importance to local people as there is a school, a church, and a post office located here. Being sheltered on the south side of Yamaska, St. Paul is the chief centre of the surrounding fruit-farming area. Because it has a railway station and a location on the major highway of the area, this settlement is much less spread out than Émileville.

Looking at the general distribution of settlement in the whole area, you will be impressed by the fact that most of the roads are lined by an almost continuous succession of buildings, and yet there are practically no buildings between the two- or three-lane roads. This type of arrangement might be called a form of *ribbon* or *linear* settlement. A knowledge of early French Canada will tell you that the farms were usually long narrow strips with a short frontage on the river or road. This map shows a similar situation, the farms having a short side or end along the road, a depth or length of a mile or more, and timberland at the end

Scale 1:50,000

1.25 Inches to 1 Mile Approximately

farthest from the road. If you examine closely the shape of the forested land between St. Paul and Papineau d'Abbotsford, you will be able to see the shape of some of the farm lots.

The effect of Mt. Yamaska on life in this area is easily determined from the map. All round the mountain we see that much of the land has been cleared for farming, although there is still considerable forest and scrub left. Yamaska Mountain, however, is itself still completely forested. If you lived here you would notice the effect of the mountain on communications. All the roads run around the mountain; none cross it. The telephone cable, too, detours around the mountain.

By using the map, locate on this photograph of Yamaska Mountain and St. Paul (a) the two lakes on the mountain, (b) the railway south of St. Paul, and (c) the cemetery northwest of St. Paul. What are the relative advantages of the map and the aerial photograph?

R.C.A.F.

Map Exercises

1. Draw a profile along a straight line joining the railway station of St. Paul with the crossroads at Jogues. Give the elevation of (a) the highest and (b) the lowest point on your profile.

2. Notice the large orchards on the south and west slopes of Mt. Yamaska. Suggest why there are so few orchards on the other two sides of the mountain.

3. You are required to make a journey on foot from east to west across Yamaska Mountain. Plan and draw on the map the easiest route to follow on foot.

4. How many (a) railway stations, (b) dams, (c) sand and gravel pits, (d) schools are shown on this map?

5. What is the area in square miles of the district shown on the map?

6. Use a good geography of Canada or an encyclopedia to find out what types of farming are done in this part of Quebec Province.

7. What other services would you expect to find in St. Paul in addition to those afforded by the churches, school, and post office shown on the map?

8. What is the distance between the school at Émileville and that at Papineau d'Abottsford via the route through St. Paul? Find a shorter route on this map. How much shorter is the second route?

9. By measuring a distance along the St. Paul road on the map and on the photograph, calculate the scale of this aerial photograph.

VANCOUVER

Maps can sometimes show us interesting contrasts within a small area. A line drawn across this map through Burrard Inlet would divide the area into two very different types of countryside. In attempting to understand or describe the area shown by a map, it is important to see whether there is such a subdivision. It would be foolish to try to lump the two distinct subdivisions into one generalized description.

Notice that the contour interval on this map is 500 feet so that the relief is shown in much less detail. What is the advantage of this wide contour interval? The mountainous region north of Vancouver repeats many of the relief features which we have already observed on the Smoky River map. As an exercise try to identify a cirque, an arête, a matterhorn peak, and other associated features. Particularly impressive are the long, narrow lakes of this area. Contours show that the mountains slope very steeply to the water's edge. Indian Arm is distinctive in that it enters the sea via Burrard Inlet. Such a long, narrow arm of the sea when produced by a glacier is known as a *fiord* and there are very many of them on the B.C. coast.

The southern half of the map represents a flat, coastal plain which is crossed by many distributaries of the Fraser River. Standing up out of this plain is the 1,000-foot forested mass of Mt. Burnaby, but all the remaining land is low-lying, much of it still being very marshy. This is the *delta* of the Fraser and most of this land and its many islands are composed of material carried to the sea by that river. That the river is still actively building this delta is shown by the extensive mud banks which extend out from the land. Notice the elongated shape of the deltaic islands and the fact that their outlines suggest the flow of water responsible for their existence.

Great as is the contrast between the relief north and south of Burrard Inlet, greater still is the contrast in terms of human settlement. To the north the mountains are almost devoid of settlement except for the line of communities along the hilly north shore of the inlet. This area is traversed by many paths and trails, but the only good roads follow the coast. It would be a mistake, however, to dismiss this area as of no importance. The Mount Seymour Provincial Park reminds us of the recreational value of mountains, lakes, and forests. Notice the underground aqueduct from Coquitlam Lake towards Indian Arm. This water falls about 500 feet before it reaches the power station from which you can see a hydro line carrying electricity to Vancouver.

Vancouver has grown on the peninsula between the North Arm and Burrard Inlet. You can see that a topographical map on this scale is of no value as a street guide since only the main arteries within the city are shown. Between Fraser Mills and False Creek you can see several roads and railways following a fairly direct course across the peninsula. Burnaby Lake suggests what is in fact true, that there is a long depression joining these two places and providing a natural route. Along the north of the city winds another railway which has direct access to the docks in Vancouver Harbour.

The functions or activities of a city this size are many and varied. Docks, warehouses, and many processing plants are located along the harbour. Around False Creek, sawmills and a number of other industrial plants are located. Between these two areas lies the shopping heart of Vancouver with both retail and wholesale outlets of large firms. The trading functions of the city are aided by its port and by the railway terminals. Education is a function which finds its highest expression in the magnificent University of British Columbia.

Scale 1:250,000

1 Inch to 4 Miles Approximately

5   2½   0   5

1. *Locate on this photograph: the railway yards, several log booms, commercial docking facilities, an anchorage for small vessels. Now pinpoint these on the map opposite.*

2. *Suggest possible reasons for the location of the three bridges in the centre of the photograph.*

ST. CATHARINES—
NIAGARA ESCARPMENT

The town in the centre of the map is St. Catharines. What is the name of the lake to the north? To what other lake does the Welland Canal lead on the south? How many sets of locks can you count on this stretch of the canal?

A steep escarpment running across the south of the map close to Thorold is part of the Niagara escarpment and is a very prominent feature of this landscape. Is there any connection between this physical feature and the existence of the Welland Canal? There are several quarries close to the steep scarp slope; locate two of these and suggest what is being quarried there. The road leading south from St. Catharines approaches this very steep slope by swinging to the west and climbing the incline on a gentler angle of ascent. An advantage of such an escarpment is seen in the power station at Power Glen on the southwest of the area, near Mile Creek. This creek meanders in broad sweeps as far as St. Catharines, but its meanders are incised well below the surrounding land; thus, flooding is seldom a serious threat.

An interesting study of transportation facilities could be based on this map. A brief examination should be sufficient to indicate the advantages of the new Welland Canal over the old one. These advantages might be listed under the two headings: the course of the canal, and the canal's facilities. What is the importance of the two dry docks shown on the map? Another comparatively new artery of communication is the Queen Elizabeth Way, which runs along the coastal lowland and skirts the northern edge of St. Catharines. At how many places in this area can you gain access to this main highway? What might be the effect of this highway on the small community of Homer close to the New Canal? There are railways of different types shown here. There is a striking similarity between the route of the main Canadian National Railway and the Queen Elizabeth Way. What do the numerous railway cuttings and embankments reveal of the detailed character of the terrain?

St. Catharines is the centre of a farming region which is marked by numerous orchards. Ontario's flourishing wine industry reminds us of grape vineyards found here. What other fruits are probably also grown in these orchards? The advantages of climate and soil make this one of the most favoured farming areas in all Canada; but a threat to this farmland is posed by new highways, new housing subdivisions, and some modern industrial developments. What attractions does this region have for these latter interests?

The cluster of settlement represented by St. Catharines-Merritton-Thorold is certainly not supported merely by local agricultural industries. In addition to the various activities associated with canal traffic and the dry docks, the map also shows three other important industries found in the area. Use an encyclopedia to find out what other industries are located here and try to find a probable reason for the choice of this site.

A better understanding of this area may be gained by drawing a profile of the land between the power house in the southwest and CKTB wireless mast close to the lake. Close to this line you will notice an educational institute. Elsewhere on the map you should find a sanitarium, an airport, a power line, a school, a railway station, and a rifle range.

On this photograph of St. Catharines locate (a) the Queen Elizabeth Way, (b) Merritton, (c) the escarpment.

Spartan Air Services Limited

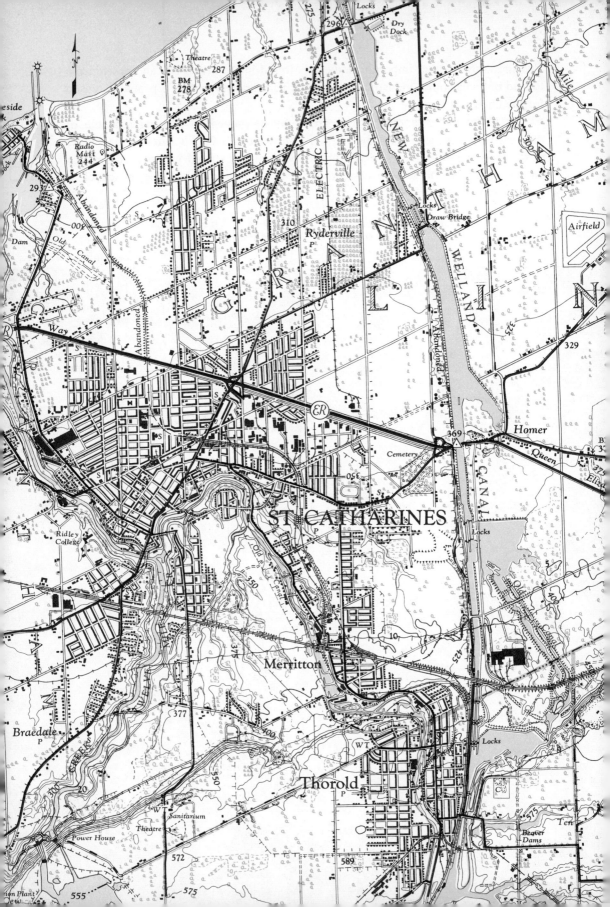

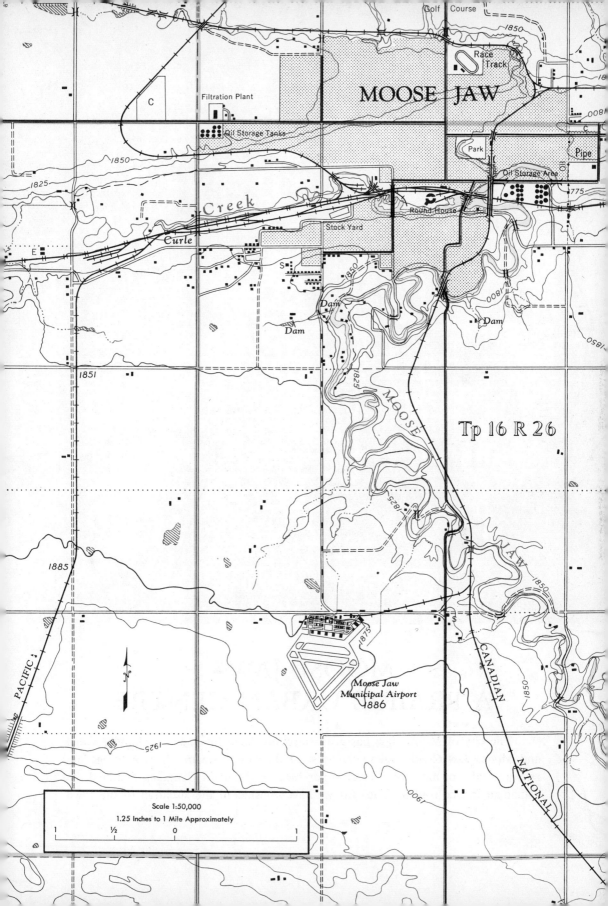

MOOSE JAW –
A PRAIRIE URBAN CENTRE

The city of Moose Jaw has grown around the confluence of Thunder Creek and Moose Jaw Creek and to the west of the latter stream. It is a bridge and railway centre of more than local importance on the main Canadian National and Canadian Pacific routes. Thus far we have considered the situation of the town.

An examination of the site of the town shows that most of the built-up area lies on a fairly flat ledge at an elevation of just over 1,775 feet. Some distance from Thunder Creek where the land rises steeply for about 50 feet, the town has spread up over this sharp edge on to the flat land above. The southern part of the town is sandwiched into a narrow promontory between the tortuous meanders of the two creeks.

Moose Jaw is fortunate in having a riverside park in the centre of the town. On the other hand, the development of the town has necessitated the building of many road and rail bridges. The oil-storage tanks, stockyards, and roundhouse tell us something about the kinds of jobs to be found in the town.

South of the town is a wide, very flat plain crossed by the meanders of the Moose Jaw, which has cut out a steep-sided, seventy-foot-deep valley. The flatness of the plain is evidenced by the wide spacing of the contours in spite of their 25-foot vertical interval, by the regular geometrical pattern of roads and railways, and by the small pockets of seasonally inundated land.

Explain why this characteristic of the land facilitates highway and railroad construction, as well as the building of modern airports. Seasonal ponds and streams suggest that this may be an area where there is a markedly dry season of the year. Why would farmers build dams in some of these hollows or small valleys?

The general flatness of the land should not lead you to overlook the steep slopes of the Moose Jaw valley and of the north section of the town itself. Examining the two railways running northward from the town, you will observe that the eastern track climbs gradually up a river valley. The track on the west, however, ascends the steep slope by running almost parallel to the contours and then by doubling back around the filtration plant.

The distribution of settlement shown on this map should be compared carefully with that on the earlier Guelph and Yamaska sheets. Here you will notice a type of rural settlement in which farms are very widely spaced and the regular geometrical pattern appears to indicate that the area was surveyed before, or at least at the same time as, the first permanent settlement was made.

Exercises

1. Comment on and explain the location of the oil-storage tanks at Moose Jaw.
2. The railway and main road both cross Moose Jaw Creek near each other on the south of the city. Which of these lines of communication *flies over* the other on entering the city?
3. The Canadian Pacific Railway track runs on an embankment for a short distance in the southwest of this area; find the embankment. What symbol is used to show this feature?
4. Locate on the photograph (a) the Park, (b) two major railway lines, (c) the Round House. Locate on the map the limits of the area shown on the photograph.

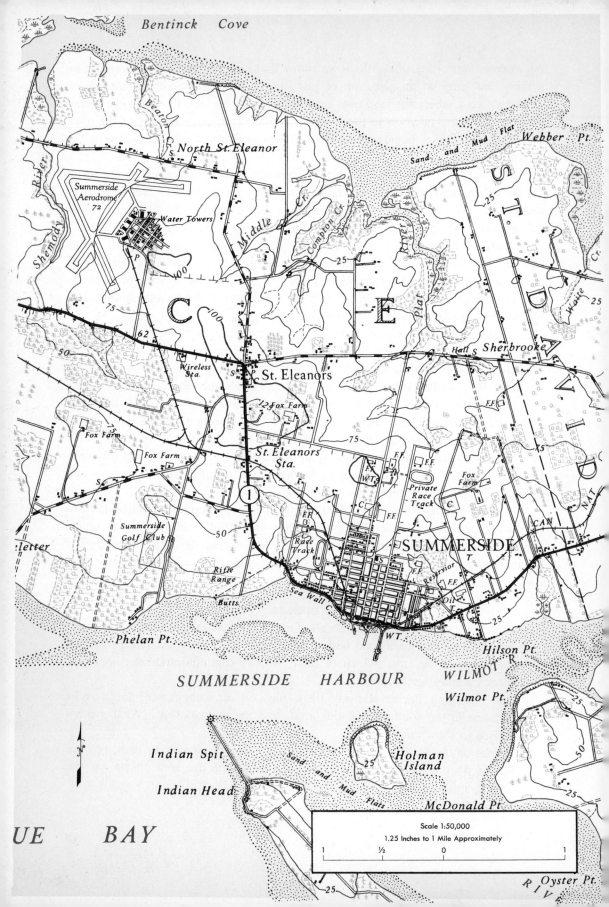

The Photographic Survey Corporation Limited

Locate on the map of Summerside the limits of the area photographed. Prepare two lists under the following headings: (a) Information gained from the photograph, (b) Information gained from the map.

39

SUMMERSIDE

This small cross-section of Prince Edward Island presents several very interesting contrasts with the Moose Jaw area. As the winding contours are not so widely spaced, this type of terrain can be described as *rolling* or *undulating*. Further variety is added to the landscape by the numerous small woods and groves of trees in contrast with the treeless plains around Moose Jaw Creek.

A fundamental contrast between the two areas, of course, lies in the fact that here we have an island on the east coast, whereas Moose Jaw is located deep in the heart of a vast continent. The coasts near Summerhill are worth some study. North of Summerhill there are three creeks whose lower valleys have been flooded to form wide estuaries. However, the wide sand and mud flats ruin these estuaries for navigation, and indeed most of the adjacent coast is handicapped in the same way. Swamps and marshes are common along this coast. Summerside Harbour, which is an inlet off Bedeque Bay, is also handicapped by sand and mud flats, but in this case the lighthouse off Indian Spit and another at Summerside serve to guide ships into the harbour. With such limited facilities, it is clear that Summerside is not a very prosperous port. Instead, it is an active fishing centre. Cliffs are to be seen around the north coast of Holman Island and Wilmot Point.

In this map we find that more detail is provided on the town of Summerhill than the previous map gave on Moose Jaw. Some idea of the local importance of this town can be gauged from the harbour, the railway station, the main road, at least one school, five churches, and a race track. Not far from the town are golf courses and a rifle range. Calculate the distance from the town to Summerhill Aerodrome. Here, as in the case of Moose Jaw, we can see one of the major problems of air travel, namely, the distance of most airports from their nearest large town. Suggest reasons why this problem has developed.

There is clearly much more settlement throughout this area than in the land around Moose Jaw. Farming is obviously the chief occupation in an area where homesteads are spaced as they are here; indeed, the numerous fox farms indicate the rather unusual type of farming common to this locality. The pattern of roads is much less geometrical than on the prairies. Here the winding, irregular road pattern is of the type that we often find in areas where settlement dates back to the early days of Canadian history—the days before government surveyors began systematic mapping.

Exercises

1. Draw a profile from Phelan Pt. to the mouth of Compton Creek. Calculate the degree of vertical exaggeration on your profile.

2. Find an area on the north coast of the island where cliffs are overlooking the mud flats.

3. Using a good reference work, find out which are the chief economic activities on Prince Edward Island.

   What evidence can you find on the map for any of these?

4. Carefully compare the number of habitations on 4 square miles of this map with the number on an equal area of the Moose Jaw map.

GABAROUSE BAY— CAPE BRETON COAST

This map shows a low-lying section of the Cape Breton coastline, which is picturesque and has many of the attractions necessary for the development of a major tourist centre. The chief drawback is not shown on the map: the coastal waters are generally too cold for bathing, even in the height of summer. Broad Gabarouse Bay is fringed on the north by several miles of long, low cliffs behind which the land rises to heights of about 300 feet. The southern shores of this bay are lower lying, with two broad sandbars enclosing Lever Lake and the smaller Harris Lake. Shielding the harbour of Gabarouse is the low but steep-sided knoll of Rouse Point, together with its isthmus, along which a protective sea wall has had to be constructed.

Gabarouse Bay is about 35 miles south of Glace Bay on the Atlantic seaboard of the island. The low-lying, hilly terrain is characterized by numerous lakes and an indeterminate drainage that results in wide marshy tracts. Extensively forested, this region resembles many areas on the Canadian Shield—an understandable similarity in view of the fact that the rocks here consist of the same hard pre-Cambrian groups that are found in northern Ontario and Quebec.

In terms of topography and settlement we can divide the area shown here into two distinct subdivisions. To the south of Rams Head the land is marshy, forested, and uninhabited. The southern coast of this area is marked by miles of sandpits and lagoons behind which are broad flat swamplands. North and west of Rams Head lagoons are less frequent and the shore much steeper. Here there are scattered settlements along the coast, with small clearings indicating that a certain amount of farming is carried on. What crops are grown on this exposed, humid coastline? Farming, however, is only one of the sources of livelihood of these islanders; in addition, they fish the coastal waters of the bay and of the adjacent fishing grounds. Gabarouse is a good example of a small maritime fishing village with its sheltered but shallow harbour and its tiny cluster of houses and other buildings. The importance of this settlement is evidenced by the presence of two schools, a church and a post office. Gabarouse is not only the heart of the local fishing industry; it is also a nerve centre for the small agricultural sector of cleared land lying between the harbour and Lever Lake.

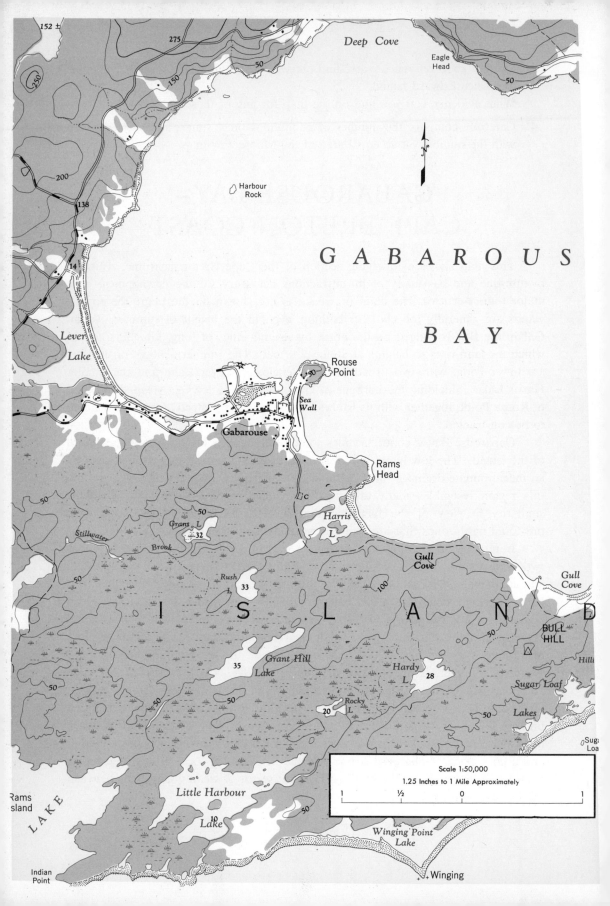

Deep Cove

Eagle
Head

152 ±

275

250

150

138

200

14

Harbour
Rock

N

G A B A R O U S

B A Y

Lever
Lake

Rouse
Point

Gabarouse

Sea
Wall

P

Rams
Head

C

Stillwater

Grant L

32

Brook

Harris
L

Gull
Cove

Gull
Cove

Rush

33

I   S   L   A   N   D

100

50

BULL
HILL

Hilli

Grant Hill
Lake

35

50

Hardy
L

28

Sugar Loaf

50

Lakes

20

Rocky
L

Rams
Island

LAKE

Little Harbour

10

Lake

50

Winging Point
Lake

Suga
Loa

Indian
Point

Winging

Scale 1:50,000

1.25 Inches to 1 Mile Approximately

1   ½   0   1

In this photograph showing Gabarouse Bay, identify the buildings and clearings R.C.A.F.
around Lever Lake. Why does this photograph give a better understanding of the
area than the map?

The elevation of the lakes in the south of the map is clearly indicated. Little Harbour Lake is a mere ten feet above sea level. This is good fishing country, salmon and other fish being plentiful in local waterways. Lack of transportation has been the one handicap that has precluded this territory's major development as a sportsman's mecca. Suggest some other drawbacks of the area from this point of view.

This map should be compared closely with the other two coastal maps provided. What are the chief differences that distinguish the three coastlines with respect to shape, elevation, possible usefulness, and human settlement?

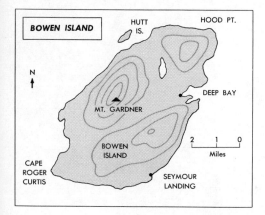

Draw a line from north to south through this island and another from east to west. Prepare a profile along each line. Write two paragraphs describing the island and its relief. Such a description should include shape, area, terrain, settlement, and any other significant features.

THE NATURAL
ENVIRONMENT

The Air We Live In

1 THE AIR

Man lives near the bottom of a great sea of gases surrounding the earth—a sea known as the atmosphere. Air is the water in this sea and is as important to human beings as water is to fish. The comparison between the air and the sea is valid in a number of respects. This part of our environment completely enshrouds us, is essential to our life, and is highly fluid, moving in different directions and at different speeds from hour to hour.

It is remarkable that this ever-present part of man's environment was one of the last fields of that environment to be subjected to accurate scientific research. Perhaps the fact that man cannot see the air explains the delay in exploring it. Meteorology, the science which studies the atmosphere and weather, is sometimes considered to date from the year 1643 when Torricelli constructed his first mercury barometer.

The Composition of the Atmosphere

Air is a mixture of a number of gases and other substances. Originally the earth's atmosphere probably consisted largely of hydrogen and helium, which are among the commonest elements in the universe. During the cooling of the earth, chemical and volcanic activity has brought about a gradual change to the point where nitrogen and oxygen together now form over 98% of the gases in the air. The proportions of the gases in the air now remain comparatively constant.

GASES PRESENT IN PURE DRY AIR

GAS	SYMBOL OR FORMULA	PER CENT (By Volume)
Nitrogen	N_2	78.084
Oxygen	O_2	20.946
Argon	Ar	.934
Carbon Dioxide	CO_2	.033
Neon	Ne	
Helium	He	
Methane	CH_4	infinitesimal
Krypton	Kr	quantities
Hydrogen	H_2	
Nitrous Oxide	N_2O	
Xenon	Xe	

    This constancy is maintained by several cycles of natural activity. By means of a process called photosynthesis, plants assimilate carbon dioxide and release oxygen into the atmosphere. Animals, on the other hand, consume oxygen and release (breathe) carbon dioxide into the air. The weathering of rocks utilizes carbon dioxide from the air in the formation of carbonates, but the decaying of organic materials on the earth's surface produces carbon dioxide which is released into the atmosphere. Nitrogen is removed from the atmosphere by various bacteria in the soil and then plays a part in the growth of plants, especially of the legumes (such as clover, beans, and peas). Conversely, nitrogen returns to the air from the excreta of animals and from decaying plant and animal remains.

Bacteria and leguminous plants transfer nitrogen from the air to the soil, from which it enters other plants and, through them, passes into animals. In turn, decaying plant and animal remains return nitrogen to the atmosphere. What percentage of the air consists of nitrogen?

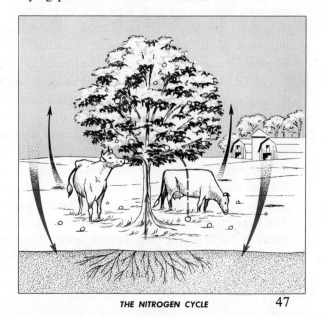

THE NITROGEN CYCLE

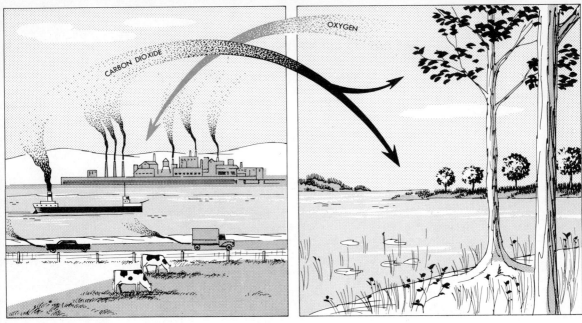

THE CARBON DIOXIDE CYCLE

Oxygen is used in combustion and the decay of plant and animal matter, but these processes also release carbon dioxide. This gas, however, is used in the photosynthesis of plants—a process which releases oxygen. How do man's activities affect this cycle?

Many cities in Canada and elsewhere now have a municipal department concerned entirely with air pollution. Air consists of more than just the 11 major gases listed in the chart, although these account for more than 99% of its total composition, and we are now learning the enormous importance of its seemingly insignificant other ingredients. Human comfort is not measured only in terms of the temperature but also of the humidity. Minute proportions of water vapour in the air are responsible for this humidity. In recent years even more attention has been given to another ingredient or group of ingredients in the air, namely the dirt, dust, and smoke that are collectively responsible for smog. Air pollution is the result of thousands of tons of gases and solids entering the atmosphere from automobile exhausts and factory smokestacks. Finally, modern scientific research has still further affected the normal composition of our atmosphere by the testing of nuclear weapons, especially by adding to it such radiation fallout as gamma rays and other dangerous particles.

These extra substances added to our air occur only in very minute proportions, but their effect on human life can be enormous. Excessive moisture in the air can not only make life uncomfortable but even affect the health of the people. Serious cases of smog can be disastrous because they can tie up transportation systems for hours or even days and, more important, can actually result in death. The huge city of London has suffered severely from smog and in 1952 perhaps as many as 5,000 people died through smog. The old and those with respiratory weaknesses are particularly vulnerable to these impurities in the air. The full effects of past nuclear testing in terms of life on our planet are not yet known, but there is general agreement that the impurities which would be released by unlimited nuclear testing could prove fatal to enormous numbers of people all over the world.

A Cross-Section of the Atmosphere

The exciting satellite and space-research programmes conducted by the United States and the Soviet Union are providing increased knowledge not only about outer space but also about the layer of atmosphere which surrounds this planet like a skin around an orange.

The exact thickness of this skin of air around the earth is not known. Part of the reason for this situation is that the air thins out, or becomes more diffuse, as one moves out from the earth's surface. The earth's gravitational force is sufficient to keep over half the total weight of air within 3½ miles of the earth's surface. Beyond that the more rarefied atmosphere continues for hundreds of miles.

Differences between the upper and lower atmosphere have led to the realization that our atmosphere is divisible into several distinct layers and that a comparison with an onion would be more appropriate than with an orange. The chief basis used for the division of the atmosphere is the variation in temperature occurring in each layer. In the lowest layer of the atmosphere are to be found the clouds and weather conditions which are so important to man. This belt, the *troposphere*, extends through an average thickness of 7 miles above the earth's surface; the upper limit of this troposphere is known as the *tropopause*. Within the troposphere, temperature falls by about 1° F. for every additional 300 feet of elevation. This is, of course, a generalized figure. Such a change in temperature due to an increase in elevation is known as the *normal lapse rate*.

Notice how tiny even our highest mountains are when compared with the depth of the atmosphere. Find out (a) the highest ascent by man other than in satellites. (b) the highest elevation a balloon has ever reached.

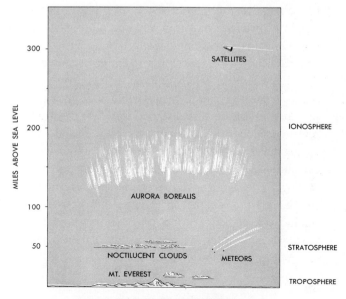

THE ZONES OF THE ATMOSPHERE

Above the troposphere is the broad layer of air called the *stratosphere*, a zone in which temperatures remain fairly constant regardless of increasing altitude. At the upper limit of this layer (called the *stratopause*) temperatures begin to rise again and we enter the *ionosphere*, which is the part of the atmosphere about which we know least. Here ultraviolet rays from the sun produce electrically charged gas atoms called ions. Part of the ionosphere is called the *ozone* layer because here there is a high concentration of ozone—a form of oxygen which absorbs a great amount of solar radiation. The air in the ionosphere is extremely rarefied, being so thin that it hardly even warms any object passing through it.

Finally, beyond the ionosphere lies the fountain layer or *exosphere*, which is the outermost fringe of our atmosphere. Here countless ions and molecules of gas keep dispersing out into space, but most of them fall back into the atmosphere again under the influence of the earth's gravity.

Air Pressure

The comparison between the atmosphere and the sea is very useful. You have only to pick up a bucket of water to realize that water has weight. Dr. Piccard, the famous scientist, found the enormous pressures of the ocean deeps to be the most serious obstacle to ocean-floor explorations. Yet certain types of fish do live under this great pressure; their bodies are adjusted to these conditions and presumably they don't even notice the pressure.

Air, too, has weight. The hundreds of miles of air exert considerable pressure on everything on the face of the earth. Each square inch of the earth's surface, of your desk, and even of your own body is under an average pressure of 14.7 pounds. Like the fish, we live without awareness of this pressure. When you ascend or descend rapidly in the elevator of a tall building or in an aircraft, you receive an indication of changing pressure in the buzzing of your very sensitive eardrums.

Air is constantly moving; you know this to be a fact every time you see the branches of a tree stir in the wind. This constant motion means that the actual weight or pressure of air on any one place is subject to considerable change. Since the human body has no means of measuring normal changes in air pressure, it became necessary to develop a scientific instrument for this task; such an instrument is called a *barometer*. A column of mercury was used in the first barometers, and the distance the mercury moved in a tube was the indication of changes in air pressure. Because this distance was first measured in millimetres or inches, these units were adopted as standards of pressure. The average atmospheric pressure at sea level is 29.92 inches or 760 millimetres. Physicists have a unit of air pressure—the *millibar*—which is now commonly used in weather maps and forecasting. The average sea-level pressure expressed in millibars is 1013.25. When you examine a weather map, you will notice a great mass of lines which may remind you of the contours on other maps. These will, however, be lines joining places of equal pressure and they are called *isobars*.

Department of Transport, Canada

This barograph is particularly useful since it not only records changes in pressure but also measures these changes. Consult your school library to find out how a barograph works.

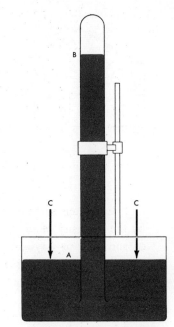

THE TORRICELLIAN BAROMETER

Invented in 1643 by Torricelli, this device showed that the weight of air pressure (c) at sea level was sufficient to balance a column of mercury (A to B) about 30 inches high.

The Heating of the Air

Just as temperature is one of the chief distinguishing factors in the division of the atmosphere into horizontal layers superimposed one on top of another, so also is it a well-known factor in the producing of differences in climate on the actual surface of the earth. Variations in climate can largely be explained in terms of differences in temperature.

The heat in the atmosphere, and even of the earth's surface, is almost entirely due to the heat energy received from the sun. *Insolation* is the term used to describe the total heat energy received by the earth from the sun's radiation. Two factors are of importance in producing variations in insolation, namely: the angle at which the sun's rays strike the earth, and the length of time that the surface is exposed to the sun's rays. Both of these factors are themselves variable. When the rays or bundles of solar energy strike the earth at right angles, they are concentrated more intensely than when they strike at a smaller angle. The lower the angle, the greater will be the area receiving the same amount of energy. Broad climatic patterns between hot equatorial and cold polar lands are largely the result of variations in insolation produced by the differing angle of the sun's rays as we move away from the equator.

51

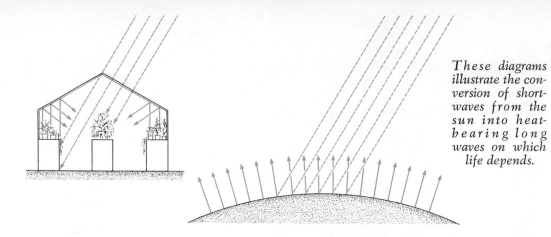

These diagrams illustrate the conversion of short-waves from the sun into heat-bearing long waves on which life depends.

Earth temperatures and living conditions will, of course, be affected not only by the intensity of insolation but also by its duration, i.e., by the number of hours of sunshine or daylight that a place receives. Moreover, this period of duration varies in a constant ratio between the equator and the poles. Accordingly, the longest day at the equator is 12 hours; at 66½ ° N. it is 24 hours; at the poles it is six months.

The operation of these two factors results in a variation in insolation according to latitude and to season.

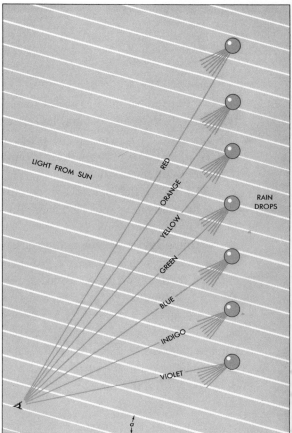

If the angle a is less than 45°, then each raindrop acts as a prism to produce a spectrum. However, the difference in angle of each drop means that each reflects just one colour to the observer.

The most important source of heat in the air is the earth itself. The process, by which, after the land and water masses have absorbed the sun's heat rays, they send some of this heat back into the air, is called *radiation*. Heat rays from the sun have a very short wave length; this means that they can pass easily through air or other transparent materials without losing much heat. These rays, however, are absorbed easily by solid substances. On the other hand, radiated heat waves from the land and the sea have a long wave length; therefore, they are absorbed very easily by the air and so heat it. Curiously, then, most of the sun's energy passes through the air and must first strike the earth before this energy will heat the surrounding air. As a radio receiver picks up waves and turns them into sound, so the earth acts to the sun's rays like a receiver and turns them into heat. An important difference between the processes of reflection and of radiation is that the latter continues even at night when the sun is not shining on a particular area.

You may have noticed a commonplace example of the different heating qualities of long and short heat waves. Sitting on a sunny day in a room that has a picture window you will notice that the temperature rapidly rises far above that outside. Similar conditions obtain in greenhouses. In both cases, the large area of glass allows the penetration of short waves, but impedes the escape of the long waves radiated by the room or the plants.

This diagram shows a major determinant of climates on the surface of the earth. The apparent migration of the overhead sun is a result of the tilt of the earth's axis and the earth's revolution around the sun. In our summer, the sun is overhead at noon a good distance north of the equator; in our winter the sun is overhead at noon the same distance south of the equator. For this reason Christmas in S. Africa and Australia occurs in summer.

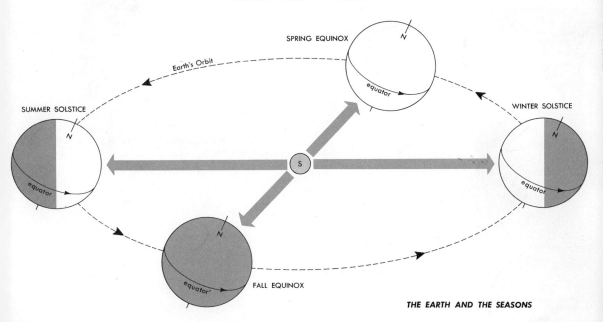

THE EARTH AND THE SEASONS

2 THE AIR IN MOTION

Air Masses and Movements

The air all around us is constantly in motion, winds blowing horizontally across the land and also moving vertically in the atmosphere. Over a particular area, air close to the ground is heated quickly on sunny days and consequently becomes lighter and less dense. Colder and heavier air may then push into that area with the result that the warmer air rises into the upper atmosphere in much the same way as lighter substances tend to float to the top of any gas or liquid. In time, the cold air will be heated, the warm air cooled, and the process repeated. The resultant circulatory movement in the atmosphere is thus the product of convection currents, which you will have studied in your science course.

In view of the fact that the heated air has become lighter, the pressure of that mass of air is less than that of the air around it and thus an area of low pressure is created. The major movements of large bodies of air are the result of air moving from regions of high pressure to those of low pressure. Since air temperatures are much higher around the equator and much lower around the poles than elsewhere on the earth, there is a general movement of air away from the poles and towards the equator.

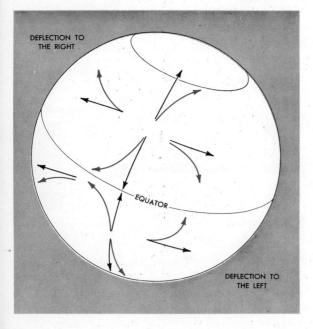

The effect of the earth's rotation on winds is expressed in Ferrel's Law which states that any object moving horizontally in the Northern Hemisphere tends to be deflected to the right regardless of its direction of motion and in the Southern Hemisphere to the left. The force producing this deflection is called the Coriolis force.

When looking at a map showing major wind move-
ments on earth, one must realize that the circulation
of the air is three dimensional. This diagram shows
one part of the pattern.

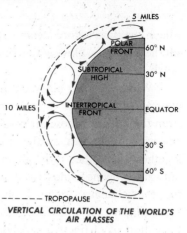

VERTICAL CIRCULATION OF THE WORLD'S
AIR MASSES

The Planetary Circulation of Air

Owing to the rotation of the earth, the paths of things moving north or south on the earth are always slightly east or west of true north or south. This Coriolis effect is expressed in the form "moving objects are deflected to their right in the Northern Hemisphere and to their left in the Southern Hemisphere", a statement known as Ferrel's Law. This rotary force exerted on an object moving at 60 miles per hour in the Northern Hemisphere could deflect it as much as 15 feet per mile of travel. Accordingly a rocket fired from the North Pole and aimed directly at New York would land in the vicinity of Chicago. Examine your atlas to see how great would be this deflection.

Great masses of moving air, or prevailing winds, are likewise under the influence of this rotary force. Winds blowing towards the equator are therefore deflected westwards, as indicated on maps showing pressure systems and air circulations. In equatorial latitudes, we find great low-pressure cells or systems where winds are erratic and where calms are very common. In the days of sailing ships, regions of such cells or systems were known as the *doldrums*. Air which ascends in these areas is cooled and moves poleward at high altitudes, much of it descending again at approximately 30° from the equator into a series of subtropical high-pressure cells. At one time, when our knowledge of meteorology was much more limited than it is today, the world's wind and pressure systems were called *belts*; in those days the area lying within 30 degrees of the equator was known as the Horse Latitudes and the calms that occurred there were dreaded by the crews of sailing ships. From the maps, it is clear that the size and location of the subtropical highs vary somewhat, partly as a result of the apparent migration of the overhead sun. It is also apparent that in the Northern Hemisphere the distribution of land and water results in a greater fragmentation of the high-pressure cells.

To the surface winds, often blowing at sea from the subtropical highs towards the equator, people gave the name *trade winds*, and these winds played an important

55

role in the days before steam navigation. The broad zone to which the northeast and southeast trades blow is the *Intertropical Front,* an area about which we still have much to learn.

Winds blowing poleward from the subtropical high follow a generally westerly course but are quite variable in actual direction and force. At approximately 60° from the equator, these air masses meet advancing cold polar air along a constantly shifting line known as the *polar front.* Westerlies rising along the polar front, together with other lofty air currents, descend in polar latitudes to replenish the outward-blowing winds from those regions. A piling up of cold air occurs along the ever-changing polar front; a powerfully active jet stream is also present. Accordingly, on this front, the mingling of cold and warm air results in the formation of distinctive revolving air masses that sweep eastwards and are known as cyclones or depressions. At times too there will be an outburst of cold polar air thrusting deep into the middle latitudes towards a subtropical high. This sudden surge of cold air often has dramatic and even disastrous results, as in November, 1962 when an outflow of this kind ruined much of the Florida fruit crop.

It is well to remember that the movements of air masses have not yet been completely explained and that the meteorologist is often in the position of having to build up a pattern when he has only half the facts. The next ten years should see marked advances in this field that could result in new and perhaps surprising discoveries.

In studying the direction and frequency of winds in your own district, do not be surprised if the general patterns outlined do not seem to apply. Complicating factors of relief and land-water differences must receive attention. Only over the oceans do comparatively simple systems of wind actually apply; indeed, this fact may explain the prominent part sailors have played in the naming of many of these winds.

On this map identify the zone of the Intertropical Front and the subtropical highs. Compare this map closely with your atlas map showing precipitation distribution in January.

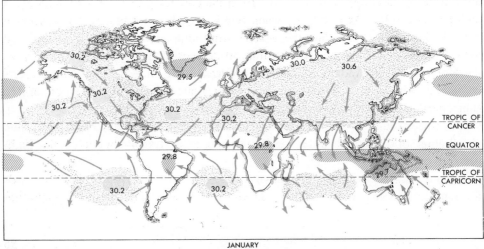

JANUARY

**A GENERALIZED MAP OF WORLD PRESSURE SYSTEMS
AND THE RESULTING AIR CIRCULATIONS**

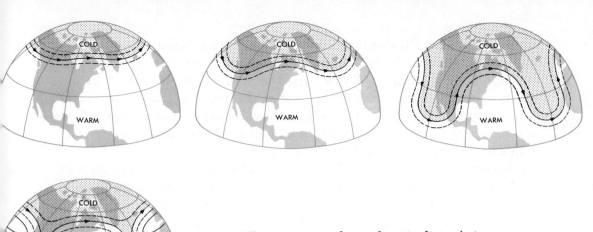

This process results in the mingling of air masses after the isolation of a cold air mass. What are the chief results?

Polar and Tropical Air Masses

As already described, air moving from the equator meets air of polar origin about the 40° latitudes. In the upper altitudes there is a wide belt of mixing air and accompanying violent winds. Here, too, as elsewhere, the air in the high altitudes is constantly moving eastwards, but at the meeting point of polar and tropical air, it moves much more strongly. The strongest of these eastward-moving air masses blows at approximately 30° N and 30° S latitude. The name given to this band of whirling warm and cold air at high altitudes is the *circumpolar whirl*.

Notice the winds blowing outward from the high-pressure cells, clockwise in the north and anticlockwise in the south. Explain this difference in direction. Carefully compare this map with a map of temperature distribution in July.

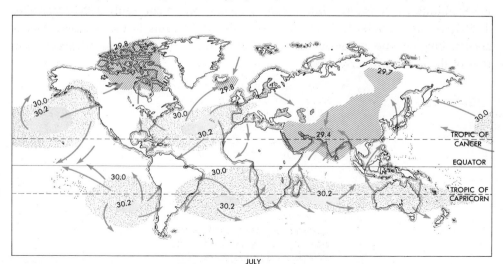

JULY

**A GENERALIZED MAP OF WORLD PRESSURE SYSTEMS
AND THE RESULTING AIR CIRCULATIONS**

57

Modern research is showing us that if we ever hope to understand thoroughly and so predict accurately the weather conditions at the earth's surface, we must first learn much more about what is happening in the upper reaches of the air. It is becoming clear that much of our weather is merely the result of air movements many miles above us. Meteorologists and physicists in many parts of the world are now steadily piecing together millions of known facts in an effort to build up a complete picture of what happens aloft.

Among the most important of the weather-making events in the high altitudes are those concerned with jet streams. These are wind systems close to the southern edge of the circumpolar whirl and, therefore, to the meeting point of polar and tropical air. There are three areas where the jet streams blow in the Northern Hemisphere; they do not, however, form a continuous band; neither do they blow constantly. The jet streams vary in extent, direction, and speed, but they are remarkable because they include the strongest winds we know, perhaps even reaching velocities of 400 m.p.h. at times but often averaging 150 m.p.h. Some of the changes in the jet stream are seasonal. Thus, in winter the jet streams are found at between 4 and 6 miles above sea level about 20° and 25° N latitude. At this time of the year they are sometimes used by aircraft, the strong tail winds considerably reducing flying time. In summer the streams occur between 35° and 45° N latitude at elevations of 7 to 9 miles—too high to be of value to existing commercial airlines.

At irregular intervals there are fluctuations in the relative strength of the polar and tropical air masses in the jet stream. As one of these air masses becomes stronger, it penetrates far into the other, and this interpenetration, coupled with the general eastward movement of air, can eventually result in a circular movement of air. The diagram shows that the waves of the jet stream can produce islands of cold or warm air which form a sharp contrast to surrounding air masses, a contrast which is of enormous importance in the weather processes of lower altitudes. During the International Geophysical Year (July 1957-December 1958), research established that there are also jet streams in the Southern Hemisphere, but our knowledge of these southern streams is much less advanced than that of the more northerly ones.

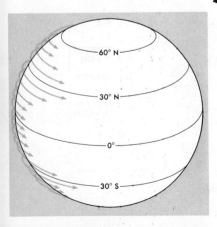

← *The general movement of air from west to east is known as the circumpolar whirl. The relative speed of winds is indicated here by the length of arrows. Where would Canada be in relation to this diagram?*

The three arrows show the general position and direction of jet streams in the Northern Hemisphere. Use a map of air routes to establish which, if any, major routes could possibly use jet streams.

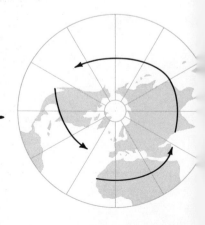

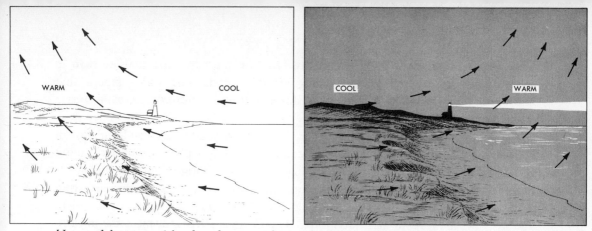

Unequal heating of land and sea results in the breezes depicted here. What will be the effect of these in terms of temperatures of places near the shore?

Local Winds

When equal areas of land and of sea, respectively, receive the same total amount of solar energy, different heating processes take place. The sun's rays do not penetrate far into the solid land; the land, therefore, heats up quickly and in turn heats the air above it. Likewise the land cools down quickly and so does its blanket of air. However, in the case of the sea—or any other large body of water—the sun's rays penetrate deeper; as a result of this, and also because of convection and other currents, the heat is widely dispersed. Consequently, the heating and the cooling are more gradual processes both in and over the sea.

This unequal heating process is important at two levels. Throughout the day and the night, temperature differences develop between the air over the land and that over the sea. During the day the warmer air over the land rises and its place is taken by the cooler air from the sea. The result is a sea-to-land wind known as a *sea breeze*. By night reverse conditions occur and the resulting seaward breeze is known as a *land breeze* after its place of origin. Generally the daytime sea breezes are stronger than the nighttime land breezes, but they are both wind patterns of only local importance.

Similarly contrasting conditions are sometimes found in mountain regions.

The arrows show the general direction taken by these storms. In the western Pacific, hurricanes are called typhoons. Find out how many hurricanes struck North America last year. Which was the most destructive and where did it strike?

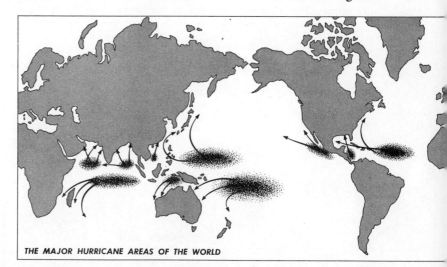

THE MAJOR HURRICANE AREAS OF THE WORLD

Here, heating and cooling are often more rapid on the bare mountainside than in the thickly forested valleys. This may result in a daytime *valley breeze* that carries air from the valley to the higher slopes and in a nighttime *mountain breeze* that carries it in the opposite direction.

Disturbances in the trade winds in low latitudes at times result in violent systems of local winds known as hurricanes. There is still some mystery about these wind storms, but it seems likely that they tend to originate when humid air begins to ascend at a particular location. Moisture condenses as this air rises, releasing into the air mass heat which in turn accelerates the upward movement and so draws in more air at ground level. The Coriolis effect influences the inward-blowing air, giving it also a rotating movement. Thick clouds circle their way into the centre.

A hurricane, which is seldom more than a few hundred miles wide, develops a force in its winds which increases steadily towards the centre. At the centre, however, there is a relatively calm area, usually about 12 miles wide, called the *eye* of the storm. In spite of its small size, a hurricane is a very important wind storm because of the enormous damage it causes, particularly in coastal areas where it can drive great waves across the land in disastrous floods. Aircraft are now used to track hurricanes and give warning of their probable course.

Much smaller than the hurricane, but in some ways more spectacular, is the tornado. On days when moist warm air at ground level is covered by cool dry air and thunderhead clouds, these twisters may develop. The funnel of rotating air wanders erratically across the ground at 40 miles an hour or less; indeed, it may lift off the ground altogether and then descend again. Within the storm, winds may reach speeds of over 400 miles an hour; these often proceed to carve a swath of destruction through the countryside. Fortunately, they seldom exceed 500 yards in width; consequently, their destruction is not as widespread as that of a hurricane. Damage is caused not only by the wind in a tornado; but also by air pressure; it appears that the air pressure at the centre of the spiralling funnel can be so low that buildings which lie under the centre may actually explode.

The tornado differs from the hurricane not only in size but also in duration, the normal life span of a tornado being about 8 to 10 minutes.

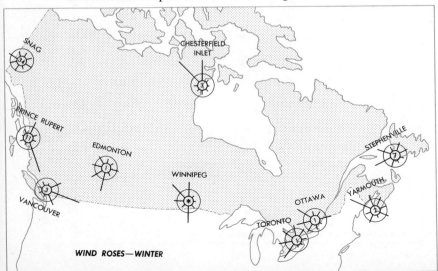

WIND ROSES—WINTER

By means of the length of the line from each compass point, wind roses show the frequency and intensity with which winds blow in a particular place. Direction frequencies are based on the time during which the wind blows, regardless of its velocity. The number in the centre indicates the percentage of time during which there is calm.

The asterisk in a wind rose indicates less than 1% calm for a particular place. On the basis of these two maps—and remember that two other seasons are omitted—which are (a) the windiest, (b) the calmest, centres in Canada? Name a centre where, in both seasons, winds are principally from the east, one wind being from the northeast, the other from the southeast.

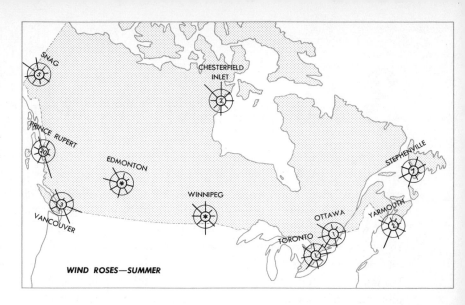

WIND ROSES—SUMMER

Wind Velocity and Beaufort Scale

Description	Miles Per Hour	Beaufort Number	Wind Effects Observed on Land
Light	1 – 3	1	Calm; smoke rises vertically. Direction of wind shown by smoke drift; but not by wind vanes.
	4 – 7	2	Wind felt on face; leaves rustle; ordinary vane moved by wind.
Gentle	8 – 12	3	Leaves and small twigs in constant motion; wind extends light flag.
Moderate	13 – 18	4	Raises dust, loose paper; small branches are moved.
Fresh	19 – 24	5	Small trees in leaf begin to sway; whitecaps form on inland waters.
Strong	25 – 31	6	Large branches in motion; whistling heard in telegraph wires; umbrellas used with difficulty.
Gale	32 – 38	7	Whole trees in motion; inconvenience felt walking against wind.
	39 – 46	8	Breaks twigs off trees; generally impedes progress.
	47 – 54	9	Slight structural damage occurs.
	55 – 63	10	Seldom experienced inland; trees uprooted; considerable structural damage occurs.
Whole gale	64 – 74	11	Very rarely experienced; accompanied by widespread damage.
Hurricane	75 – 136	12 – 17	Very rarely experienced; accompanied by widespread damage.

3 THE AIR AND ITS MOISTURE

Were it not for the water vapour in the air, most of the earth would become arid, barren desert. Water vapour plays a key role in the air's ability to absorb and retain heat. Yet, in spite of its strong effect on the absorption and retention of atmospheric heat, water vapour forms at most only 5% of our atmosphere, and even within this narrow percentage the actual proportion is extremely variable. In recent years people have been paying more attention to water vapour in the air, or *humidity* as it is called, because it has become clear that the comfort of human beings depends in large measure on this humidity of the air. Temperatures alone are not adequate criteria in selecting a pleasant place for next summer's vacation.

Measuring the Moisture in the Atmosphere

Each year billions of tons of water enter the atmosphere as a result of the sun's activity, most of it to return to the oceans, lakes, and rivers as precipitation. Every day much of the exposed water surfaces on earth loses water through the process of *evaporation*. This process is, of course, a gradual one, and we are seldom aware of its occurrence. Evaporation is most rapid in areas of high temperatures, such as the tropical regions. Winds also aid evaporation, for still air soon becomes completely saturated and so hinders the continuance of the evaporation process. A certain amount of moisture also enters the air from moist land surfaces and from burning fuels.

All plants also give off moisture to the air. This process is called *transpiration*, and its effects are considerable. It has been estimated that a single tree in one year may release several thousand gallons of water into the atmosphere.

Different terms are employed relative to the measurement of the amount of humidity in the air. The term *absolute humidity* is used to describe the weight of water vapour contained in a given volume of air. Absolute humidity is usually measured in grains per cubic foot, a grain being .002 ounces. The capacity of air to hold moisture varies with its temperature. This is a fact of the utmost importance in the understanding of weather processes. The higher the temperature of the air, the greater its capacity to hold water vapour. Consequently a rise in temperature increases the air's capacity to hold moisture, a lowering of temperature decreases this capacity. For every temperature there is a definite limit to the amount of water vapour that the air can hold. This limit is called *saturation point*, and air at or above this point is described as saturated. Saturated air cannot retain any further moisture in the form of vapour and, therefore, such excess moisture condenses into a liquid. This condensation appears in the atmosphere in the form of rain, snow, hail, and clouds.

In terms of the probability of rainfall and of degree of human comfort it may now be clear that knowledge of the absolute humidity alone is of little value. For a particular temperature we must know the relationship or proportion between the amount of moisture in the air and the amount of moisture that the air is capable of holding. This proportion is called the *relative humidity* and it is usually expressed as a percentage. Changes 'in the temperature of the air or in the amount of moisture it holds, will be reflected in changes in relative humidity. Thus air at 50° F. reaches the saturation point when it holds slightly over 4 grains of water vapour per cubic foot. If it contains 3 grains, its relative humidity is about 75%. Were that body of air warmed up to 70° F., it would be enabled to hold 8 grains per cubic foot and its relative humidity would fall to about 36%, even though it still held exactly the same quantity of moisture. By the same token, if the temperature of that mass of air fell to 40° F., it would be completely saturated with 3 grains per cubic foot; in other words, its relative humidity would be 100%.

Here we see a magnification of dew drops on blades of grass. Briefly explain how dew is formed.

Department of Public Relations,
Ontario Agricultural College, Guelph

How Condensation Occurs

In the previous example we saw that the cooling of moist air could result in its reaching saturation point. Continued cooling below this point will result in the changing of the vapour into a liquid or solid. The temperature at which water in the atmosphere begins to condense is called the *dew point*. At night many objects are sufficiently cold to chill the surrounding air to just below the dew point, with the result that the atmospheric moisture condenses on their surface as dew. The same scientific process takes place at parties when water droplets appear on the outside of glasses which contain iced drinks.

An important law of meteorology states that rising air becomes cooler even though no heat may be lost to the outside. This cooling is the result of decreasing pressure and is known as *adiabatic cooling*. It is important not to confuse the rate of adiabatic cooling with the lapse rate; the latter applies only to still air, the temperature of which is measured at different levels. The normal dry adiabatic rate is about 5.5° F. for every thousand feet. Most air, however, is moist and the water vapour present alters the adiabatic rate to the extent that the moist adiabatic rate is about 3° F. for every thousand feet.

Clouds

Air is constantly in motion and masses of air are always rising and falling as restlessly as do the waves in the ocean. The temperature of rising air masses is reduced to dew point by adiabatic cooling until the water vapour condenses to form clouds. Cooling alone is not sufficient, however, for cloud formation. Microscopic dust, smoke, or salt particles serve as nuclei upon which the vapour can condense to form water droplets. Such a dust particle is called a condensation nucleus. All clouds are composed of billions of these same tiny droplets; but the clouds assume different outlines and form at different altitudes. On the basis of these differences clouds are classified.

Within a belt of 20,000 feet above sea level to about 40,000 feet are to be found the highest clouds. These clouds are often thin and wispy and are composed chiefly of minute particles of ice. Such thin, featherlike streaks across the sky, often in slow-moving bands, are called *cirrus* clouds. Associated with them are sheets of white cloud which may cover the whole sky and may produce a halo around the sun and moon—the *cirrostratus* clouds. Groups or lines of small globular patches of cloud are sometimes described as *mackerel* sky and such clouds are classified as *cirrocumulus*.

Between 6,500 feet and the lower limit of the cirrus clouds occur the *alto-cumulus* and *altostratus* families of clouds. The latter is a greyish blanket, often with dark streaks on the underside or with the sun showing as a bright spot in the centre of the cloud. This type of cloud is often a sign of bad weather to come,

HIGH CLOUDS — — — — — **35,000 FEET**

Cirrocumulus

Cirrus

Cirrostratus

DEVELOPMENT

Cumulonimbus

MIDDLE CLOUDS — — — — — **20,000 FEET**

Altostratus

Altocumulus

VERTICAL

Cumulus

OW CLOUDS — — — — — **6,000 FEET**

CLOUDS WITH

Stratus

Nimbostratus

Stratocumulus

65

whereas the altocumulus is often related to fine weather. The altocumulus consists of geometrical masses of rounded, white clouds. Below these two groups of clouds and down to ground level are the low clouds. *Stratus* cloud is a dense, uniform, dark grey layer very similar to fog. Separate masses of low-lying grey cloud are called *stratocumulus*; these are often arranged in long lines with spaces between. Often accompanied by rain or snow are the thick, dark, shapeless masses of the *nimbostratus* group.

There are a few types of cloud which can be found anywhere between 1,500 and 35,000 feet above sea level. Thick, white, fleecy clouds, which usually have flat bases and are often widely spaced, are called *cumulus*. Larger than these and having cauliflowerlike tops are *cumulonimbus* clouds, which reach high into the atmosphere, where they may be associated with thick cirrus clouds; they are the thunderhead clouds.

Fog

Fog is really a type of stratus cloud formed from an air mass in which the cooling has been slow and has taken place throughout the whole mass. Usually the cooling of this air has taken place near the ground and so is not the result of rising air. Fog can be produced in several ways:

Ground or radiation fog is produced on clear, cool nights when the ground loses heat rapidly by radiation and the air close to the ground is cooled below dew point. This type of fog can be particularly thick in valleys and often occurs in the fall.

Advection fog is produced when warm, moist air passes over a much colder surface. This frequently happens in spring when the ground is still frozen or snow-covered.

Conditions opposite to those of advection fog can produce the same result. At times water may evaporate into a body of air which is too cold to hold it as vapour; so it condenses once again in the form of fog.

Similar to advection fogs are those produced by the mixing of contrasting air masses. Such mixing is most likely to occur in areas where cold or warm ocean currents meet. An outstanding example of such an area is the Grand Banks off the Newfoundland coast, where the Labrador Current brings cold air into contact with warmer air over the Gulf Stream.

Other Precipitation

"What causes rain?" is one of the most difficult questions in the whole science of meteorology. The following explanation is the most commonly accepted one, but it still leaves many questions unanswered. The droplets of water in a cloud vary in size according to the size of their condensation nuclei. Most cloud droplets are only 1/2,500 inch in diameter and so are easily kept in the atmosphere by even gentle air movements. The larger droplets, however, may gradually drift downwards; in doing so they collide, and unite, with other smaller droplets, thus increasing still further their own size. This kind of growth is called *coalescence*. When the droplet has reached about 1/125 inch, it is usually heavy enough to fall even through rising air currents and has now become a raindrop.

Ice crystals, too, can cause rainfall. In cooling the air around it, each crystal increases its own size by the water vapour which crystallizes on its surface. Eventually the falling ice crystals melt and continue their passage to the ground as raindrops. This is the basis of one of the two chief methods of scientifically producing rain, namely, seeding rain clouds with ice crystals from an aircraft. As silver iodide crystals have an effect similar to ice crystals, they are also used in this modern and very important application of meteorology.

Ice and frost can present scenes of great beauty. They provide us with facilities for winter enjoyment. However, here you can see one of the disadvantages. Name four other drawbacks.

Courtesy Ontario Hydro

As has already been pointed out, condensation is usually the result of the cooling of an air mass. On the basis of the cause of this cooling, types of precipitation can be classed as convectional, orographic, or cyclonic.

Convectional precipitation is the result of the rapid heating of the air over part of the earth's surface with the resultant development of convection currents in the atmosphere. Thunderhead clouds form under these conditions and the precipitation which occurs is usually sudden and violent. In Canada this type of precipitation is most common in the summer months; in hot tropical latitudes it is common throughout the year.

Air can be forced to rise, too, by the shape of the land over which it is moving. Humid air blowing towards a mountain range is forced by the relief of the land to rise and in rising is cooled adiabatically. Sufficient cooling results in precipitation on the windward slopes of the mountains where air is rising. On the other, or leeward, side the air is falling and is becoming warmed; consequently the wind now has a drying effect. This dry leeward side is called the *rain shadow*, and the type of precipitation which occurs on the windward side is called *orographic*. The high mountains along our Pacific seaboard provide excellent examples of orographic precipitation and rain shadows.

A cold, and therefore heavy, air mass may act in a way similar to that in which a great mountain range acts. In this case the rising warmer air produces *cyclonic* precipitation. Much of the rainfall occurring in the lands between 35° and 65° North and South latitudes is of the cyclonic type. Cyclones, or depressions, are very complex weather masses and they will require detailed treatment later in the book.

Precipitation can also be classified on the basis of the size and form of the drop of water that is falling. Thus droplets of less than 1/100 inch diameter are called *drizzle*. These droplets are so small that they will normally remain suspended in the air if there is even a slight upward air movement. Drizzle, therefore, is associated with very still conditions. In the case of the rain, droplets may range up to ⅕ inch in diameter; such droplets will fall even against fairly strong air movements. At times the falling raindrop passes through a layer of very cold air and freezes. This forms *sleet*. In other conditions the frozen raindrop is buffeted up and down through the cold air by successive currents of air. Each of these movements results in the formation of another layer of ice around the already frozen drop. Such precipitation is called *hail* and occurs most commonly in thunderstorms—a type of storm where strong vertical air currents are created. The commonest form of solid precipitation is *snow*; this occurs when ice crystals fall to the ground without melting. Before reaching the ground these crystals may pass through a belt of warm air which can cause some melting and lead to several crystals' sticking together to form large snowflakes. Hard, fine snow results if the falling crystal passes through a belt of colder air near the ground.

68

4 THE WEATHER MAP

Maps and geography go together. One famous geographer once said, "If it's geography, it can be shown on a map". This can be partly explained by the fact that this subject is concerned with the relationship between places and conditions on the face of the earth. Mapping things helps us to understand them more clearly, picture them more vividly, or explain them more quickly and accurately. Weather conditions are mapped by meteorologists for all three of these reasons.

The weather map is an attempt to show by symbols the existing weather conditions of a large number of places. By using such a map we can describe the weather of a number of these places at a particular time and, after a certain amount of practice, describe the future weather conditions in any of them. This is called forecasting.

National Aeronautics and Space Administration

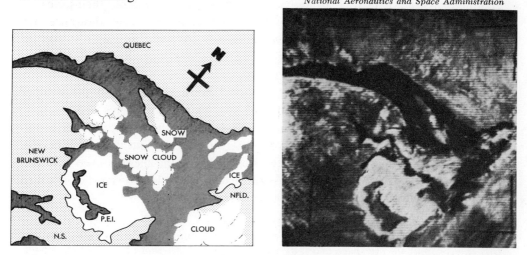

Tiros IV took this photograph of 300,000 square miles of the estuary of the St. Lawrence. Snow is seen on Anticosti. Snow clouds hang between it and P.E.I. which is locked in ice. Ice also blocks much of the channel between Newfoundland and the mainland.

Every official weather map is the result of the work of hundreds, perhaps even thousands, of highly trained meteorologists. All over North America and throughout most of the other advanced countries of the world, these men take a host of weather readings every six hours and transmit them to a national agency which rapidly combines and plots them on maps. The information gathered includes atmospheric pressure; temperature; wind direction and speed; amount and form of precipitation; extent, type, and height of clouds; humidity; and visibility. All of this information is then plotted on a large map until a general pattern begins to emerge.

The first thing which strikes us on examining a weather map is the mass of winding, whirling lines many of which are in concentric patterns. These lines are drawn to connect points which have an equal barometric pressure, and are called *isobars*. By means of these lines we can recognize the various high- and low-pressure systems. In view of the fact that winds blow from high- to low-pressure areas, these isobars can tell us something about their probable direction. However, owing to the Coriolis and other forces, these winds do not blow at right angles to the isobars but are actually deflected as you can see on the map. The relative spacing between isobars is called the *gradient*; this can tell us much about force or velocity of the winds. When isobars are close together, we have a steep gradient and strong winds will result. Widely spaced isobars mean gentle gradients and generally slower winds.

In reading a weather map it is important to bear in mind that in the middle latitudes—an area which includes much of Canada and the United States—the general movement of great masses of air is towards the east. This fact is of enormous assistance in forecasting; but, of course, the air masses themselves do change direction as they move and so the forecaster has to make allowances for such changes. Low-pressure cells move across our continent in winter at average speeds of about 30 miles an hour. In summer they are generally slower—usually about 20 m.p.h.

The location of meteorological stations is shown by circles on the weather map. Each of these circles is accompanied by a number of figures and symbols; by means of these, important information is given about the actual weather conditions at any particular place. In order to facilitate the interpretation of this information, the symbols used have been standardized, and there is even a special position for each figure used. This mass of weather symbols and statistics is called station model. Examine the accompanying model closely.

Here you see a complete station model, although it is actually much larger than it would be on a weather map. Write a paragraph describing the weather conditions at this place. Compare the space taken by your paragraph with that of the station model.

1. Figures showing force of wind in knots (each ½ barb = 5 knots).

2. Arrow showing direction of middle cloud movement.

3. Figures showing temperature in degrees Fahrenheit.

4. Arrow shaft showing direction of wind (from northwest).

5. Symbol showing present state of weather (snow).

6. Visibility in miles and fractions.

7. Coverage of lower clouds in tenths.

8. Height of base of clouds in hundreds of feet.

9. Symbol showing type of low cloud (stratus).

10. Figures showing dew point in degrees Fahrenheit.

11. Symbol showing type of middle cloud (thick stratus).

12. Figures showing barometric pressure at sea level (1024.7 millibars—9 or 10 omitted).

13. Figures showing net amount of barometric change in past 3 hours (in tenths of millibars—2.8 millibars).

14. Symbol showing barometric tendency in past 3 hours (rising, then steady).

15. + or − sign showing pressure higher or lower than 3 hours ago.

16. Code figure showing time precipitation began or ended (in this case ended since present and past weather are of different types).

17. Past weather during 6 hours preceding observation (rain).

18. Figures showing amount of precipitation in the last 6 hours (.45″).

19. Symbol showing amount of total sky covered by clouds.

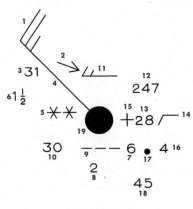

A STATION MODEL

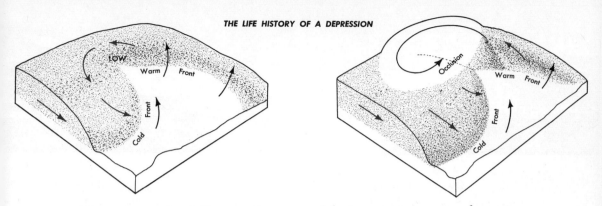

These cross-sectional diagrams show some of the important stages in a depression.

The Depression

Mention has already been made of the large low-pressure cells which are so characteristic of our latitudes. These usually appear on the weather map as concentric patterns of isobars stretched out on a northeast-to-southwest direction and covering an area of perhaps 500 to 1,000 square miles. These pressure systems, called *depressions*, have very regular weather patterns which make the forecaster's work easier. During World War I, Bjerknes, a Norwegian meteorologist, developed an important theory which explains most of the weather conditions found in a normal depression. At that time huge armies were facing each other in France on a line of fighting called the *front*. Bjerknes explained the depression in terms of two constrasting air masses, a polar and a warm air mass, and his theory, named according to the terminology of World War I, became known as the *Polar Front Theory*.

THE LIFE HISTORY OF A DEPRESSION

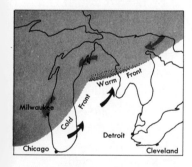

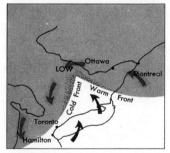

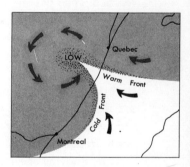

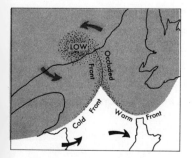

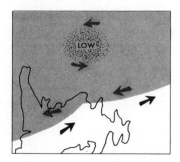

Here you see the changes which might take place in a depression as it moves across eastern Canada.

71

This cross-section of a depression gives some idea of the processes involved and the resulting weather conditions. Bear in mind, however, that the cold air mass in front actually "wraps around" the warm air to reappear again at the rear.

The line of contact between the polar and the warm air is known as a *front*, and at first there will normally be one continuous front. As the air masses turn in towards each other and as the warm air is gradually lifted off the ground by colder air, two fronts begin to form. These two form an inverted *V* pointing at the centre of the depression with the warm air between its two arms. Since the first (that is the eastern) of these two lines is the front of the warm air mass, it is called the *warm front*. Moving west we again enter an area of cold air when we cross the second line or *cold front*.

A cross-section of the air masses close to the warm front would show that here warm air is gradually rising over a wedge of cold air. Associated with this rising warm air is a succession of cloud formations beginning with the lofty cirrus, and culminating in a vast expanse of dull, stratus layers. These clouds may give warning of a depression as much as a thousand miles before the warm front is reached. The passing of the warm front over an area is marked by rainfall, which may be quite heavy and continuous. Conditions at the cold front are quite different. Here the warm air is being lifted much more sharply, partly owing to the fact that friction with the ground slows down the advancing cold air; the rapidly rising warm air produces towering cumulus and cumulonimbus clouds and violent rain-storms and thunderstorms often occur. Strong winds which shift direction suddenly are also characteristic of cold fronts and in the days of sail these could present serious danger to sailors, who called them squall lines. In the case of slower-moving warm fronts the winds are normally not so strong and storms are less likely.

In studying the life story of a depression, we notice that the second, or cold, front gradually overhauls the warm front. When this happens the warm air mass is lifted completely off the ground and as the depression progresses steadily, more of this air is lifted ever higher into the atmosphere. The term *occlusion,* or *occluded front* is used to describe this area where the two fronts have merged and often the storm is most intense here, the winds moving anticlockwise around the centre of lowest pressure. Eventually, however, the occlusion becomes complete, all the warm air is far above ground level and is rapidly cooling, and the depression gradually dies out.

72

Sometimes a depression may halt its eastward movement and the fronts may linger in one locality; they are then called *stationary fronts*, but they retain the general characteristics of normal warm and cold fronts.

The Anticyclone

The low-pressure system which forms a depression is sometimes called a temperate cyclone. There is, however, another pressure system which is of importance, the anticyclone, which is a high-pressure cell. Winds associated with the anticyclone blow in a clockwise direction out from the centre. The anticyclone has no division by fronts and there is no lifting of a large cold air mass. Weather conditions in an anticyclone are often fine and clear—cold in winter, but a heat wave in summer—and they often remain settled for long periods as the anticyclone moves very slowly once it is well established.

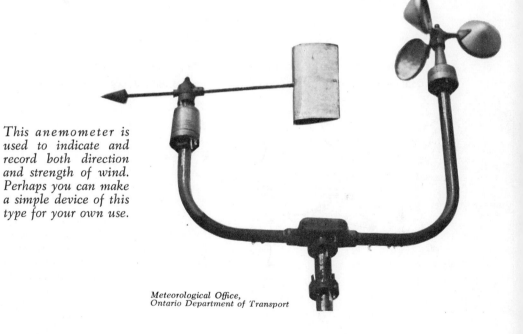

This anemometer is used to indicate and record both direction and strength of wind. Perhaps you can make a simple device of this type for your own use.

Meteorological Office,
Ontario Department of Transport

The Thunderstorm

The storms associated with depressions usually cover a wide area but are seldom of exceptional violence. Rain rather than gale-force winds is their chief characteristic. In certain parts of the world, however, destructive winds and storms can assume the proportions of a national disaster. The thunderstorms which we experience in warm weather are the result of warm air's rising very rapidly. This air causes a cumulus formation to tower as high as 25,000 feet, where condensation begins to take place. An immense amount of turbulence takes place at this time owing to the fact that some air is still rising while sharp downdrafts are accompanying the rain or hail. Lightning takes place in these storms because the upper layers of the cloud become positively charged with electricity while the lower levels are negatively charged. In certain cases lower cloud levels may even become positively charged. The ground, too, usually has an electric charge with reference to the adjoining air masses. When the difference between any two of these electrical charges becomes too great, a discharge takes place between them. The clap of thunder is caused by the rapid heating and expansion of the air as the lightning passes through it.

Every year over 200 people are killed by lightning in North America alone, but in many of these cases a little care could have saved a life. Lightning tends to strike prominent objects such as a person standing in a large open field. Avoid trees, bodies of water and metal towers on these occasions. Automobiles and buildings with a steel framework, however, are generally safe.

Air Masses

It should now be clear that to understand our weather we must know a great deal about atmospheric conditions many miles away from our own area.

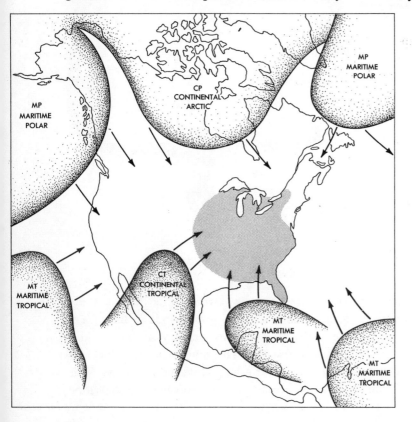

The major air masses of North America and their general classification are shown here. The dotted area shows the chief "battleground" of polar and tropical air. This is also the region of most frequent tornadoes in this continent.

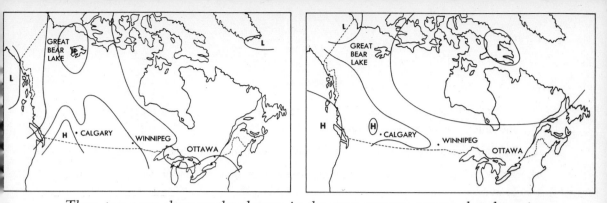

These two maps show us the changes in the great pressure systems that determine the weather conditions of the various parts of Canada. Correlate these maps carefully with the even more generalized one of air masses. What conclusions can you draw from these maps about probable wind direction?

There are certain great semipermanent air masses over the continents and oceans whose interaction produces the cyclonic pressure systems already considered. Each of the vast air masses is characterized by fairly uniform conditions of temperature and humidity and they are classed by their source as polar (P), arctic (A), or tropical (T), maritime (m), or continental (c). At times these great air masses expand or send out long arms over distant areas, thus the tropical continental air mass often produces weeks of hot, dry weather in summer over the Central United States, the Prairies, and parts of Ontario. In winter cold air from the Polar Continental mass sometimes penetrates as far south as the Gulf of Mexico.

UNIT REVIEW

Vocabulary Review

Match the phrase in the left column with the correct word or phrase in the right column. Do not write in this book.

1. Measures air pressure
2. Band of high altitude winds
3. Equatorial low pressure belt
4. Sheetlike clouds
5. Layer of atmosphere closest to earth
6. Low pressure belt 65° N and S of the equator
7. Ratio between capacity and actual amount of water vapour
8. Particle around which water droplets collect
9. Large mass of low pressure air
10. Measures wind velocity
11. A wind blowing towards the sea
12. Science of the atmosphere
13. A form of oxygen which absorbs solar radiation
14. Connects places of equal atmospheric pressure

a. troposphere
b. horse latitudes
c. relative humidity
d. circumpolar whirl
e. barometer
f. doldrums
g. stratus
h. depression
i. isobar
j. land breeze
k. station model
l. condensation nucleus
m. anemometer
n. meteorology
o. coalescence
p. ozone

Questions

1. Approximately how thick is each of the four layers of the atmosphere? List the chief characteristics of each.

2. Explain the differences in air conditions which produce dew, rain, and frost.

3. Draw a diagram of a depression and explain in what direction the wind would blow:
   (a) directly east of the centre
   (b) southwest of the centre
   (c) directly north of the centre.

4. What are the main similarities and differences between hurricanes and tornadoes?

5. Construct a station model with the following information:
   (a) sky, overcast
   (b) southwest wind, 20 knots
   (c) temperature, 69° F.
   (d) dew point, 47° F.
   (e) pressure, 1026.3 millibars
   (f) barometric tendency last three hours, rise of 3.8 millibars
   (g) present weather, drizzle
   (h) cloud type, stratus
   (i) past weather, showers
   (j) precipitation, 0.73 inches

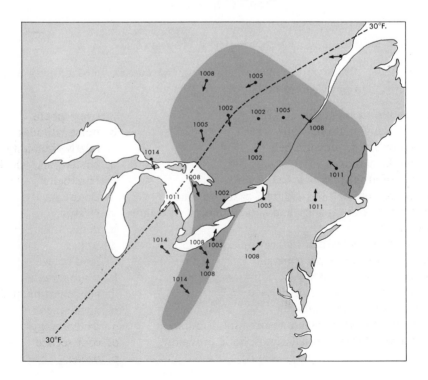

6. This generalized weather map shows a depression passing over the Great Lakes-St. Lawrence region. Pressure in millibars and wind direction are given for each station. The shaded area is experiencing precipitation at the time of the readings. The area north and west of the isotherm shown has temperatures below 30° F.; all other areas are warmer than that.

   (a) Draw in the isobars of this depression.

   (b) Find the centre of the depression. Mark it "L".

   (c) Paying close attention to wind direction, draw in the warm and cold fronts. There is no occlusion here.

   (d) Estimate the wind direction at the stations where this is not shown.

   (e) Indicate areas where cirrus, stratus, and cumulus clouds might occur.

Research Assignments

1. Use a good encyclopedia to find out what the following instruments are used for. Prepare a statement explaining how any one of them works.

   (a) Hygrometer

   (b) Barograph

   (c) Radiosonde

   (d) Psychrometer

   (e) Aneroid Barometer

2. Using good encyclopedias and magazine articles prepare a detailed report on the theory and technique of rain making.

3. Draw up a chart with the following headings:

Day	Temperature		Precipitation		Wind		Cloud	
	Maximum	Minimum	Type	Amount	Direction	Force	Type	%

Each morning and evening for the next two weeks use the wind and cloud charts and your local radio station to fill in the chart. At the end of that period draw a wind rose and temperature graphs of your district.

What was the commonest cloud type? At what elevation is this cloud found?

Unit Two

Waters of the Earth

1 THE WATERS OF THE LAND

Land, water, and air in various forms make up the physical environment in which man lives. Of these three the one which is perhaps the most widespread is water. Immediately we think of the water environment as meaning oceans, seas, rivers, and lakes, but this is only part of the water in our surroundings; in addition there are the clouds, rain, humidity in the air; there is water in the soil, in sedimentary rocks, in underground caverns. In this chapter we will concern ourselves only with the water in the ground.

The Earth's Water System

Paul Gallico has written a book called *The Snowflake*, in which he tells the story of a snowflake's falling on the mountains; it melts and enters a river, reaches the sea, is evaporated, and returns once again to the atmosphere. This particle of water had fulfilled a complete cycle in different forms: solid, liquid, and vapour. Practically all the water on the earth repeatedly undergoes such a cycle with some slight variations. The entire process is called the *hydrologic cycle*.

The first stage in the hydrologic cycle is the passing of water into the atmosphere by evaporation. Carried by atmospheric movements over the world's landmasses, this moisture falls back as rain or snow to the surface of the earth. Part of the water which falls is evaporated on its way downwards; part is evaporated from the ground, plants, ponds, rivers, and other bodies of water. Some reaches the sea again in streams and rivers, while other water enters the soil to join in a great underground circulation about which we still have much to learn. An idea of the proportion of total rainfall which is taken up by each of these processes can be gained by the following. In our temperate latitudes a place with a total precipitation of 30 inches would have nearly 6 inches of run-off in streams and creeks and about 3 inches that would percolate deep into the soil; the remaining 21 inches re-enters the air as evaporation.

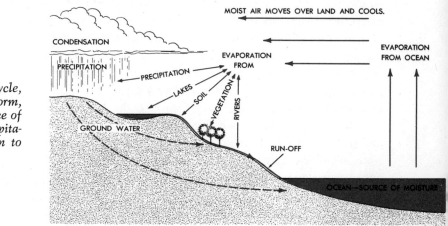

The hydrologic cycle, in diagrammatic form, illustrates the source of moisture, its precipitation, and its return to the ocean.

Lakes

Lakes, quite small lakes, are among the very beautiful features of many landscapes and their place in the art and literature of most countries is a very important one. In terms of economics, too, the lake has an important multiple role to fulfil: it provides transport, power generation, water supply, and recreational resources. The number and variety of lakes on the surface of the earth is incalculable; indeed, no one has yet been able to count the lakes of Canada alone. In order to classify and, therefore, understand lakes more clearly, geographers usually examine their origins and then group them into certain categories on this basis.

Glacial lakes are perhaps the most important in the geography and activities of the North American continent. Many glacial cirques now contain a completely enclosed small lake, called a tarn. In places, glaciers gouged in the earth great holes which were subsequently filled with water; in, other places, the dumps of glacial moraine have so interfered with the normal drainage that streams have wandered wildly filling up one depression after another in a chain of small ponds and lakes.

Eventually glacial lakes may disappear either through silting or else through the wearing down of the moraine barrier and the draining away of the impounded waters. This is what happened in the case of Lake Agassiz, of which our present lakes Winnipeg and Winnipegosis are mere relics. Glaciation also played a significant part in the formation of the Great Lakes, which were probably merely wide river valleys deepened and further widened by glacial scouring. Hundreds of moraines were dumped along the southern margins of these valleys. As the glaciers melted, their water flowed into the great depressions, was trapped by the morainic mounds, and found its outlets through the Illinois and Wabash, then the Mississippi, and later through the Susquehanna and Hudson. During this period, the area and shape of the lakes were different from those of today; accordingly, geologists have given these ancestors of our present lakes different names. Thus the enlarged form of Lake Ontario is called Lake Iroquois and those living close to Lake Ontario can take part in useful field trips to trace the former shore line of Lake Iroquois, which in many places is still quite evident. Eventually, adjustments in the level of the land after the removal of the ice led to these lakes taking their present form and finding their only large outlet through the St. Lawrence.

Diastrophic lakes are those produced by earth movements such as folding and faulting. Faulting followed by tilting, can result in depressions which become water-filled and form lakes, but deeper lakes usually occur in grabens or cracks occurring between two more or less parallel faults. The world's deepest lake—Lake Baikal in the U.S.S.R.—is of this type and reaches a depth of over 5,700 feet. Lake Tahoe between California and Nevada, is a smaller lake of this type. In Africa, the great rift valley includes Nyasa, Tanganyika, Rudolf, and many other lakes.

Volcanic activity, too, can produce lakes by the damming of rivers by lava and by the filling of extinct calderas or craters with water. Crater Lake in Oregon is a particularly beautiful and much-photographed lake of this latter type.

Rivers can form lakes in many ways. Abandoned meanders, called ox-bows, can remain as sealed-off lakes for many years. Obstruction of a river can lead to the filling up of part of the adjacent valley just as a reservoir fills up behind a dam. A delta, too, may cut off a large body of water and so form a lake; the Salton Sea in California is a particularly fine example of this type of lake.

Lakes may also be formed in a variety of other ways. Wind erosion, landslides, mudflows, and the removal of salts and limestone in solution can all produce depressions which may eventually become lakes. Finally, by the building of dams, man himself has been an important agent in the formation of large lakes. In the United States and the Soviet Union there are several particularly large lakes of this type, e.g., those behind the Hoover (Colorado R.) and Grand Coulee (Columbia R.) dams, and the Rybinsk and Kuibyshev lakes of the U.S.S.R.

Tectonic depressions can often be obscured by the presence of lakes. Here we have a small lake in a simple fault, but many large lakes occur in important grabens. Find one such lake in Africa and one in Asia.

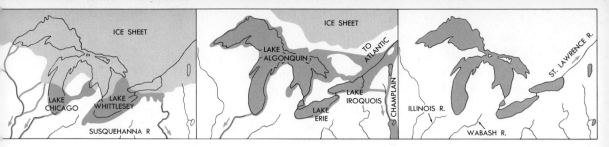

STAGES IN THE FORMATION OF THE GREAT LAKES

The retreating ice not only shaped the land but also, in this case, shaped the lakes and rivers.

The Water in the Earth's Crust

Wells play an essential part in the life of most of our villages and small towns, thus reminding us of that part of the precipitation which enters deep into the soil. Since this water originated in the atmosphere, it is known as *meteoric* water; after it falls, it gradually seeps through soil and spaces in the rocks. Within deep sedimentary rocks there is often salt water that has been trapped in pockets ever since the time that these rocks were formed on lake or sea bottoms. This water is said to be *connate* because it was sealed in at the time the rock was *born*. Unlike meteoric water, this water is usually static and does not move within the rock. Finally, there is *magmatic* underground water which is of chemical origin, having been released in the rock by volcanic heating processes.

In a study of underground water we distinguish two layers of rock—the lower layer into which water has penetrated until it can hold no more and an upper, drier layer. These are respectively known as the zones of saturation and of aeration and are separated by an imaginary line called the *water table*, which is defined as the upper limit of the saturated layer. The water table rises and falls in accordance with major changes in precipitation and with the quantities of water drawn off from the depths. The shape of the water table more or less follows that of the surface above but is usually rather more gentle in its slopes. It is rather like a shadow of the surface contours.

Ground water flows in much the same way as surface streams, i.e., it flows down the slope of the water table at a rate proportional to the gradient. Another variable factor affecting the rate of movement of ground water is the permeability or impermeability of the rocks through which the water has to pass. In some cases this water has been known to move at a rate of several feet a day. Igneous and metamorphic rocks are often of very low permeability; they, therefore, are often of little value in affording a water supply.

This diagram shows Lake Agassiz—a great lake of the past. Lakes are transitory features on the earth's surface; they drain away or silt up with the passage of time. Notice the size of Agassiz compared to our present Great Lakes—yet now only small fragments of it remain.

Wherever the water table reaches the surface, ponds, marshes, lakes, or streams commonly result. Along hillsides this occurrence will result in a series of springs, but many of these may dry up if the water table falls in times of drought. Perhaps the most reliable springs are those which emerge close to the point where a permeable rock lies immediately above an impermeable layer, the result being that the water flows along the surface of the impermeable rock to emerge on the hillside. Settlements often found at these springs are known as *spring-line settlements*.

More spectacular, but often less useful, are the ground waters which appear at the surface as hot springs and geysers in many parts of the world. Ground water may be heated by underground volcanic activity or by its being mixed with steam or hot gases, so that its temperature on reaching the surface may range from lukewarm to boiling. In cases where the evaporation of water by boiling exceeds the normal inflow, mineral particles become concentrated in the water, and thick, porridge-like *mud-volcanoes* result. Because hot water always has a much greater capacity to dissolve minerals than cold water, these hot springs carry large quantities of minerals towards the surface. Here the minerals may accumulate as terraces around the hot spring, a calciferous substance known as travertine being their main constituent. Normally white, travertine often assumes quite gay shades of red, yellow, or brown depending on the algae present in the area. You have probably seen picturesque coloured posters showing this type of formation in the Yellowstone National Park or perhaps in the beautiful Rotorua district of New Zealand.

Sometimes a series of underground cavities linked by small passages becomes filled with heated steam and water. If the outlet of this system is narrow and crooked, the trapped water may continue to heat above the normal boiling point of 212° F. This *superheating* occurs because of the pressure of the water blocking the outlet from the cavities. Eventually, the trapped water does boil and forces its way to the surface; in so doing it reduces the pressure on the underlying waters. These then boil explosively, driving hot water and steam high in the air until the chambers are practically emptied of their original water. More ground water then floods in and the process begins all over again. This is the explanation of the magnificent, and sometimes frightening, *geysers* which are such tourist attractions in many parts of the world. Geysers generally occur in areas of such considerable faulting as the downfaulted formations known as grabens.

Notice the underground relief of the water table. Bear in mind that water within the saturation zone is also probably moving.

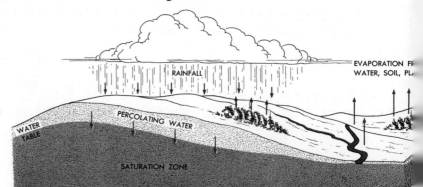

These diagrams show the effect of underlying geology on drainage and on settlement pattern.

Water Supply and Man

Modern industry, social organization, settlement patterns, civilization, and even human life itself are impossible without an adequate water supply. Think how difficult life would be in New York, Vancouver, or Toronto if everyone still had to go down to a stream, lake, or well for all the water he needed for washing, cooking, and drinking.

Wells still supply much of man's water requirements, although most of this water is now pumped through complex supply systems. To be effective, a well must penetrate below the water table, preferably in an area where the flow of ground water is quite fast and where rocks are highly permeable. In view of the fact that the upper level of the water table is liable to fall in periods of prolonged drought, the reliability of a well may easily depend upon the well's being sunk to a considerable depth below this upper level. Since bringing this water to the surface usually demands pumping, such wells are known as *pump wells*.

In large areas of Australia, the Middle West of the United States, and other parts of the world, there are many productive wells which do not require pumps, but rather the water from them can pour forth like a powerful fountain. As the first wells of this type were found in Artois in northern France, they have sub-sequently been called *artesian* wells. These wells are the result of a depression in geological structures which consists of a permeable layer of rock sandwiched between two impermeable layers. If these rocks become exposed to the surface in a particular area, water penetrates the permeable layer, called the *aquifer*, and accumulates in the lower parts of this layer. As such water is under some pressure, it rushes up wells without the need of pumps. This artesian water may come from very great depths and is often at a high temperature when it reaches the surface. More important still, artesian water is often very salty and hence of little value for irrigation.

The meeting of permeable and impermeable rock is often the source of springs. This diagram shows how a fault may produce such a spring.

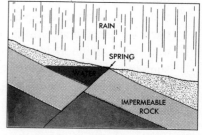

In the semi-arid lands of the world, man often creates his own water reservoirs by building structures to catch and hold water in great tanks, in vast underground

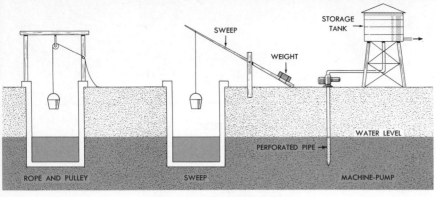

WELLS OF THREE DIFFERENT TYPES

The rope and pulley was extensively used in medieval western Europe. Many Egyptian villages still use the sweep. Your community perhaps uses the machine-pump system. Find out three other types of wells and relate them to the correct place and period of history.

caverns, or in basins. During and since World War II many such water-storage systems have been developed in North Africa from water resources which had been forgotten since the days of the Roman Empire. This *catchment* water is often of very good quality and can be an important factor in the life of these areas.

Previous comments on spring-line settlements serve to emphasize the fact that the surface water in many areas may play an important role in the location of human habitations. In more recent years we can find many examples of huge industrial plants whose locations have largely been determined by the need for vast quantities of water; some idea of the quantities required can be gained from the list on this page. Since surface drainage patterns may vary as between permeable and impermeable rocks in a particular area, the variation is often reflected in different patterns of village distribution. Here, too, we see man's heavy reliance on natural water supply. Vast cities, of course, require immense quantities of water and often spend astronomical sums to guarantee their supply. It has been calculated that the average North American uses about 15,000 gallons per year. The city of Los Angeles has developed its sources of water in the Sierra Nevada, from which it pipes water for 200 miles into the city.

Probably 90% of the water used in cities and factories is subsequently returned to rivers and streams after use. You might immediately say that this should solve the problem of where to get more water, and certainly considerable quantities of this returned water are purified for further use. However, many industrial concerns dump waste materials into rivers and streams; this waste so contaminates the water that normal purification methods are of no value. Government and industrial agencies concerned with the conservation of water resources are now giving more and more attention to control of water pollution. Man can no longer afford to squander the bountiful supplies of water, air, soil, and many other things that he has so often taken for granted in the past.

Water Used in Industrial Processes

5 gallons	—	to process 1 gallon of milk
10 gallons	—	to produce 1 gallon of gasoline
80 gallons	—	to generate 1 kilowatt-hour of electricity
300 gallons	—	to manufacture 1 pound of synthetic rubber
65,000 gallons	—	to produce 1 ton of steel

Areas of Excessive Water

In many areas of the world the surface water is more than enough for man's requirements; indeed, in places where the water table is at the surface, extensive swamps have resulted. Four large areas in Africa which are lakes in the rainy season become swamps during the drier part of the year. Other swamps are found in areas of glacial deposition, on low-lying coastal plains, and by deltas and low-lying flood plains such as the Mississippi, Rhone, Volga, and many other rivers. When drained, such swamps sometimes prove to be extremely fertile lands. Others provide great quantities of peat, a low-grade fuel of great importance in the. U.S.S.R., Ireland, and certain other countries.

Man has shown great ingenuity and tenacity in his struggle to reclaim flooded land; undoubtedly his most remarkable achievements in this field have been in the Netherlands. One can see some justification for the statement that "God made the sea, but the Dutch made the land". So skilled have these people become in reclaiming marshy or flooded land that they have played an important part in the reclamation of land in many parts of the world. The rich farms of the Holland Marsh in Ontario provide an example of this type of work.

Waters of Disaster

The water which plays an essential role in the maintaining of human life can also play an equally destructive part if it appears in the form of floods. In many parts of the world, flooding is a normal, if rather unpredictable, part of the hydrologic cycle, and in areas of the Mississippi basin and the Hwang Ho valley, to mention only two, flooding is an ever-present threat to human life.

The network of rivers and streams which make up the drainage system of any district is proportionate to its normal supply of water, most of which comes from the atmosphere as direct precipitation. The total precipitation, however, may vary enormously over a period of months or years, falling far short of normal to cause a drop in river levels or rising far above normal to produce floods. Owing to the fact that the low-lying flood plains of these rivers are usually very fertile, they have often become so densely peopled that floods can result in heavy loss of life. Several times in the past century the flooding of the Hwang Ho has resulted in over a million deaths.

Spring floods occur in parts of Canada and elsewhere as a result of a thaw's taking place while the ground is still frozen and so unable to absorb the newly released waters. When spring rains fall at the same time, these spring floods can be very extensive. Of similar type are the floods produced by a river's thawing along its upper reaches while still frozen at its mouth. This is a common happening in Soviet Siberia, where northward-flowing rivers such as the Ob spread out to cover miles of low-lying land every spring when the meltwater pours downstream. A special category of flood is the one produced by violent atmospheric or other disturbances. The *double punch* of hurricanes *Connie* and *Diane,* which struck Connecticut only a week apart in 1955, resulted in 20 inches of rainfall and widespread flooding by over-swollen streams. Earthquakes, too, can result in sudden disastrous floods called *tsunamis*, which will be described separately later.

The *special* types of flood man can do very little about, but there are measures which can effectively reduce the dangers resulting from the ordinary processes of river flooding. Direct methods of flood control include the damming of major streams and channels, the building of artificial levees or walls to protect human settlement, and the preparation of permanent overflow channels to handle excess waters in time of flood. Flood controls which are indirect but equally important include extensive soil-conservation practices and widespread reforestation throughout entire river basins. Such measures can prevent a quick run-off of water from the land and thus act as regulators of the river flow.

Ground water as well as surface water can contribute to great disasters. Landslides, which are described elsewhere in this book, can be the result of the movement of underground water and of its subsequent effects on overlying masses of rocks.

2 THE OCEAN

Man lives on the land surface of the earth completely enclosed by the world of air which we have already considered. Encircling the landmasses on which we live are the vast bodies of water, the oceans and seas, which form a whole mysterious world for man to investigate. From the earliest times this realm of water has played an important part in the life of man—as a source of food, a highway, and even a place of recreation. Only in very recent times has man been able to study the oceans scientifically and so the science of *oceanography*, like that of meteorology, is a very young one.

Oceanic Exploration

In the past few years many articles have been written in magazines about Piccard's Bathyscaph and the Moho project, both of which have drawn attention to all the other forms of underwater exploration. The exploring of the deep oceans has been compared to space exploration in that both must be done largely by instruments since there are enormous obstacles to man's activities in them. One author has called the oceans *inner space* because of this parallel. Much of the work of oceanographers consists in designing new types of instruments which can be used to reveal more and more kinds of marine information.

Some of the most widely used instruments in oceanographic research are described below, the first three being concerned with the investigation of the water of the seas and the remainder with the exploration of the ocean floor.

Water Samplers

These are containers of various shapes which are lowered to the desired depths where they are then closed by a weight-and-cable system. By means of these, samples of water at various depths are obtained for biological and chemical analysis.

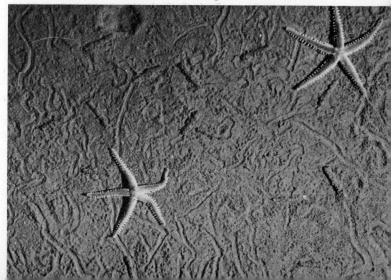

This photograph was taken at a depth of 100 fathoms in Hudson Bay in the summer of 1961. The Marine Sciences Branch of the Department of Mines and Technical Surveys is using the latest oceanographic instruments to study carefully the coastal waters of Canada.

Marine Sciences Branch,
Department of Mines and Technical Surveys

Oceanographic Thermometers

The temperatures of different levels of the water world can be just as important as those of the atmosphere. However, since the pressure in the deep water is enormous (12,000 lbs. per square inch at five miles down), specially constructed thermometers are necessary. One of these special thermometers is the bathy-thermograph which, as it is lowered through the water, provides a continuous record of temperature changes. There is also a type of electronic thermometer which keeps a continuous record of the water temperature at a fixed depth over a lengthy period of time.

Current Meters

Some of these are attached to the vessel conducting the research and provide information on the direction and speed of the great rivers in the ocean which we call currents. Similar information is provided by the *pinger*, an electronic device which is released at a fixed depth and floats independently at this depth. This instrument emits *ping* sounds, which can be tracked by the ship. The *underwater satellite* is one name which has been given to this useful piece of equipment.

Depth Recorders

Originally the simplest form of depth indicator was the plumb line—a long line attached to a weight which was lowered into the sea at regular intervals by a sailor, who called out the length of line each time it was lowered. This method was useful, but it could be used only in quite shallow water; moreover, its results were not scientifically accurate. Most modern depth recorders make use of the fact that sound waves pass easily through water and will echo back from a solid surface. These *echo sounders* measure the time taken for the sound produced in the ship to return after striking the ocean floor. In this way, as the ship progresses, the machine is enabled to draw a profile of the submarine floor.

There is an important commercial application of the echo-sounder in the fishing industry. On the profile chart the sea bottom is shown by a thick black line, but often there are shadowy patches above this. Such patches are produced by dense schools of fish from which some slight echoes rebound.

Explorers of the Floor

It is not sufficient to know merely how deep the oceans are. There are many fields of science in which it is important to learn more about the composition and shape of the floor and also about the forms of life found in that remote, mysterious world. Special movie and television cameras have been built to help us discover these things. For studying the effect of submarine explosions, there is a camera which can take more than 20,000 pictures in a few seconds. Gradual changes in the ocean floor can be recorded by another camera which takes 1000 photographs a day for 8 consecutive days.

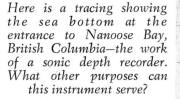

Institute of Oceanography, U.B.C.

Here is a tracing showing the sea bottom at the entrance to Nanoose Bay, British Columbia—the work of a sonic depth recorder. What other purposes can this instrument serve?

Fish and plant organisms of the deeps are studied by the use of trawls and dredges, which collect samples. This method, however, cannot be used in the deepest parts of the ocean abysses.

Some of the most valuable findings regarding the ocean deeps have been made by Jacques Piccard. In his bathyscaph he descended in 1960 to the record depth of 35,800 feet in the Marianas trench in the Pacific. In the field of science and exploration, the work of Piccard should be ranked with that of the Soviet and U.S. astronauts; yet the latter have received much the greater publicity.

One of the most important means of obtaining information about the ocean floor is the use of instruments which gather samples of the floor itself. Some of these merely scoop up the soft rocks and clays which lie there. Others, called *corers* or *drills*, drive down into the solid rock below the sea and bring up long, narrow cores or columns containing cross-sections of the submarine geology. The Moho project is undoubtedly the most famous of all the ventures into oceanic geology, but there are countless similar, though smaller, projects being pursued in many parts of the globe.

Nuclear-powered submarines have still further expanded the horizons of man's underwater exploration. Several expeditions have been made under the Arctic ice by U.S. submarines of this type, and we now know that the sea is about 13,500 feet deep at the North Pole. During the International Geophysical Year scientists were astonished by the discovery that Marie Byrd Land and the Ellsworth highlands are really islands and that the landmass of Antarctica is about 20% smaller than had been previously calculated.

Submarine research is steadily increasing as more scientists with better equipment enter the field each year. At present a buoy is being prepared which will consist of a column extending to a depth of 300 feet below the surface; within this oceanographers will be able to make their observations. New research ships— which are really floating laboratories—are being built and from these all the complicated exploration of the sea will be conducted.

Why Explore the Oceans?

It is now clear that considerable work is being done in many parts of the earth in order that we may learn more about the water world that surrounds our continents. As you may quite reasonably question the value of all this research, a few major reasons for this interest are indicated here in outline only. Use your school encyclopedias to find out more about the following points as a basis for a class discussion of "the value of oceanographic research".

In many of the countries of Asia there is already a serious weakness in normal food supplies and a similar situation could eventually develop in North America and western Europe. Experts maintain that the sea is potentially more productive in food than is the land, yet only between 1% and 2% of the world's food comes from the sea. Professor Hardy, one of these experts, writes about the day when sea farmers will clear weeds and less desirable creatures from areas where edible fish can then grow fat and provide a regular harvest.

Food alone is not enough; man needs water also to live—but the normal water supply on the continental landmasses is strictly limited. Already, in the United States, man is using over 60% of the natural water supply and the consumption is increasing rapidly each year. At present great expense is involved in the distilling of fresh water from the sea on a large scale. However, the day may not be far removed when man in certain regions may turn to the sea for both food and water.

Sea water contains larger reserves of certain minerals than the land. At present some salt, bromine, and manganese are extracted from sea water on a commercial scale, but rich nodules of iron, cobalt, nickel, copper, and manganese are lying on the ocean floor awaiting the development of new methods of removal. One expedition calculated that parts of the eastern Pacific hold over a million dollars worth of mineral nodules per square mile.

The effect of the sea and ocean currents on the climates of the continents is immense, but has never been exactly calculated. A clearer understanding of this relationship may help us forecast weather more accurately. If man ever reaches the point of controlling climatic conditions, probably such control will begin with the diversion of large bodies of water. One spectacular undertaking of this type, which was suggested by a Soviet engineer, involved the building of a 46-mile dam across the Bering Strait. Use the map on page 100 to examine the currents and adjoining landmasses which would be affected by such a construction.

The Water World

The earth has sometimes been called the *watery planet*, a title which is excellent in view of the fact that water covers about 70% of its total surface. In the other planets of the solar system, temperatures are either too high or too low for the existence of vast oceans like ours. Here again we find a part of our natural environment which may not be duplicated anywhere else in the immense regions of the solar system.

It is believed that the vast quantities of water which now form the *hydrosphere*, or water surface of the earth, were originally a chemical constituent of the rocks. Ages of volcanism and a period of cooler temperatures have released these waters at the surface and into the atmosphere. Probably the total volume of the hydrosphere now remains fairly constant and the greatest changes nowadays are the result of the increase or decrease of glacial masses.

Salinity

Everyone knows that the water of the sea is salty but that that of rivers and lakes is usually fresh. Where does the sea's salt come from? It is, of course, true that minute quantities of minerals and salts are carried by river water, but the accumulation of these salts does not explain the vast quantities of salt in the sea. Salt is also derived from the rocks of the ocean floor. Finally, there is a constant growth and alteration in the salt content of the sea as the result of the presence of fish and plant life in this watery world.

The amount of salt in the sea is measured in terms of parts of salt per 1000 parts of water and the average salinity of the sea is expressed as 35 $^o/_{oo}$. However, the salinity varies enormously as between one sea and another. The factors which regulate this variation include:

> the temperature—high temperature means high evaporation, which in turn results in a higher accumulation of salts in the sea.
>
> rainfall—very heavy rainfall increases the amount of fresh water in any large lake or sea.
>
> large rivers—these, too, add more fresh water to the seas into which they flow.
>
> heavy cloud cover—this can reduce evaporation and also produce heavy rainfall, both factors in the decrease of salinity.

However, detached or partially enclosed seas may be sufficiently cut off from the oceanic circulation of water for the factors affecting salinity to operate independently in their case. Thus, the Baltic Sea, with a low rate of evaporation and with many large rivers flowing into it, has a salinity of 7 $^o/_{oo}$; this means that its water is almost fresh. The Red Sea, however, has a salinity of 40 $^o/_{oo}$. The completely enclosed Dead Sea as a result of long-continued evaporation now has a salinity of almost 240 $^o/_{oo}$.

Although these may seem to be insignificant proportions of salt in comparison with the enormous volume of salt in the oceans, we shall find that their final total is not inconsiderable. There are about 3½ pounds of salt in every 100 pounds of oceanic water. It has been estimated that if all the salts were extracted from the seas there would be a sufficient quantity to cover the world's land surface with a layer of salt about 450 feet deep.

The salts in the sea are important not only because they make it easier for swimmers to swim and because they ruin the water for drinking purposes, but also because they can be extracted in great quantities. In many places beside the sea, common salt (sodium chloride) is extracted for human use. In addition, most of the world's magnesium is also derived from the sea. Bromine, too, is derived chiefly from the sea. Magnesium is an important element in the new alloys used in aeronautic construction, whereas bromine is used in photography, in the manufacture of gasoline, and in several chemical industries. Gold, too, is to be found in ordinary sea water—perhaps as much as 90 million dollars worth in one cubic mile of sea water. Unfortunately, there is still no economic way of extracting this precious metal from the sea.

The Temperature of the Sea

Insolation occurs equally on the sea and on the land, but water has a greater capacity to absorb heat than rock or soil; moreover, the fluidity of water allows this heat to be carried several feet deeper into the sea than into the earth. Land surfaces heat and cool rapidly; thus, their seasonal contrasts are great, whereas water surfaces heat and cool more slowly. This is a fact of the utmost importance in the understanding of the climates of the world. The explanation of the land-water temperature difference is to be found in the transparency of water, which allows the heat rays to penetrate for several feet, and also in the constant movement of great water masses in currents and drifts. As the ground is opaque and solid, normal heating occurs only in the top few inches, where it takes place very rapidly, as does winter cooling.

Heating of the sea, like that of the land, varies considerably between the equator and the poles. Surface temperatures of 70° F. are about normal in tropical seas, whereas in polar regions 28° F. is about average. The freezing point of sea water varies with the salinity, but it is always below that of fresh water. Even so, there is a permanent crust of 10 to 15 feet of ice on top of the Arctic Sea. On the other hand, probably the warmest of sea bodies is the partially enclosed Persian Gulf, where temperatures of 96° F. are recorded regularly.

Just as the temperature of the air varies at different altitudes, so does that of the different depths of the sea. Somewhere between 200 and 1,000 feet below the surface in the great oceans, there is a sudden drop in temperature; thus we have a mass of warmer waters moving over the colder deeper waters. The imaginary line dividing these two layers is called the *thermocline* and its depth varies with the season. Name a similarly changing temperature level in the atmosphere.

Our knowledge of the floor of the Atlantic is still incomplete but present information gives a picture like this.

The Ocean Floor

Sometimes when we look at the wave-rippled flat monotony of the ocean, a sea, or a wide lake, we instinctively think of the submarine floor as being a wide, flat plain. This is a common but quite mistaken notion. The ancient legend of Atlantis comes much closer to the truth—the story of a highly civilized country with mountains, hills, plains, rivers, and cities, all of which sank thousands of years ago below the waters of the Atlantic. Essentially, the ocean floor is like the land surface of the earth.

Modern mapping of the ocean floor has revealed three distinct types of submarine landforms. The first of these is the *continental shelf*, which is a ledge or shelf fringing the continents and covered by comparatively shallow water. This shelf is really a vast accumulation of deposits carried down to the sea by countless rivers and streams and subsequently planed flat by the work of the sea. In view of this origin it is not surprising that the shelf is usually widest along old coastlines where deposition has long been active, and is extremely narrow along young shore lines. The effect of wide continental shelves on fisheries and on tides is considerable and will be outlined elsewhere in this book.

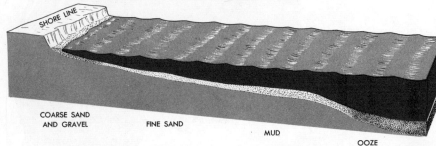

Weakening wave action tends to sort out rock fragments. Near the shore, the heaviest particles are deposited and there is a gradation to the fine ooze of the ocean deeps.

About the 100-fathom line the smooth-sloping plain of the continental shelf ends and an area of very steep slopes gashed by deep canyons occurs. This is known as the *continental slope* and it extends approximately to the 2000-fathom mark, which is the beginning of the *deep-sea basins*. The steep-sided chasms which are found at the edge of the shelf long puzzled oceanographers as they are mostly too deep and too far from the land to be drowned river valleys. It is now generally believed that many of these were formed by powerful *turbidity currents*, which are powerful ocean-bottom currents produced by an underwater landslide or avalanche on the continental slope. In 1929 an earthquake took place on the Grand Banks of Newfoundland which started just such an avalanche and its consequent turbidity current. The effect of this current was recorded by the breaking of transatlantic cables one after another until one 300 miles away from the avalanche eventually snapped.

The average depth of the deep ocean basins is about 2½ miles, but in many places it is very much deeper than this. Trenches about 35,000 feet deep scar the ocean bottom in many areas. These trenches are usually long, narrow, and V-shaped in cross-section; often they are found in proximity to chains of volcanic islands. In contrast, several of the earth's greatest mountain ranges lie entirely covered by the waves of the sea. Volcanoes, some of which do not appear above the surface, are common in some parts of the submarine terrain. Some of these oceanic volcanoes are girdled by coral reefs in tropical seas; in some cases the volcano is no longer above the sea but the reef has remained as an *atoll* such as is shown in the diagram on page 204. Many undersea volcanoes have been mapped which have curious flat tops as though the top had been sawed off. These are known as *guyots*.

If you look at the sketch of the Atlantic Ocean, you will be struck by the enormous mountain range which extends throughout the length of that ocean.

Recent research has shown that this Mid-Atlantic Ridge is continued via the Indian Ocean into the Pacific. Although exploration is still incomplete, we now know that this is a 40,000-mile range varying in width between 100 and 1,200 miles and having many peaks towering 20,000 feet above the ocean floor. These startling proportions are enough to let us know that this is one of the greatest natural features on the crust of the earth.

Some mystery is attached to the origin of a trench which extends like a backbone along the centre of most of this range. Having a width of 8 to 30 miles and a depth of a mile or more, this trench or crack is almost as interesting as the surrounding mountains. Some scientists maintain that the earth is at present expanding and that this crack is the result. The great Canadian geophysicist, Dr. Tuzo Wilson, has estimated the expansion at one inch every 50 years; however, we are not yet able to measure it. Whatever the solution to the mystery, the fact remains that most of the major movements in the earth's crust are associated with this range and its trench.

The Oceans

For convenience we have given different names to different oceanic bodies of water, but a glance at the map is sufficient to show that all oceans are connected. There is no disconnected ocean in the way that Australia is cut off from the other landmasses. Altogether about 75% of the earth's surface is covered by water.

The largest and deepest of the oceans is the Pacific, which includes about three-eights of the total oceanic area. The Atlantic forms about a quarter of the total area. Among the three smaller oceans the Arctic Ocean is remarkable in that much of it is permanently covered by ice—in places to a depth of 10 feet.

The floor of all the oceans is covered with a variety of sediments. In the vicinity of landmasses, the sediments consist of pebbles, gravel, and sand, which originated on the land and were carried seawards by rivers and currents. The strength of such currents decreases in proportion to their distances from the shore, with the result that they can transport only smaller and smaller particles the farther out they flow. In this way the sediments which fall to the ocean floor have first been sorted out by the water. Far out at sea, however, the deposits on the bottom usually consist of an extremely fine but heavy slime called *ooze*. This ooze originates in wind-blown dust, dust from meteorites, and the remains of plankton and other forms of marine life. The rate of deposition of these deep-sea sediments is calculated at only one inch in every 2500 years.

The slow rate of deposition in the oceans has encouraged geologists to examine ocean-bottom cores to find out more about the past. Already important discoveries about past changes in climate have resulted from this work.

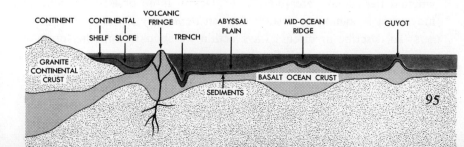

This generalized cross-section gives some idea of the general pattern of submarine geology and of the correct terms.

95

3 WAVES, TIDES, AND CURRENTS

If you lived most of your life far from the sea and then moved to a place on the coast, you would probably be most impressed by the constant, endless movement of the sea or ocean. Should you have experienced a passage across the ocean on a great liner, you would certainly remember the unceasing motion of the waves and perhaps have become curious about the forces in the sea. Having reviewed the chief facts about the composition of the ocean water and the nature of the ocean floor, let us now turn our attention to the movements of waters near the surface—movements which can be classified as waves, tides, or currents.

In these diagrams the extent of the tides is much exaggerated. Notice that spring tides occur at times of both new and full moon.

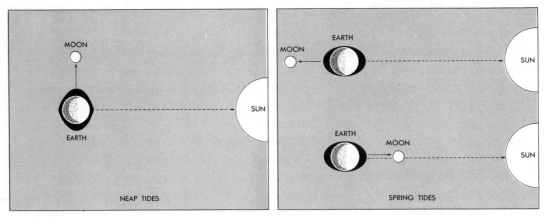

THE PATTERNS EXPLAINING SPRING AND NEAP TIDES

Waves

Waves are affected by all the other movements in the oceans, but their most important feature is the manner of their motion. One of nature's finest deceptions is observable in the fact that the waves of the sea give the impression that the water is constantly moving forward. This is not the case. Actually, as you can see if you watch a piece of wood or cork floating in rippling water, the particles of water (and with them any floating object) show a more or less circulatory motion. Analysis of this motion shows that each particle moves in a circle whose diameter is equal to the height of the wave, and that this movement is passed on to adjoining particles so that the *movement* or *wave* or *wave shape* advances or moves forward, whereas the actual water merely revolves in more or less the same area. Such a movement is sometimes described as an *oscillatory wave*.

To describe or discuss wave action we should know the terms used in wave study. Every wave has two major parts—the mound of water, the top of which is called the *crest*, and the adjoining depression or *trough*. The vertical distance between the crest and the lowest point of the trough is called the *wave height*. The distance between two consecutive crests is called the *wavelength* and the time it takes for two crests to pass a given point is called the *period*. The disturbance of water created by a wave usually extends to a depth equal to about a half of the total wavelength.

The terminology of waves is illustrated here as the movement of water particles.

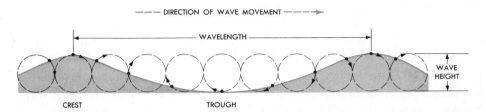

The shape and size of waves can vary in accordance with changes in winds. Generally the stronger a wind and the longer it blows, the higher will be the waves; but the *fetch* of the wind is also significant, i.e., the distance over open water that a wind has blown. A gentle breeze will produce tiny wavelets, but the unevenness produced by these presents a greater surface to the wind, the result being that these wavelets will usually increase in size. Rolling waves with a very long wavelength can be produced by steady winds; such waves may continue for very long periods of time in the open sea, where they are known as *swells*. Sometimes the force of the wind may be sufficient to topple waves over, causing their crests to tumble forward as *whitecaps*.

The waves used by surfboard riders are essentially different from those already described. In the first place they are waves of translation, in which the water is actually moving forward. As the bottom becomes shallower, the normal circular movements of water particles is impeded and an elliptical pattern develops. This ellipse is accompanied by a slowing of the movement along the bottom and by a piling up of following waves. Even within one wave we find the back of the wave overtaking the front until a peak is formed. When the point is reached where the ratio between the height of the wave and the depth of the water is in the proportion of 3 to 4, the wave spills over as a *breaker*. If the wave enters shallow water very quickly, the size and violence of the wave is increased. A very long, gradually shelving shore line, however, results in smaller, less spectacular breakers.

The advancing wave enters shallower water until it spills over. Of importance is the ensuing undertow and backward movement of sediments along the shore.

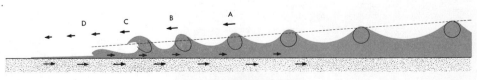

THE DEVELOPMENT OF A BREAKER

Underneath the forward movement of the shore-line breakers there must obviously be a return movement of water to the sea. This returning water is known as the *undertow*. Along beaches where there is an offshore sandbar—even if it is submerged—water will race back to sea through any gaps in the bar and so produce a swift *rip current*. Many misconceptions exist on this subject. Undertows are seldom serious hazards to swimmers; rip currents always are. The swimmer caught in a rip current should not battle against it but should either swim across and out of it or else let it carry him until he feels the current weaken, when he can swim ashore at some other point.

You have all read descriptions of great storms at sea and may have seen movies showing the powerful waves which can develop in such storms. Sailors tell us that the height of waves in feet during a storm is usually about half the speed of wind in miles per hour; i.e., a sixty-mile-an-hour gale will produce 30-foot-high waves. A battering of several hours by such waves as these can do enormous damage to even the largest ships. However, many waves far exceed the usual nautical rule of thumb. The captain of an American tanker in the Pacific once encountered waves over 110 feet high. The Tillamook lighthouse in Oregon has had a metal grating placed around the beacon because of frequent damage by waves—at a height of 139 feet above the sea. It was at this station, too, that waves once tossed a 135-lb. boulder through the roof of the lightkeeper's house.

Great as the destruction of these waves may be, it is still true that wind-caused waves are less disastrous for mankind than are the *tsunamis*—waves resulting from movement on the ocean floor. Such movements may result from volcanoes, earthquakes, or simply large underwater landslides. Tsunamis, fortunately, are fairly rare; so far fewer than 250 have been recorded in history. In the open sea a tsunami may be a wave with a height of a few feet, a wavelength of a hundred miles, and a speed in excess of 400 miles an hour. On entering shallow water this wave will pile up to heights of 50 feet or more and so will ravage many miles of low-lying land. An earthquake on the Alaska coast caused a tsunami in 1946; in that area it killed 159 people as it carved a scene of destruction among the unsuspecting towns and farms. More recently the terrible Chilean earthquakes of 1960 resulted in extensive damage and heavy loss of life in Japan. Use your atlas to estimate the distance this deadly tsunami must have travelled. (Note that a tsunami is a very severe *seismic sea wave*, familiarly known as a *tidal wave*.)

New Brunswick Travel Bureau

Here we see the tidal bore on the Bay of Fundy. What is a tidal bore? What is its cause?

Tides

It is a common mistake to describe a tsunami as a tidal wave when it has, of course, no direct connection at all with tidal processes. Tides are movements of oceanic waters resulting chiefly from the gravitational pull of the moon and sun. In your science class you will already have learned that bodies exert an attraction on one another in relation to their mass and the distance between them. The moon, though smaller than the sun, is so much nearer the earth that its gravitational pull on the oceans is about double that of the sun. However, when the positions of the sun, moon, and earth form a straight line, the tides are at their highest and are called *spring* tides. When the sun and moon are tugging at right angles to one another, the tides are lower than usual and are called *neap* tides.

This simple planetary explanation of tides, however, is not sufficient to explain the details of the frequency and height of tides in particular areas. The shape and size and depth of the oceans and seas, together with the particular features of their coastal outlines, all modify the pulsating movements of the waters that constitute tides. Many coastal areas experience very high tides as a result of the shallowness of the sea floor, or else, as in the Bay of Fundy, of a narrowing funnel up which the tidal water must move. Such exaggerated tides are called *tidal bores*.

Tides are by far the most extensive movements of the world's waters, billions of tons of water both at the surface and at some considerable depths moving twice daily. The economic consequences of this movement are enormous. Without tides most of the large rivers of the world would silt up at their estuaries, for tides continually remove much of the sediment carried down by these rivers to the sea. In many ports the ships cannot enter or leave except at the slack period between tides; elsewhere, a ship will make use of the tide to clear harbour more easily. Recently, at the estuary of the Rance River in France, a power station has been built which utilizes the force of 37-foot tides; there are many places in North America also where this vast force could be harnessed.

Currents

There are many stories of people placing messages or notes in bottles which were then thrown into the sea from a liner far out at sea or else from a lonely oceanic island. In many instances these bottles have been picked up on beaches thousands of miles away. Waves cannot account for such long journeys, but currents and drifts can. These currents are great, steadily moving masses of water corresponding to the major wind systems of the atmosphere. Throughout the following paragraphs we shall continue to refer only to currents, but it should be kept in mind that currents and drifts are essentially the same; sailors use the word *current* to denote water that has a speed of over a half knot per hour and the word *drift* to denote any speed slower than that.

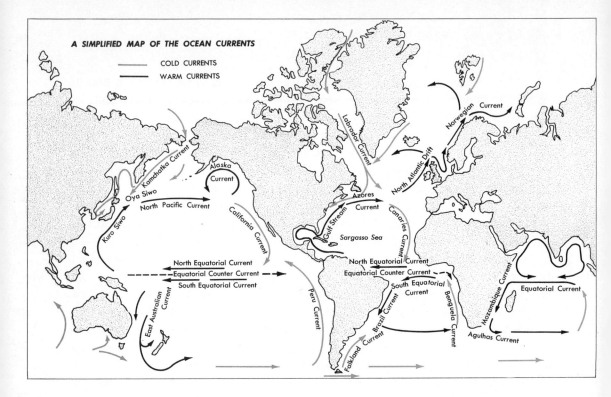

A SIMPLIFIED MAP OF THE OCEAN CURRENTS

The causes of currents are diverse and not yet completely explained. A comparison of a map showing prevailing winds over the oceans with one showing ocean currents will immediately indicate so many similarities that it should be clear that such winds must be listed among the important causes of ocean currents. It is also clear now that variations in insolation also contribute to the formation of currents. In equatorial latitudes, the water is heated much more than that outside the tropics. Heating results in an expansion of water, just as cooling produces contraction; this means that equatorial seas are a little higher than those to the north and south. This unevenness results in a general surface flow of water away from the equator.

The density of the sea depends not only on its temperature but also on the salinity. Cold, salty water tends to be heavier than warm, less saline water; consequently, in places it sinks towards the bottom, thus setting up a circulation of water between the surface and the deeps.

In addition to the factors which cause ocean currents, there are others which are better described as controlling factors. The first of these is the rotation of the earth from west to east. Near the equator, because the earth is moving at about 1,000 miles an hour, the waters tend to swing towards the western shores of equatorial seas. A French mathematician studying the physics of the earth's movements has pointed out that all moving bodies tend to turn to the right in the Northern Hemisphere and to the left in the Southern. Named after him, this

100

tendency is known as the *Coriolis effect*. The Coriolis effect influences the ocean currents not only directly but also indirectly through the winds. Finally, the shape of the landmasses acts as an important controlling factor upon the actual course which the currents will follow. In a few areas we may go even further and point out that even the submarine relief of the ocean floor can play an important role in diverting or dividing a broad current.

The story is told that Benjamin Franklin was intrigued by the fact that in his day many American sea captains were regularly crossing the Atlantic from the United States to Europe in a much shorter time than equally skilful and experienced British mariners. His enquiries revealed that his countrymen knew of a very strong eastward-flowing current near the American coast which they were using on the way out and avoiding on the way back. Franklin then prepared a chart showing this current and applying the name *Gulf Stream* to it. This current is probably the most widely studied of all such bodies of water and it might also be described as the main artery of the North Atlantic oceanic circulation.

A map of ocean currents reveals a steady, westward-moving current in equatorial latitudes which does not continue all round the globe because of the Asian, American, and African landmasses. In the Atlantic these North and South Equatorial currents are respectively deflected north to become the Gulf Stream and south to become the Brazil Current. There is also a return, or eastward, movement of water known as the Equatorial Counter Current. The Brazil Current meets the colder Falkland Current about 40° S latitude and then swings east across the Atlantic, where, as the Benguela Current, it completes an anti-clockwise circulation of oceanic waters. In the north the waters of the Equatorial Current stream into the Caribbean Sea and Gulf of Mexico. Between Florida and Cuba this great oceanic river pours forwards at speeds of over 5 miles an hour. Along the U.S. coast, every minute, billions of tons of water swing northward in a stream 50 miles wide and about 1,500 feet deep. No river on earth can compare with this. From Cape Hatteras the Gulf Stream turns out to the Atlantic, but near the Grand Banks it meets the colder Labrador Current; thus the widely known fogs ensue. Ocean floor relief (as well as other factors) results in the dividing in mid-Atlantic of this enormous body of water, the main stream continuing as the North Atlantic Drift, a southern branch becoming the Canaries Current, and a much smaller northern arm swinging south along the south coast of Iceland to be known as the Irminger Current. The basic circulation of the North Atlantic you will notice is in a clockwise direction.

Between the Bahamas and the Azores, a map of currents reveals a large area of comparatively calm water known as the Sargasso Sea, so named because of the Sargassum seaweed that floats on the surface here. This area has been compared to an enormous hub of the Atlantic Current wheel. The calmness of this area, the almost stagnant water, and the sinister floating weeds resulted in this area's acquiring an almost legendary status among seamen; indeed, it was invariably avoided by sailing vessels. Even in the early days of steamships, many captains steered clear of this huge region until it was realized that the seaweed presented no real threat to the propellers.

One of the major tasks facing oceanographers at present is the mapping of submarine currents. In several instances important but deep countercurrents exist below those flowing closer to the surface. This is certainly the case with respect to the Gulf Stream, although its countercurrent has not yet been accurately mapped.

The Importance of Currents

The effect of many ocean currents is so far reaching that it would take a whole book to do justice to their importance in terms of man's life and activities. Currents are classified as *warm* if they are flowing into areas where the surrounding waters are of a lower temperature and as *cold* if the reverse is the case. Warm currents may carry their heat thousands of miles, and by warming the winds which blow over them have an enormous effect on climatic conditions of adjoining land-masses. Cold currents can have an opposite effect. Western Europe—especially Norway—is an area where temperatures are beneficially affected by currents. Use an atlas to find summer and winter average temperatures in Norway and compare them with those of similar latitudes elsewhere in the world.

In certain areas cold currents can actually contribute to the aridity of nearby land areas. This curious effect is brought about by the fact that air passing over the colder water is chilled, with the result that, when it crosses over the much warmer land, it is heated and so its capacity to hold moisture is increased. These conditions serve to intensify the other circumstances that militate against an adequate supply of rainfall. Find two areas in Africa where such conditions may have some significance.

The importance of currents to navigation has diminished with the development of modern steam and motor vessels. However, Thor Heyerdahl's exciting journey from Peru to Tuamotu on the Kon-Tiki in 1947 showed that in certain circumstances currents can still be of considerable consequence.

Fifteen tons of seawater in the stem of this Flip will make it stand upright in 300 feet of water. Built-in research facilities will aid in the study of ocean sounds and waves.

Wide World

UNIT REVIEW

Vocabulary Review

Match the word or phrase in the left-hand column with the correct one in the right-hand column:

1. water-bearing layer
2. water-filled caldera
3. underwater extension of continental mass
4. ocean-floor sediment
5. ancient lake
6. extent of open water over which wind blows
7. long, rolling wave
8. giant wave caused by submarine earthquake
9. occurs during rising tide in estuaries
10. depression between two waves

(a) ooze
(b) fetch
(c) swell
(d) aquifer
(e) continental shelf
(f) Crater Lake
(g) tidal bore
(h) trough
(i) whitecap
(j) tsunami
(k) Lake Agassiz

Questions

1. In what ways has man increased and also decreased the possibilities of flooding?
2. What are the factors necessary for an artesian formation?
3. Discuss the processes which result in the formation of lakes, giving examples of each.
4. Describe five types of instruments used in oceanographic research.
5. How are continental shelves developed? What is their chief importance?
6. Compare and contrast the currents of the Atlantic and Pacific oceans.
7. Briefly discuss the effect of the earth's rotation on the movements of currents.
8. Describe the factors which control the speed and movement of ground water.

Research Assignments

1. Prepare a detailed report on the Moho project describing what it aims to discover and the methods being used.
2. By reference to specific examples describe those ways in which lakes may disappear.
3. What are the major difficulties in the exploration of the great ocean deeps and how are these being overcome?

Materials of the Earth

~

1 ROCKS

The solid part of man's environment, the *solid earth* as we call it, is called *lithosphere* or *stone-sphere* in contrast to the gaseous atmosphere and liquid hydrosphere. The study of the materials making up the surface of the earth is the field of the geologist. Yet, in many cases, the actual type of rock or mineral present in an area is the most significant factor in the human environment, determining occupations, distribution and extent of settlement, and also local standards of living. In view of these and other factors, the student of geography must often begin his study of a region by studying its broad geological distributions.

Because of the looseness with which we commonly use the words, it is very easy to become confused by the terms *rock* and *mineral*. A rock is any naturally occurring solid mass making up an essential part of the earth's crust and composed of several minerals. A mineral, however, is a naturally occurring element or inorganic compound possessing a definite chemical composition as well as definite chemical and physical properties. You will have studied the terms *element* and *compound* in your science class; the former is a substance that cannot be broken down into simpler substances by ordinary chemical means, and the latter is a chemical combination of two or more elements. Most minerals are compounded. In ordinary usage the term mineral is also applied to any substance that can be obtained by mining, but our basic scientific definition of mineral includes natural gas and oil, and even water.

Find the man in the middle foreground of this photograph of The Devil's Postpile. Notice his size. Jointing in this fine-grained igneous rock results in the remarkable columnar structure.

The Classification of Rocks

If you begin to collect different kinds of rocks, you will soon reach the point at which you realize that the number of different types of rock seems to be infinite. In order to give your collection more meaning, you will begin to group the specimens on the basis of certain similarities. Geologists had the same problem and they used the origin of rocks as one basis of classification. On this basis, we have rocks described as *igneous* if they are the result of the cooling of magma or lava into a solid state. *Sedimentary* rocks, as the name signifies, are those that were previously sediments laid down by the action of wind or water. The term *metamorphic* describes a wide variety of rocks the present composition of which is the result of changes brought about by intense pressure or heat either deep in the earth or resultant from violent earth movements. All the rocks found on the earth belong in one of these three broad categories.

Igneous Rocks

Igneous rocks were described as *intrusive* if the magma solidified below the earth's crust and never appeared at the surface as liquid. Most intrusive rocks solidified slowly in their subterranean birthplace, and this resulted in their consisting of a mass of large crystals thus giving the rock a very coarse texture. More quickly cooling *extrusive* rocks have finer crystals and, therefore, a much smoother texture—in many cases almost glassy in appearance and feel. Igneous rocks may also be subdivided on the basis of their mode of occurrence (see the chapter on Volcanism) or on the basis of their mineral content. Quartz, feldspar, mica, and hornblende are a few of the many minerals found in a great number of igneous rocks. However, some igneous rocks, being particularly rich in iron and magnesium, are known as *basic*. The basic igneous rocks are usually heavy and are dark in appearance. Other igneous rocks may contain a very high proportion of silica—thus producing a rock relatively light in colour and weight. These are called *acid* or *acidic* rocks.

You may wonder why we trouble to classify rocks that have solidified below the earth's surface as they might seem to have no importance in terms of man's life. In reality, however, these rocks are to be found across large areas of the earth's surface as they have often been exposed by the erosion and denudation of rocks that previously covered them. Granite is to be found, for example, in every province of Canada and in many states in the United States. This is by far the most common intrusive rock. It is easily recognized by the clear, glassy grains of quartz, white or pink feldspar, and smaller amounts of dark hornblende and black mica. The coarse grains and speckled appearance of this rock are distinctive, but its final colour will vary according to its feldspar content. Granite is an acidic rock, popular as a building stone because of its hardness, decorative appearance, and very widespread distribution. Similar to granite is *gabbro*, a darker rock covering wide areas in the region of the Canadian Shield.

Other interesting extrusive igneous rocks include basalt, obsidian, and pumice. *Basalt* is a common fine-grained rock that is essentially a type of lava often perforated by many holes through which gases previously escaped. An extruded lava, which has cooled very quickly under certain conditions, can produce *obsidian*, which has a shiny, glasslike surface. Very thin pieces of obsidian may be almost transparent. *Pumice* is an igneous rock which sometimes is light enough to float. This curious fact is explained by the spongelike quality of pumice due to its rapid cooling around trapped gas bubbles. Were it not for its colour, we might be tempted to call pumice nature's *solidified soap suds*.

Lava, which solidifies at the surface of the earth, can also solidify in different forms depending on the chemical composition and the surrounding conditions. Rough, honeycomb-like scoria, tuff or consolidated ash, and other lava forms are discussed at greater length in the chapter on volcanism.

Sedimentary Rocks

At times, on a very warm dry day, you will have seen the wind picking up dust, sand, or soil and swirling it away in quick gusts; or you will have noticed a little stream, swollen by heavy rains, running thick and milky with mud or carrying branches, stones, and other debris on its turbulent way. Here you are seeing the forces of nature acting as great *transporters* of material. However, the sudden gust of wind does not blow forever, nor the stream remain in perpetual flood, and when the wind ceases or the stream slows down, then they deposit their heavy loads. Glaciers and the seas, too, play a part in this redistribution of material on the face of the earth. The process of dumping this material is known as *deposition*, and the materials deposited are known as sediments. In time these sediments can become compacted and combined to form once again a solid rock, and rocks of this type are naturally known as *sedimentary rocks*.

COMMON SEDIMENTARY ROCKS

	ROCKS		SEDIMENT	
FRAGMENTAL	Conglomerate	—	Garvel	**COARSE**
	Sandstone	—	Sand	**MEDIUM**
	Shale	—	Mud (clay)	**FINE**
CHEMICAL	Limestone (calcium carbonate)		⎱ Chemical and/or organic precipitates, often with embedded shells	**CRYSTALLINE**
	Dolomite (calcium magnesium carbonate)			
	Salt (halite) Gypsum and Anhydrite		⎱ Purely chemical precipitates	

Sedimentary rocks are described as *fragmental* if they are composed of millions of fragments of other rocks cemented and compressed together. *Chemical* sedimentary rocks consist of materials such as calcite and gypsum that precipitated in solution. Many sedimentaries, consisting of plant or animal remains, particularly of fish in the sea, are termed *organic* sedimentaries.

The manner of formation of sedimentary rocks is reflected in several characteristics shared by most sedimentaries. There are usually quite distinct layers in these rocks and they vary according to their age and mineral content. This *stratification* (the layers are called strata) is the chief characteristic of such rocks and the lines between the strata are called *bedding planes*. *Fossils* are found only in sedimentary rocks. Odd-shaped pieces of stone and other materials occur in these rocks, too, these objects being known as *concretions*. Finally, in some sedimentaries, the wind and water have carved their autographs by the survival of distinctive solidified ripple-marks and similar lines that we can see repeated every day on our beaches.

Fragmental sedimentaries are classified by geologists on the basis of the size of fragments involved. Thus a *conglomerate* is composed of compacted boulders, stone, or gravel—in other words, any fragments larger than 0.08 inches. Sand, which is not a particular type of rock but merely an indication of the size of the particles (0.08 to 0.008 inches), ultimately may form sandstone. Clay, composed of particles smaller than 0.008 inches, is the basis of shale.

These thin-bedded sandstones have very clear bedding planes. What do these planes tell us about the rock's origin?

Probably the easiest of all sedimentaries to identify is a conglomerate. This is simply a mass of cemented and often rounded gravel and small stones. Sandstone is probably the most widely distributed sedimentary as it consists of cemented sand grains that, remaining porous, can act as important reservoirs of water or oil. Quartz is the commonest of the grains in sandstone, but any mineral may be the dominant one in a particular formation with the result that there can be enormous differences between one sandstone and another. The intensely compressed clay, forming shale, still remains quite weak and tends to be eroded very easily by water or ice. This material has usually been pressed into parallel layers, and the resultant shale splits quite easily into flat pieces.

In the subsequent study of landscapes, you will find that one of the most distinctive types of rock, in terms of its effect on topography and human life, is limestone. One source of limestone is the calcium carbonate, extracted from the earth's crust by river and lake waters rich in carbon dioxide, and later deposited on the ocean floor. Plants and fish also extract calcium carbonate from the water to provide the materials for their shells and bones. In turn they die and accumulate on the ocean floor. The type of limestone so formed will obviously depend on the conditions of this accumulation—corals and certain plant species can live only in warm, clear, relatively shallow water and result in an almost pure calcareous limestone, whereas clams, mussels, and similar species inhabit muddy waters and are associated with limestones that are mixed with sands and clays. Limestones are extremely porous and are quite resistant to erosive forces except rain water, which is really a weak carbonic acid and soon decomposes the rock and removes much of it in solution.

Chalk is a particularly soft, white, limestone in which silicious plant and animal remains have formed very hard flint nodules. This flint is one of man's earliest sources of fire, and the caves associated with limestone provided our primitive ancestors with some of their finest homes. For this reason, the chalk and limestone regions of Europe have long been centres of important historical research.

Coal, in its various forms from low-grade lignite to rich anthracite, is a very important organic sedimentary rock. Bacterial action and compression are the chief forces accounting for the transformation of timber and vegetable matter into our most important source of fuel. Because of this transformation, some authors classify coal among the next set of rocks—the metamorphics—and there is still no absolute agreement on the subject.

Metamorphic Rocks

Igneous and sedimentary rocks do not always remain undisturbed after their initial formation or deposition. Instead, many of these rocks are subsequently subjected to intense pressure during folding or faulting movements in the earth's crust or to the great heat found deep underground and in areas of active volcanism. Heat and pressure can cause the recrystallization of the minerals within a rock or can lead to a reaction between adjacent rock masses. The word *metamorphic* is derived from the Greek for *changed form* and is a good term for these rocks that have undergone physical or chemical change.

Metamorphic rocks with a large proportion of mica or iron-magnesium minerals have a distinctive characteristic due to the tendency of these minerals to form flat flakes or needles lying in parallel planes. These rocks tend to split fairly easily along these planes and they are described as *foliated* metamorphic rocks. For the subdivision of all metamorphic rocks into foliated and nonfoliated rocks, foliation is the main criterion.

In some of the older classrooms, you may have seen old-fashioned slate blackboards. *Slate* is also used as a roofing material in some parts of the world. This hard, fine-grained rock splits easily into thin slabs—a fact reminding you that it is really metamorphosed shale. Quite different in appearance is *marble*, one of the most beautiful of stones. The coloured veins in marble are of mineral origin whereas the basic white marble itself is merely recrystallized limestone. *Gneiss* is a common rock on the vast Canadian Shield and is a foliated metamorphic rock formed from granite and other rocks. The rock is usually streaked with mineral colours and is quite coarse in texture. However, its appearance varies considerably—depending on its parent material. Sandstone, too, can become metamorphosed in which case the quartz grains are compacted to the point that the rock is no longer porous but becomes extremely hard and resistant. This rock is known as *quartzite*.

These are the stumps of a so-called petrified forest; the natural casts represent the lepidodendron, a tree of the Carboniferous period. Even the roots and bark show clearly.

Corporation of Glasgow, Parks and Botanical Gardens Dept.

Identifying Rocks

Many students get satisfaction from examining the rocks of their own district and trying to work out the geological history of the hills and valleys, plains and depressions in the land around them. The following are just a few ideas as to how you might go about doing your own field work in rocks.

The first thing to keep in mind is that rocks, exposed to air and water, are likely to undergo physical and chemical change. For this reason, geologists use a hammer in field work, chipping off the rock surface to obtain a specimen less altered by exposure. Nevertheless, even the first brief examination of a rock exposure can be instructive. The presence of fossils tells us immediately that the rock is sedimentary; as does conspicuous bedding or stratification. If the rock breaks in closely spaced planes and has a shiny surface, then it is probably a foliated metamorphic. At the first examination, you will try to place the rock in its general classification on the basis of origin.

After considering the general *structure* of the rock formation, examine its *texture* by breaking off a small piece for minute study. Distinctly visible separate grains, merely cemented together, indicate a sedimentary. A honeycomb texture suggests an extrusive igneous rock of which pumice is the best-known example. The best, and only thoroughly reliable, test of rocks is the identification of the minerals present in the individual specimen, but this involves more detailed study and equipment. Acid, or even ordinary vinegar, can provide a useful test of the carbonate rocks such as chalk, limestone, or marble. Powder a small quantity of the rock and add acid or vinegar; if it fizzes persistently, then the rock is a carbonate. Beware, however, of the fact that sandstones and even some igneous rocks do contain small quantities of carbonates, but these will not effervesce persistently.

Colour can sometimes be a useful general clue as to the classification of a rock. On the other hand, it can often be misleading and should be used only after a good deal of practice.

This cutting shows an exposure of limestone. Road construction often provides such excellent opportunities to study rocks.

2 MINERALS

Classification

At this point you should review the definition of the terms rocks and minerals and avert any possibility of confusion in the following pages. As with rocks, so with minerals: one of the first major tasks of the geologist and collector is to work out a broad system of classification into which he can fit the more than 1,800 existing minerals.

One simple classification divides minerals into silicious, metallic, nonmetallic, and gems. The silicious minerals, the commonest of all, are those which contain silicon. Most of the minerals in granite are silicons and actually about 40% of the common minerals belong in this group. The *metal-ore* minerals usually receive more attention because of their economic value; but only a few of these, such as gold, silver, and copper, occur in their natural state. Most of them are found in chemical combinations with oxygen, carbon, and other elements. The term *ore* is used to describe a mixture of a worthwhile metallic mineral with other unwanted minerals, which are then called *gangue*. Whether a metallic mineral is considered worthwhile or not depends on its concentration and on the price and demand for the mineral on the market. Ores can occur in any type of rock.

Nonmetallic is a convenient term to apply to a diverse group of minerals which have some economic significance but which are not sources of metals. Sulphur is an important member of this group; indeed, a wide variety of compounds, such as the sulphates and carbonates, belong here.

Of great interest, owing to their use, is the final group—the *gem* minerals. These occur most commonly in igneous and metamorphic rocks, but in some cases they have been worn from their place of formation and deposited in younger sedimentary rocks. The value of a gem is determined by its size, beauty of colour, lustre, hardness, freedom from flaws, and perfection of crystallization. Among the most popular are diamonds, emeralds, and rubies; there is also, however, a great variety of gems described as semiprecious, which are less expensive but often very beautiful.

When broken open, this apparently uninteresting piece of calcite reveals a beautiful world of crystals. Such a stone is called a geode.

American Museum of Natural History

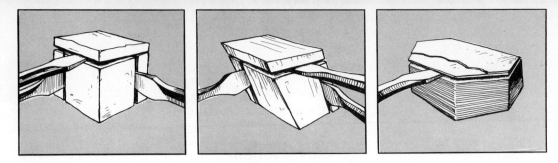

These diagrams present a few different types of cleavage. Here you see cubic, rhombohedral, and basal cleavage. Find out the other types of cleavage and prepare similar diagrams.

The Identification of Minerals

One of the first problems for the amateur mineralogist in identifying a mineral, is the basic one of isolating it. Seldom is a mineral clearly indicated by one test. Indeed, other substances present with the chief mineral can often give a reaction which leads to false conclusions. Ultimately, only careful laboratory testing can give absolute certainty in the identification of most minerals. If you are interested in minerals and rocks, however, you will want to undertake certain tests for yourself, and there are many basic tests which can easily be applied.

Colour is usually the first thing you will notice about a mineral—even before you pick it up. Beware of discolouration by exposure to the air and always try to observe a freshly broken surface of the mineral. Any good text on mineralogy will provide detailed descriptions of the colour of various minerals. It would be better still if you could obtain one which provided colour plates of the minerals you are studying.

Streak should not be confused with the colour of the mineral, as this term applies to the colour of a thin, powdered layer of the mineral. This can be obtained by rubbing the substance against the unglazed porcelain at the back of a tile. Nonmetallic minerals have a light or even colourless streak; metallic minerals usually have a dark streak.

On picking up a mineral, you may immediately be impressed by its **hardness.** Since it was found to be much more difficult to determine the gradations of hardness than to distinguish colour or streak, a scale of hardness was developed by Friedrich Mohs, a celebrated mineralogist. Mohs' scale is a table only of relative hardness beginning with talc, one of the softest minerals, hence rated as 1, and running up to the very hard diamonds, which are rated at a hardness of 10. To use the scale find out which of the minerals your sample can scratch and which it cannot. Any mineral which can scratch carborundum but not diamond has a hardness of between 9 and 10.

As with colour, so with hardness: be cautious about using the exposed surface of a mineral for testing as the weathered surface may be much softer than the native mineral. Scratch marks on a weathered surface can often be simply rubbed off and, therefore, are not true scratches.

Lustre is a scientific term used to describe the ability of a mineral to reflect, refract, or absorb light. Basically, we speak of a metallic or nonmetallic lustre. There is a wide variety of other terms to describe lustre: brilliants like diamonds are described as *adamantine*, a shiny rosin-like appearance is *resinous*, a glassy appearance is *vitreous*. Other terms used include pearly, oily, dull, silky, and earthy.

A few minerals are described as *massive* or *amorphous* if their molecules do not form a fixed, orderly arrangement. Most minerals, however, are distinctly crystalline. The **crystal form** is one of the surest clues as to the character of a mineral. Crystallography is a highly specialized form of mineralogy which makes it possible to identify many minerals even from only part of the crystal; nevertheless, in some cases the crystalline structure can be detected only by X-rays. There are six basic crystal forms and a variety of combinations of these which occur in minerals.

Crystalline minerals have another distinct quality, namely, **cleavage**. This means that they split easily in definite directions and with smooth planes. Mica splits easily into thin sheets and so has one direction of cleavage; other minerals may have up to six directions of cleavage. In addition to number and direction, cleavage is also calculated on the basis of the ease with which it occurs; thus we have poor, fair, good, perfect, or eminent cleavage. The *perfect octahedral* cleavage of the diamond makes much of the jeweller's work possible. Most minerals exhibit no cleavage but instead simply break or fracture irregularly.

The weight of a mineral relative to the weight of an equal volume of water is described as its *specific gravity* and this too can be a useful clue. Thus we have a full range from pumice, which floats on water, to gold, which has a specific gravity of 19.3 and, therefore, is almost 20 times heavier than water.

The photograph shows an example of conchoidal fracture in obsidian.

Special properties of certain minerals are of great assistance in their identification. Thus, some feldspars have a surface which is described as striated—the striations being due to the grating of parallel ridges and grooves on the surface. Magnetite attracts small pieces of iron. Sulphur and several other minerals become electrically charged when rubbed. Calcite, tungsten, and some uranium are phosphorescent—giving off light after being subjected to ultraviolet rays. Invisible radiations given out by radioactive minerals such as uranium and pitchblende can be detected by a Geiger counter. Chlorite is flexible and will remain bent after a little pressure; mica, however, springs back unless broken; it is, therefore, described as elastic. Gypsum and several other minerals can be easily cut with a knife and will pulverize if hammered. These are described as *sectile* minerals. Malleable minerals are those, such as gold and copper, which can fairly easily be hammered into sheets.

Laboratory Tests

Many of the above tests are best carried out in a laboratory. This is particularly true of the specific-gravity test. In the chapter on rocks we have already described the simple acid test for calcite.

Phosphorous can be identified by dissolving the mineral in boiling concentrated nitric acid and then adding drops of the solution to an ammonium molybdate solution; the result is a canary yellow compound.

Other laboratory tests include the flame test, the bead test, and the blowpipe test. The first of these entails moistening a small quantity of the powdered mineral and placing it in a flame at the end of a platinum wire. The colour of the flame will indicate the presence of certain minerals. Broadly similar methods are used in the bead test; in this, a bead of borax is threaded on to a platinum wire, dipped in powdered borax, and placed in a flame. If the bead is then dipped in a powdered mineral and placed again in oxidizing flame, it will change colour. One of the blowpipe tests consists in beating a powdered mineral on a charcoal block and subjecting the powder to the blowpipe flame. The fumes produced may provide clues as to the nature of the mineral. Otherwise, the nature and colour of the residue on the charcoal will provide the necessary evidence.

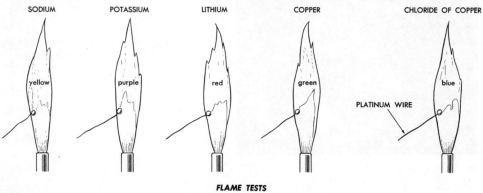

SODIUM   POTASSIUM   LITHIUM   COPPER   CHLORIDE OF COPPER

yellow   purple   red   green   blue

PLATINUM WIRE

FLAME TESTS

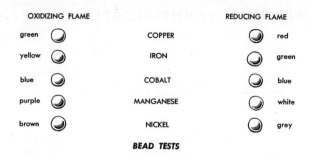

OXIDIZING FLAME				REDUCING FLAME
green		COPPER		red
yellow		IRON		green
blue		COBALT		blue
purple		MANGANESE		white
brown		NICKEL		grey

BEAD TESTS

A Few Common Minerals

Three of the commonest silicious minerals are quartz, mica, and talc. Quartz has a hardness of 7, a specific gravity of 2.65 and a glassy-to-greasy lustre. The hardest of the common minerals, quartz, may occur in a variety of colours. Crystals of this mineral are used in optical and electronic instruments; in powdered form it appears in paint and porcelain; as sand it is used in concrete. Some forms of quartz are listed as semi-precious stones. These include the **cairngorm**, beloved of Scotland's national dancers. **Mica**, hardness 2.5 to 3, specific gravity just under 3, and glassy or silky lustre, is remarkable for its flaky cleavage and thin, transparent sheets. Also used in electrical equipment, this mineral is particularly important in fireproof equipment. **Talc** has a hardness of 1, a specific gravity of 2.7, and a pearly-to-greasy lustre. This mineral has perfect cleavage. Sinks are often made of soapstone, a type of talc which is resistant to most minerals. Other uses for talc include paints, paper, and talcum powder.

Among the nonmetallic minerals are calcite, sulphur, and graphite. **Calcite**, hardness 3, specific gravity 2.7, lustre glassy or earthy, is the most common carbonate in the limestones and chalk. Great quantities of calcite are used in smelting, in fertilizer, and in whitewash. **Sulphur**, a basic material in the chemical, insecticide, rubber, and paper industries has a hardness of about 2 and a similar specific gravity. Graphite, hardness of 1 to 2, specific gravity of 2.2, and a metallic lustre, is the substance used in lead pencils. Recently used in nuclear reactors, this mineral is of interest because, like the diamond, it is practically pure carbon.

Hematite is an interesting metallic mineral which is a major source of iron ore. **Chalcopyrite**, often called *fool's gold* because of its golden appearance, is actually one of the most widely distributed copper ores. **Bauxite**, strictly speaking, is a rock and not a mineral; but its importance is such that it is usually grouped with these. Coloured white, gray, red, or yellow, it is an earthy substance which is our chief source of aluminum.

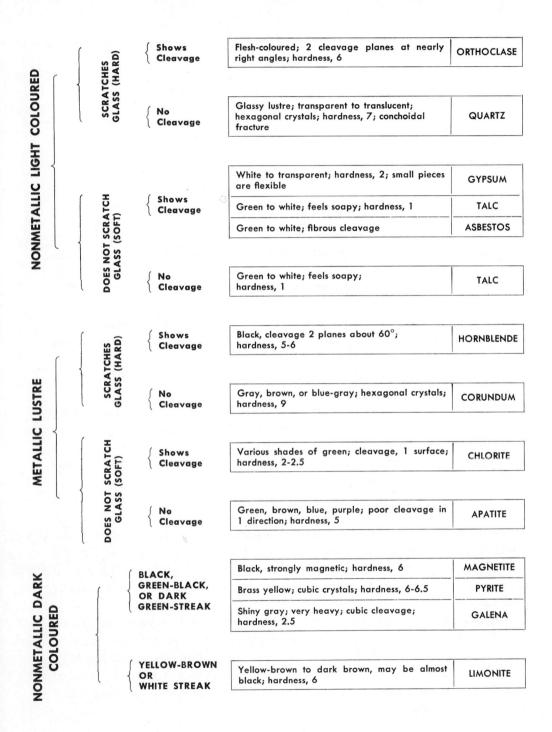

NONMETALLIC LIGHT COLOURED

SCRATCHES GLASS (HARD)

Shows Cleavage — Flesh-coloured; 2 cleavage planes at nearly right angles; hardness, 6 — ORTHOCLASE

No Cleavage — Glassy lustre; transparent to translucent; hexagonal crystals; hardness, 7; conchoidal fracture — QUARTZ

DOES NOT SCRATCH GLASS (SOFT)

Shows Cleavage —
White to transparent; hardness, 2; small pieces are flexible — GYPSUM
Green to white; feels soapy; hardness, 1 — TALC
Green to white; fibrous cleavage — ASBESTOS

No Cleavage — Green to white; feels soapy; hardness, 1 — TALC

METALLIC LUSTRE

SCRATCHES GLASS (HARD)

Shows Cleavage — Black, cleavage 2 planes about 60°; hardness, 5-6 — HORNBLENDE

No Cleavage — Gray, brown, or blue-gray; hexagonal crystals; hardness, 9 — CORUNDUM

DOES NOT SCRATCH GLASS (SOFT)

Shows Cleavage — Various shades of green; cleavage, 1 surface; hardness, 2-2.5 — CHLORITE

No Cleavage — Green, brown, blue, purple; poor cleavage in 1 direction; hardness, 5 — APATITE

NONMETALLIC DARK COLOURED

BLACK, GREEN-BLACK, OR DARK GREEN-STREAK
Black, strongly magnetic; hardness, 6 — MAGNETITE
Brass yellow; cubic crystals; hardness, 6-6.5 — PYRITE
Shiny gray; very heavy; cubic cleavage; hardness, 2.5 — GALENA

YELLOW-BROWN OR WHITE STREAK — Yellow-brown to dark brown, may be almost black; hardness, 6 — LIMONITE

 SOILS

Of greater importance than either rocks or minerals are the soils which cover most of the land around us. The science of soils is quite distinct from geology and is called *pedology*. This science tells us that soil is the surface layer of disintegrated rock; it is usually mixed with humus and in it plants grow. Soil is the result of the close interaction of the gases of the atmosphere and the organic matter due to the presence of plants and animals, with the underlying rock. A fertile soil is a combination of gases, liquids, and solids in a remarkable state of balance. You probably think of soil as *just a heap of dirt*, but this is not the view of the pedologist; he knows that chemical, physical, and biological activity is unceasing in the soil, that soils change and develop in response to climatic or vegetational change, that soil is almost a *living* thing. Indeed, a soil that has lost its fertility is sometimes called *dead* soil.

The Components of the Soil

The basic material—or *parent* material—from which soils are formed, is usually the underlying original rock. According to the nature of this rock, the soil will contain more or less of such materials as sand, silt, or clay. Certain areas, however, have such parent materials as glacial drift, volcanic lava, or other debris.

In addition to these *inorganic* components, soils also have a variety of organic materials, the most important of which is undoubtedly humus. Decomposed vegetative (and animal) particles, or *humus*, provide soils with the darker element in their colouring; this material may be completely decayed and in colloidal form, or it may be only partially decayed. Worms and various bacteria, which add to the fertility of the soil, are found to be commonest in soils that are rich in humus.

Department of Public Relations,
Ontario Agricultural College, Guelph

In studying a soil profile, digging will reveal the horizons or, as in this case, the subdivisions within each layer.

The water present in the soil is important not only for plant growth but also for maintaining the processes that are always going on in most soils. *Soil water* is actually a complex solution in which chemicals such as chlorides, nitrates, phosphates, and sulphates are present. Gases present in a good loamy soil are sometimes described as *soil air*, but these gases differ from ordinary atmosphere gases in having an excess of carbon dioxide due to the presence of growing plants; the soil air also has a slight deficiency in oxygen and nitrogen as compared with the air that we breathe.

The Processes and Factors in Soil Formation

In examining and classifying soils, pedologists frequently use the terms of profile and horizon. A *profile* is a vertical section of soil showing each of the layers from the surface down to the original parent material. Each of these layers or zones is called a *horizon*. We might describe a full slice of a layer cake as a profile and each layer as a horizon. Horizons are classified as A, B, or C depending on their nature and closeness to the surface.

The story of the formation of a soil begins with the weathering of exposed rock by wind, water, and temperature change. There follows the appearance of mosses, lichens, and bacteria in tiny niches and crannies; this vegetation in turn provides the first humus and mould in which ferns and grasses take root. In time various seeds carried by wind and birds add variety to the plant life until even shrubs and trees are well established. The plant kingdom itself has a vital part to play in the formation of soils. Penetrating roots break up and aerate the soil in which they grow; the aeration encourages worms and burrowing animals to work downwards and bring inorganic particles closer to the surface. The work of weather is not limited to the initial weathering of the rock but also includes two vital processes which continue to play a part in determining the character of the fully formed soil. Precipitation provides the water which is essential for the normal chemical and biological processes which occur within soils. However, when precipitation is excessive, water percolates through the upper layers, carrying away humus and other materials into a deeper layer of the soil. This is the process of *leaching*. In arid regions, evaporation and capillary action bring ground water rich in salts to the surface, where the salts are deposited.

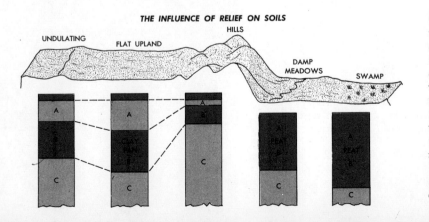

THE INFLUENCE OF RELIEF ON SOILS

Changes in relief can result in changes in drainage pattern and also in important changes in climate and vegetation, which in turn affect the soil type. For this reason, we can describe a vertical zonation of soils in addition to the horizontal zonation described in this text and outlined on most soil maps.

Temperature, too, can affect the formation of soils. High temperatures favour bacterial action; this action reaches its peak in the humid tropics where soils may be starved of humus because of the immediate destruction of fallen plants by other organisms. Very low temperatures on the other hand retard chemical and bacterial action and thus protract indefinitely the whole soil-forming process. The thin, rocky soils of the Canadian tundra lands are examples of soils produced under this handicap.

The final quality and character of any soil thus depends on a large number of variable factors. Most important of these are *parent material* and *climate*. Parent material, however, is probably the less important of these two. For example, the rich black soils of the U.S.S.R. are developed equally well from basalt, granite, and loess. The *relief* of the land plays an important role in that soil on gentle slopes or level ground is less influenced by erosion and so is usually deeper and more stable. *Slope*, too, can have importance because slopes facing the sun will usually be warmer. This increased temperature affects the soil not only directly but also indirectly through the vegetation which results. The time during which soil-forming activities have been continuous also has an effect on the actual type of soil which will result. Differences in the *age* of a soil result in a division of soils into young and mature. *Mature* soils are those which have such a well-developed profile that it is now stable and does not suffer change. In *young* soils the horizons either do not exist or else are in an early stage of development. It it not possible to say how old a soil must be to become mature; in some places it may take 200 years, in others closer to 2,000 years.

A Classification of Zonal Soils

Since there are so many variable factors, it may seem astonishing that it is possible to draw up a systematic classification of soils and produce a world map depicting soil regions. Nonetheless, such a division and mapping has been achieved and is of supreme importance in any attempt to understand such problems as the world's food supply, patterns of international trade, and at a different level, the way of life of man, especially as a farmer, in different lands.

The basic classification of soils is into azonal, intrazonal, and zonal soils. By *intrazonal* is meant those soils which have formed in swamp, marsh, or bog conditions. *Azonal* soils are those found on steep slopes. Neither of these types of soil ever develops the normal profile with distinct horizons; but the intrazonal soils can at least become mature and acquire their own distinctive characteristics. Possessing an understanding of climate, relief, and soil-forming processes, the pedologist is able to prepare a soils map of the world reducing the classification to comparatively few major groups of *zonal* and intrazonal soils.

In equatorial climatic conditions of high temperatures and heavy precipitation, lateritic soils develop. Here leaching is just as rapid a process as is decomposition.

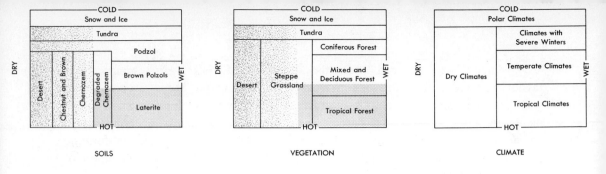

A CORRELATION OF CLIMATE, VEGETATION, AND SOIL ON A HYPOTHETICAL NORTHERN CONTINENT

These diagrams should also be used when you are studying climates and vegetation later in the course. The colouring in two diagrams represents desert and tropical climates. How far does North America correspond to this generalized pattern?

Humus, however, is scanty owing to the rapid bacterial action. The soil is reddish in colour because of the presence of iron oxides and hydroxides. Cultivated laterites quickly become infertile owing to leaching, but forests of hardwood trees and scrub with deep roots can flourish. The weathering and erosion of other materials in laterite often leave important residual ores of bauxite, manganese, and limonite (iron oxide).

In regions of high temperature but alternate droughts and heavy rains, the lateritic soils are modified in some important respects. Humus is richer in these soils and their general fertility is high. However, the long drought results in the drying up of the soil and thus encourages rapid soil erosion at the time of the rains—a serious threat in these regions. The high rate of evaporation during the dry season results in the accumulation of alkaline salts near the surface and these can be harmful to plant life when they become too thick. Sometimes these salts and minerals collect in a thick layer just beneath the surface and become cemented by soil water into a hardpan which can interfere with the normal soil renewal processes. A further drawback is sometimes found in the semi-desert or tropical-steppe regions where the surface may become baked to the point that it cannot be broken even by a plough. All of these soils are laterite—red laterites in the savanna; chestnut, red, or brown laterites in the tropical and subtropical steppes.

Saline soils reach their maximum development in the arid desert regions lying beyond the savannas. Here, evaporation being excessive, the light-coloured soils have a thick accumulation of salts close to the surface; the accumulation may even form a hard, broad salt pan formed by *caliche* (crusted calcium carbonate) in some areas. Rich in carbonate of lime, these soils can be quite fertile when irrigated; but the sparsity of vegetation results in a serious deficiency in humus, which has to be supplied artificially.

Some of the finest soils in the world are to be found in the temperate lands that lie on the poleward side of the tropics. Of enormous significance in providing the world's food supply are the temperate steppes, where the chief vegetation is the tall grass that is characteristic of the pampas, prairies, steppes, and veld. The *chernozem* (or black earth) soils of this area are rich in calcium; they are also rich in humus owing to the actual decomposition of grass roots within the soil. The conflict between the downward and upward processes of leaching and evaporation, respectively, is here practically a tie, and we may, therefore, in terms of soil formation, describe these areas as the *zones of balance*. The wind-borne, fine-grained soils known as loess cover extensive areas in this region and provide particularly rich grasslands. The great wheatlands of the world are developed largely on chernozem soils, including much of our Prairie Provinces.

Closer to the poles in the temperate latitudes, the climatic balance is tilted once again—this time in favour of accelerated leaching due to greater precipitation accompanied by generally lower temperatures. This dominance of the leaching process produces a soil in which shortly beneath the surface there occurs a strongly leached horizon which has an ash-grey colouring and from which the soil is named—*podzol*. This Russian word means *like ash*. Podzols reach their full development in the areas of coniferous forest which are so extensive in Canada and the U.S.S.R. In these forests the acidity of rainwater is increased by its passing through the needles and cones which mantle the forest floor; at the same time this acidity increases leaching and reduces the beneficial bacterial action in the soil. In certain areas excess oxides solidify in the B horizon to form a hardpan which impedes the downward percolation of water and may lead to marsh conditions developing at the surface. Lime and fertilizer and much hard work can make farming on podzols worthwhile, but these soils are not naturally fertile. Much of the world's farming, however, is done on podzolic soils; in these cases measures are taken to counteract the acidity. Regular ploughing retards any further leaching. In the true deciduous forest the trees are normally widely spaced so that a ground cover of grasses and herbaceous plants takes root. These,

The depth of the boundaries between the different horizons is subject to a considerable variation. Suggest reasons why these boundaries are sometimes sharp and sometimes indistinct.

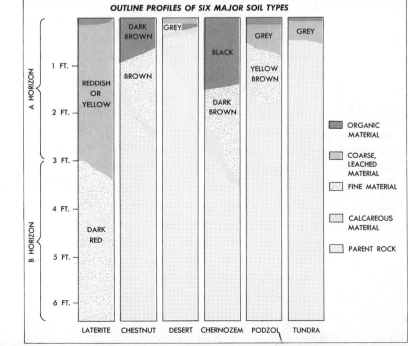

OUTLINE PROFILES OF SIX MAJOR SOIL TYPES

together with the decaying leaves of the trees, add greatly to the humus content of the soil. This brown-forest soil or brown earth resembles the podzols in that it suffers leaching, which is the dominant process, although to a less violent degree. Finally, as precipitation diminishes, trees become more widely spaced until they become mere clumps in a grassland scene. In such an area the soil type is essentially a chernozem, but the precipitation that is sufficient for tree growth is often enough to promote a certain amount of leaching on grassland. The leaching-evaporation balance then becomes tilted slightly in favour of the former and the soil is called a *degraded chernozem*. While this soil is really less fertile than true chernozem, it often produces much better crops owing to the fact that the rainfall is greater and more reliable.

Similar to the laterites of the tropics are the red and yellow earths of the monsoon lands of Asia. Here temperatures are lower and leaching less violent than in the rainforest, with the result that the soils are able to retain their humus and mineral content. The resultant soil is quite fertile as long as measures are taken against the soil erosion which monsoon rains can easily produce. A marked wet season and dry season is also the chief characteristic of the Mediterranean region, and here a red, clayey soil, often based on limestone, is widespread and is called *terra rossa*—an Italian term which is now generally accepted.

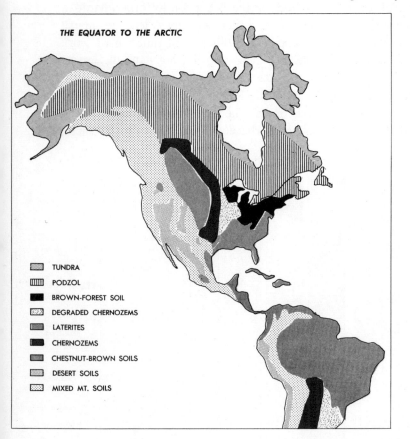

THE EQUATOR TO THE ARCTIC

TUNDRA
PODZOL
BROWN-FOREST SOIL
DEGRADED CHERNOZEMS
LATERITES
CHERNOZEMS
CHESTNUT-BROWN SOILS
DESERT SOILS
MIXED MT. SOILS

How far does this map correspond to the generalized diagram showing a hypothetical continent? Account for any major differences.

The owner of this hill used fertilizer on the left half to grow strong grass and thus check erosion. Gullying has continued on the other half of the hill. What effect will the trees on the surrounding hills have on erosion there?

Soil Erosion

In most countries in the world there are now government agencies devoted to preserving the soil and its basic fertility. These agencies have been made necessary by the fact that man, through succeeding generations, has often ruined good farmland by sheer mismanagement and ignorance. In a world of increasing population the limited food-producing surface of the earth assumes ever greater importance.

Wind and water are the main agents of soil erosion. Once deforestation, overgrazing, overcropping, or overcultivation has removed a soil's humus and so lowered its porosity and cohesion, widespread *sheet erosion* or deep-carving *gully erosion* soon develops. The ultimate tragedy is that once these processes start they accelerate and soon spread to cover wider areas. Measures adopted to prevent such disasters include:

    Terracing—in which a slope is cut into a series of shelves, each with a low retaining wall. Best developed in the Orient, this method has long been used also for dry farming in Mediterranean Europe.

    Contour ploughing—wherein the farmer ploughs parallel with the contours. In effect this creates a series of terraces each of which checks the run-off water and also the downward movement of soil.

    Strip farming—is a method in which alternate parallel strips of land are planted or left fallow. The idea behind this practice is that the standing vegetation will reduce run-off and will also limit wind erosion.

Shelter belts—of trees are often planted to act as wind breaks in arid or very hot regions. In California these lines of trees are also used to protect orchards; in New Zealand to shelter flocks of sheep and young lambs; in the U.S.S.R. for the waving grain of the wheat fields. Soviet scientists have found that in certain cases shelter belts have increased cereal yield by over 20%. However, this measure, as carried out on the Soviet scale, is still subject to discussion.

One of the chief obstructions to the remedying of soil erosion problems is the fact that such huges areas are often involved that only large-scale government action is of any value. The efficacy of such action, however, is often hampered by international or state boundaries' crossing the area and thus dividing the authority. When this political difficulty is overcome, excellent examples of intelligent planning and teamwork result. The first such major scheme was the Tennessee Valley Authority, initiated in 1933, and still a classic example of man's working with, instead of against, his environment. An area in which international understanding is a still unfulfilled prerequisite for sound planning, is the Jordan Valley and Dead Sea area, where much yet remains to be done.

Here we see systematic shelter belts around some Texan farms. What function does a shelter belt serve and how does it do this?

U.S.D.A. Photo

124

4 OUR GEOLOGICAL BACKGROUND

When Robinson Crusoe saw a footprint in the sand, this clue told him of the proximity of Man Friday. In some such way, the modern geologist looks at rocks and sees there the footprints of each of the ages of the earth's long history. Sometimes the nature of a rock may speak clearly of its origin; at other times its position gives a valuable clue to its past. Often the best clue is locked within the rock in the form of the remains or imprints of long-dead plants and animals; such relics, or fossils as they are called, provide invaluable data concerning the period during which the rock was formed. One of the most exciting aspects of the study of geology is this detective work—this search for different types of clues leading to the building up of a scientific account of events which happened, not yesterday, but hundreds of millions of years ago.

Since many types of sedimentary rock are laid down in horizontal layers, or strata, it is obvious that the youngest strata will be on top and the oldest beneath. This conclusion will hold true only so long as the strata remain undisturbed. As long as they do so, however, they give us a very clear indication of the sequence of the geologic periods in which they were formed. The deposition of these layers would occur in great seas, or lakes, which would form whenever an area of land subsided. *Stratigraphy* is the branch of geology which is concerned with the study of strata as clues to the past.

More often than not, the original layers of rock were folded or faulted, tilted or broken, by the intrusion of other rocks. In these cases the geologist cannot presume that the rock lying nearest to the surface is the youngest, and he must, therefore, make use of a variety of scientific methods to work out the story of the succession of rock layers. Fortunately, modern research in radioactivity and the employment of complex mathematical calculations have provided two useful tools for the discovery of the age of rocks. Many comparatively recent sedimentary rocks contain the remains of ancient plants and animals, thus they also contain the carbon 14 which is found in the composition of all living things. Carbon 14 is a radioactive element which decomposes at a constant rate which we can measure; hence, by examining the proportion of carbon 14 in any rock, we can tell how long it is since the plants and animals were buried in it. In the older rocks, where fossils are lacking, there are often instead several radioactive minerals such as uranium. As these minerals decompose very slowly to produce lead, graphs can be drawn to indicate their successive stages of decomposition over a period of millions of years. Here, too, intricate calculations permit fairly accurate dating of extremely old geological formations.

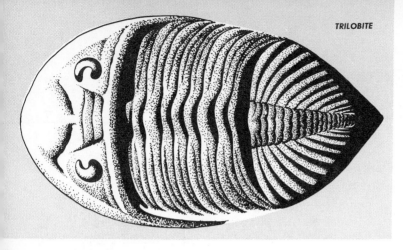

TRILOBITE

The trilobite is an interesting fossil that experienced considerable variation during the period of its comparatively short existence. This short existence makes the trilobite an excellent index fossil for dating the rocks in which it occurs. Many trilobites can be found in Canada and the United States.

Less accurate methods of geological detective work involve the study of the processes of erosion and deposition which are active today, and the application of this knowledge to the past. By estimating the rate of river erosion we can arrive at some idea of how long a river canyon has taken to form or a waterfall to cut back to its present site. On the other hand, climatic changes have certainly occurred during the past 10,000 years and allowances must be made for them when this method is used.

Fossils

The most widely used method of dating and classifying rocks is based on our knowledge of fossils—a subject which is called *paleontology*. We know the types of plants and animals characteristic to various ages and, when these occur as fossils, they indicate the age of the rock in which they occur. However, just as today we have deep oceans, salty seas, fresh-water lakes, sandy deserts, and wide forests each having its own peculiar forms of life, so in the past there was diversity even within one period.

There are few more interesting branches of geology than that of paleontology with its endless search for more and better preserved fossils. Just as the detective searches for clues, so the geologist searches for fossils; to both men these are the vital steps towards more knowledge.

Royal Ontario Museum

Some plant fossils such as eqatheites dentatus can be found in the Royal Ontario Museum.

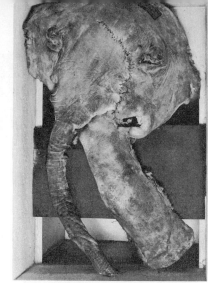

The photograph shows part of a well-preserved woolly mammoth which was found in a glacier in Alaska. How has this animal been preserved for so long?

In the normal process of nature, after a plant or animal dies it is either consumed by some other animal or attacked by bacteria and decay. There are many humorous songs about the chain of events which begins with fertilizer in a meadow and ends with someone's enjoying a tasty steak. As a result of this process, the great majority of the living things that appear on the surface of the earth eventually disappear completely. However, under certain circumstances the processes of decay can be delayed or halted altogether; indeed the refrigerators in our homes remind us of one way in which this can happen. A dramatic proof of the effectiveness of ice in preserving animals was provided by the discovery in 1900 of a woolly mammoth in Siberia. This huge elephant had been preserved almost completely intact for thousands of years in a glacier. Other similarly preserved animals were found later in Alaska. An interesting mystery is attached to these discoveries. The remarkable preservation of the flesh, and even of uneaten buttercups in the mouth of the mammoth, have shown frozen-food experts that the animal was frozen at below —150° F.—much lower than any natural temperature ever recorded. The problem is this: Was there a time in the not-so-distant past when large areas experienced such excessively low temperatures for a long period of time?

Volcanic ash, wax, certain soils, and a gum called amber also act as preservatives in certain circumstances.

Fossils in which an organism, or part of it, is preserved in its original state are very rare indeed. It is more common to find a specimen in which the original material has been altered by chemical processes or in which merely a trace of the plant or animal has survived. In the distant past, calcium carbonate, pyrite, and silicon dioxide sometimes were carried by water into the cell spaces of recently dead plants and animals. As the water evaporated, the minerals would accumulate; this process may have been repeated many times. Eventually the organism would decay leaving a solid mineral framework in its own outline. This process, called *petrifaction*, accounts for the greater part of our knowledge of earlier types of life.

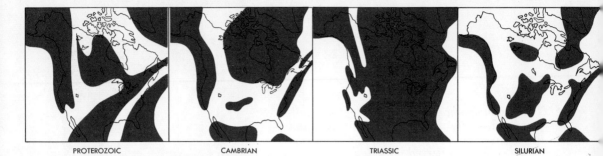

PROTEROZOIC CAMBRIAN TRIASSIC SILURIAN

The Geological Time Sequence

According to the reckonings of geologists, most of the continent on which we live is very young. As the *Story of a Continent* shows, the *landmass* now known as North America has been subject at different times to elevation and depression, folding and flooding, glaciation and volcanism. We can think of this huge continent as a mighty giant whose face has become more and more wrinkled with the passage of aeons of time. This giant, moreover, has several times been restored to his youth—only to begin the long ageing process all over again.

The earliest division of time in the earth's history was the period when the earth was just taking shape as a planet. This cosmic era has already been discussed. Name and explain two of the theories which have been advanced as explanations of the earth's origin.

Subsequent to this cosmic era there was the Azoic (*a*, without + *zoe*, life) Era, a time when temperatures were falling, a hard crust was forming, and the earth's chemistry was undergoing important changes—a time also when there was no plant or animal life of any kind.

The Pre-Cambrian Era

The first great geological era of which we still have clearly visible evidence and concerning which we can hold scientific discussion, is the Pre-Cambrian. It is significant, however, that the name used for this era merely tells us that it was *pre* or *before* some other era. Even though it covered a much longer period of time, we know much less about the Pre-Cambrian era than about any of those which come later.

More than two billion years ago an era began, called the Archeozoic—a term meaning *very ancient life*, although it is not certain that there was any life at that time. During this time the vast Canadian Shield comprising Alaska, Newfoundland, and several other parts of North America, formed distinct lands whose outline repeatedly changed as the surrounding seas advanced and retreated. This period ended with a great series of crustal movements (called the Laurentian-Algoman) which formed mountains in the areas of the present Laurentians, Adirondacks, and Great Lakes. Ultimately these mountains were reduced to peneplains but their appearance marked the beginning of the next geological era.

128

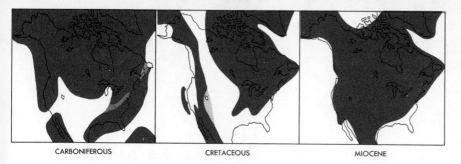

CARBONIFEROUS   CRETACEOUS   MIOCENE

Locate on each of these maps the present position of Vancouver, San Francisco, Winnipeg, Montreal, and Halifax. Prepare a list for each place outlining the periods during which it was above sea level.

Primitive plants and such soft-bodied creatures as worms and jellyfish appeared during the Proterozoic era. This was a time of widespread volcanism—a period associated with the formation of rich iron, copper, and silver deposits.

The Palaeozoic Era

During the Cambrian period of Palaeozoic time much of our continent lay at the bottom of warm shallow seas which were inhabited by a variety of such invertebrates as sponges, snails, and jellyfish. Since a small, segmented creature called the *trilobite* was particularly numerous at this time, it is possible to arrange the succession of Cambrian rocks according to the gradual growth and evolution of the trilobite in its fossilized forms. The principal scene of Cambrian life was the sea and most of the exposed land surface was either bare or else occupied by primitive fungi and algae. Tectonic action in the region of New England brought an end to the Cambrian, and initiated the Ordovician period. Most of North America was still under shallow seas at this time and vast areas were covered by thick deposits of limestone. This rock is often very rich in fossils and among these we find traces of the first vertebrates.

This Ordovician seascape shows what the Toronto area looked like about 500 million years ago.

Royal Ontario Museum

Our coal came from the forests of t h e Carboniferous period.

Throughout the Silurian and Devonian periods, life became ever more advanced with the appearance of many new species and gradual disappearance of the most primitive forms. Stories have been written about adventures with time machines, but if a time machine were possible, surely the most exciting adventure would be a journey through the millions of years necessary for the modern plants, animals, and fishes to reach their present stage of development. In Silurian times we would see most of North America as land and would see the first land animals—scorpion-like creatures. Coral reefs were common around the shallow inland seas. By this time, too, the impressive rocks which form the Niagara escarpment were already in their present position. Fish were numerous, but more and more varieties of fish appeared in Devonian time—a period marked by the presence of the first amphibians, and of trees and ferns some of which were over 30 feet high.

Forests were perhaps the principal characteristic of the next period—the Carboniferous. At that time much of North America was under water and we would have seen vast areas of warm, humid swamps with great evergreen trees, especially ferns and horsetails. Plants and animals grew to maturity amidst the sweet decay of the contemporary organic life around them. Among the fossil remains of this time that have been classified, there are over 800 species of insects and a number of fish and amphibians. Great alligators, snakes, and dragonflies, with wings each a foot in length, would impress us by their activity. Gradually the shallow waters from Newfoundland to Pennsylvania deepened as the land subsided and the sea covered the rich plant remains with thick sediment. In time the pressure and heat transformed them into coal, hence the name *carboniferous* for this period. A visit to the Carboniferous period would be very much like experiencing some of the adventure stories which are set in hot, equatorial forests, although there would be many important differences.

In the time between the flooding of the Carboniferous *everglades* and the activity heralding the great earth movements which produced the Appalachian mountains, most of the continent stood well above the level of the seas and experienced a much drier climate. Plants became modified and adapted to the new conditions, and reptiles became more numerous. This was the Permian period.

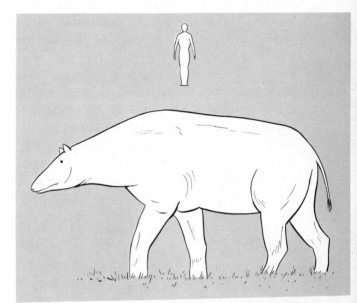

The Baluchitherium, an Oligocene animal from Asia, is compared in size with man.

The Mesozoic Era

The word Mesozoic tells us that in the story of the organisms of earth this was the period of *middle life*. During the previous period increasing dryness had killed off many of the simpler animals and plants; and during this period most of the animals that are popularly known as *prehistoric* began to appear.

During the Triassic (or three-layered) period much of North America was a huge desert. Under these desert conditions there developed the salt and gypsum deposits of Canada's Atlantic provinces and of various parts of the United States. Dinosaurs began to appear. Also, towards the end of the quite short Triassic period there was much volcanic activity and many of the igneous fractures between the Great Lakes and the Atlantic occurred.

Perhaps the most fascinating period to visit in a time-machine would be the Jurassic, sometimes called *The Age of Reptiles*. This was the age when both the 80-foot-long diplodocus and the 20-ton brontosaurus lumbered through the marshes and ponds where grew the fragile plants which formed their only diet. In the air we might have heard the sound of wings as a lizard of 20-foot wing-spread, the *pterosaur*, or a bird with sharp teeth, the *archaeopteryx*, flew past.

Long-necked sea monsters known as *plesiosaurs* and porpoise-like *ichthysaurs* inhabited the Jurassic seas. Crustal movements took place towards the end of this nightmare period, with the result that the Coast Ranges of North America were formed; and with them probably the gold deposits of California.

The word Cretaceous is derived from the Latin word for *chalk* which was one of the chief deposits laid down in the Cretaceous period, the third geological period (of the Mesozoic era), which immediately followed the Jurassic. King of the earth at that time was the carnivorous tyrannosaurus—a 20-foot-high dinosaur. In Canada there lived at this time the ceratopsia—a 50-foot-long horned reptile somewhat similar to the rhinoceros. A visitor to Cretaceous North America would probably have observed extensive forests of maple, poplar, willow, and other trees which are still common today. In the air he would have seen the largest flying creature of all time—the pteranodon with its 25-foot wingspread. The Cretaceous period concluded with the great earth movements which formed the Rocky Mountain systems and re-elevated the now ancient Appalachians. The close of this period, too, saw the final disappearance of the many species of dinosaurs which had characterized the Mesozoic era.

A more modern scene is an Oligocene landscape. In how many animals or trees here can you see a resemblance to creatures of the present?

The Cenozoic Era

The word Cenozoic means *recent life*; it is the name given to the geological era in which we now live—an era during which the relief and the plants and animals which surround us today began to emerge in their present forms. The rich oil, gas, and sulphur deposits of North America are largely found in rocks laid down in this era when subtropical climatic conditions prevailed over most of our continent. *Eohippus*, the first horse, was a small dog-sized animal found during the *early dawn of modern life*, or Eocene epoch. In the Oligocene epoch we might have seen the first foldings of the earth's crust which were to produce the mighty Alpine and Himalayan mountains and we would have seen hundreds of volcanoes in western North America. The climate was now a little cooler and in the animal kingdom the division into cat and dog families had just begun.

During Miocene times we would have seen great herds of horses and camels roaming the plains of North America; it was also at this time that animals similar to the present rhinoceros, deer, monkey, and pig were very common.

Towards the end of the Tertiary period an important change took place in the world's climate. The beginning of the Quarternary period is known as the Pleistocene epoch—a word associated with the great ice ages which have been discussed elsewhere. At this time great continental glaciers covered much of the earth and the general level of seas and oceans fell. Land bridges developed between Asia and North America and the resultant mixing of the animals of the two continents led to the disappearance of some species. Fossils of this time give us a picture which includes man, the sabre-tooth tiger, mastodons, great herds of bison, and enormous wolves.

After the close of the Pleistocene epoch, the world moved into the period, characterized by its diversity, in which we now live. We know what extremes of climate are to be found today; for instance, cold Arctic conditions contrast with the damp heat of tropical forests. The surface of the earth is being altered by a great variety of erosion cycles, as well as by volcanoes and earthquakes. Life, too, is more varied than in any previous age, for we now have an enormous number of species of plants, animals, and fishes.

Considering the entire period of the earth's history, man is seen to be a very recent arrival. This makes our geological detective work even more difficult, for we are trying to solve mysteries which happened millions of years before our time.

Man appears on the geological scene. It is one of the greatest human achievements that primitive man, living in dark, crude caves, was inspired to paint figures on the walls around him. In addition, these ancestors of ours showed a high degree of skill.

ERA	PERIOD	EPOCH	TIME OF ORIGIN	DURATION	SOME PLANTS
			(millions of years)		
CENOZOIC	QUATERNARY	RECENT			
		PLEISTOCENE			
	TERTIARY	PLIOCENE	55	54	
		MIOCENE			
		OLIGOCENE			
		EOCENE			
MESOZOIC	CRETACEOUS		120	65	
	JURASSIC		155	35	
	TRIASSIC		190	35	
PALAEOZOIC	PERMIAN		215	25	
	CARBONIFEROUS		300	85	
	DEVONIAN		350	50	
	SILURIAN		420	70	
	ORDOVICIAN		480	60	
	CAMBRIAN		550	70	
PROTEROZOIC			1200	650	
ARCHEOZOIC					
			2100	900	
AZOIC					
COSMIC			2500	400	

SOME PLANTS: FLOWERING PLANTS, CONIFERS, FERNS · HORSETAILS, MOSSES, ALGAE, BACTERIA · FUNGI

SOME ANIMALS	MAJOR LAND MOVEMENTS	A "SHAPE" OF THE TIMES
MAMMALS	the major existing cycles of erosion	
REPTILES	the great ice ages	SABRE-TOOTHED TIGER
BIRDS	cooling down • appearance of Bering Land Bridge	
INSECTS	great mountain-building activity and volcanism in the west	MONKEY
FISHES	subtropical deposition	
WORMS	volcanism and faulting in the west	EOHIPPUS
	thick deposition in extensive seas	
	building of the coast ranges	ARCHAEOPTERYX BRONTOSAURUS
	volcanism in many areas	
	Appalachian mountain building	
	gradual submergence of shallow, low-lying plains	DRAGONFLY
TRILOBITES	mountain building in Nova Scotia and Newfoundland	SPIDER SHARK
	thick sedimentaries laid down	CORAL
	ancient folding in the Maritimes and New England • submergence elsewhere	CEPHALOPOD
	wide seas • thick deposition	JELLYFISH TRILOBITE

135

UNIT REVIEW

Vocabulary Review

Match the word or phrase in the left column with the correct word in the right column.

1. Relative Weight
2. Mohs' scale
3. Ultraviolet light
4. Study of rocks
5. Concentration of minerals in stream bed
6. Main mineral in limestone
7. Rock that may float on water
8. Bead Test
9. Foliation
10. Quartz

(a) calcite
(b) borax
(c) arrangement of minerals in layers
(d) pumice
(e) a common mineral composed of silicon dioxide
(f) flint
(g) hardness
(h) petrology
(i) fluorescent
(j) specific gravity
(k) placer deposits
(l) lava

Questions

1. Explain why such minerals as quartz, corundum, and diamond are used as abrasives.

2. Briefly explain why it is difficult to identify a mineral by its colour.

3. Describe the process by which an original rock surface changes until it is one of deep, fertile soil.

4. Differentiate between cleavage and fracture.

5. What is the usual way of obtaining the streak of a mineral?

6. Briefly explain the system normally used in the classification of soils.

Research Assignments

1. Prepare a list of ten objects in the school, identifying, as far as possible, the lustre of each.

2. Place some clay, sand, and gravel in a tall vessel of water and stir the water well. Then allow it to stand and record the time it takes for the deposition of each sediment.

3. Using the *Atlas of Canada* or a similar reference work, prepare a map showing the location of each of the major mineral deposits in Canada.

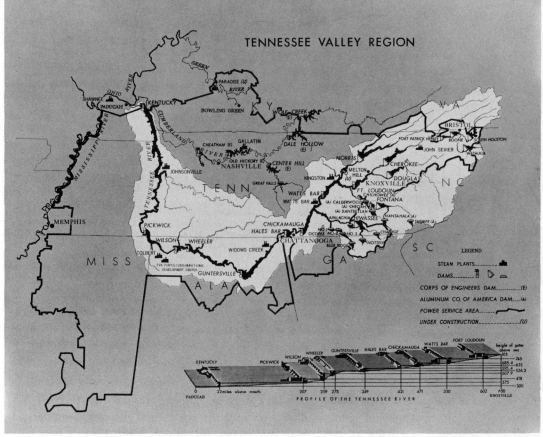

Tennessee Valley Authority

4. "Major soil conservation programmes often involve the complete rehabilitation of the economy of large areas." Discuss the aptness of this expression with respect to the Tennessee Valley scheme, which is mapped here.

5. Use the mineral identification key and your knowledge of the basic tests to identify four of the chief minerals in your class collection. Explain the methods you used and the results obtained.

6. Visit a quarry or some rock exposures in your neighbourhood and collect several rock specimens. After attempting to identify these, carefully compare your results with those indicated by a geological map of the area.

Movements within the Earth

1 THE EARTH: ITS ORIGIN, AND STRUCTURE

The earth is just one, and, at that, one of the smaller, planets of our solar system. Very little is known about its origin, or about the origin of any planet for that matter. As we have not witnessed the birth of our planet, we can only surmise the nature of its formation and draw on our knowledge of present conditions to guide us.

Earth's Origin

One theory which attempts to explain this phenomenon of a planet's birth is known as the *planetesimal* theory. This idea suggests that the sun may have experienced a glancing collision with another star with the result that masses of matter were scattered in a wide arc about the sun. These eventually cooled and formed planets, moons, and planetoids. A similar theory holds that the stars did not actually collide but passed close enough to draw out from each other masses of gas or molten material by the force of gravity. Whether either of these events actually occurred is difficult to say. Some proof of the theories can be adduced from reversing the procedure of solidification of liquid material. This is carried on every day in refineries where solid rock is melted to remove the minerals.

Another attempt to explain the origin of the earth is advanced in the *binary* or *companion-star* theory. According to this idea, the sun once had a companion star, which exploded or disintegrated leaving only the smaller bodies which we call planets. Exploding stars are very rare, but there is some evidence that such explosions occur, and, therefore, this theory could be correct.

The *nebular theory* differs considerably from the above-mentioned conjectures. Here, the author of the theory envisions a cloud of hot gaseous material revolving in space. Because of cooling and contraction the gaseous material liquefied and the decrease in size caused an increase in the speed of rotation. The liquid material bulged about the equator and eventually rings of molten material broke away from the cloud or nebula. In time these rings split and formed the planets. The moons are thought to have been formed from the planets in the same manner. The rings of Saturn are thought to be incompletely formed moons.

A parallel theory suggests that some of the gaseous material from which the sun evolved continued to rotate about the equator of the sun. In time convection currents within this material established giant whirlpools and the planets emerged from these. Both these theories assume the formation of dense bodies from gaseous material. As this process of contracting and condensing is hard to visualize, we can offer the spectacle of the reverse process, namely, the explosion of an atomic bomb, as proof that such contraction and condensation could have occurred.

The above-mentioned theories are discussed in the hope that the student will read them critically and attempt to prove or disprove them. There are some other theories, not mentioned here, which the author hopes will provide some interesting research for the reader.

Earth's Structure

Our knowledge of the structure of the earth's interior is limited. Indeed, we know more about the stars millions of miles away than we do about the earth's interior 20 miles below the surface. Our lack of knowledge seems astonishing, for man has inhabited the earth for thousands of years yet has been unable to overcome the obstacles which hinder him from penetrating to its core. The two chief obstacles are heat and pressure. In mines at a depth of even one mile a considerable rise in the temperature of the rock has been recorded, and, on the average, temperatures rise 80° F. for every mile of depth. As shafts are sunk deeper, cool air must be pumped underground and in many cases a bonus is provided in the wages of the miners for heat risk. These factors make the sinking of a shaft to great depths a very expensive proposition.

Pressure is, however, an even greater obstacle. If you have ever lifted a large boulder, you can imagine the tremendous weight that even a slender mile-depth cylinder of excavated rock will have. This weight, or pressure, compresses and compacts the rock underneath it. If this pressure were suddenly released, the rock would expand and, perhaps, actually explode. When a shaft is sunk to great depths this situation is created and because of the release of pressure, rock may explode into the shaft. Thus, it seems that if the interior of the earth is to be explored, some other methods must be used. Drill holes can penetrate to greater depths than shafts, but as yet these are limited to the first few miles of the earth's crust.

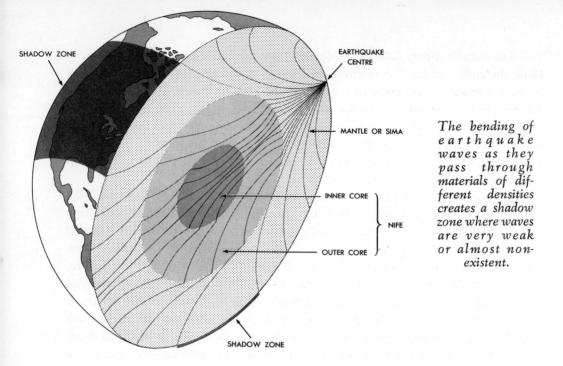

The bending of earthquake waves as they pass through materials of different densities creates a shadow zone where waves are very weak or almost non-existent.

Some knowledge of the earth's interior has been gained by careful seismographic recordings of shock waves set up by earthquakes. Because these waves, which spread out in all directions from the centre, travel at faster speeds in denser material, it is possible to determine that the earth's core is much denser than its surface. This is done by measuring the time it takes shock waves to travel through the earth.

Another useful property of these waves is the fact that they bend as they pass through materials of varying densities. One of the effects of this bending is a *shadow zone* some distance from the earthquake centre where shock waves are very faint or nonexistent. The presence of this shadow zone had been interpreted by scientists as proof that the earth has a very dense core.

Basing their conclusions mainly on the study of these shock waves, some scientists believe that the earth consists of three distinct layers. The *crust* or *sial* layer, which is the outer layer and which in places reaches depths of 30 miles, is separated from the next layer by the Moho discontinuity. Beneath this is the *mantle* or *sima* layer, 1,800 miles thick, and then beneath that is the *core* or *nife* layer which may or may not have a liquid centre.

The Sial

This is the thin, outer layer known as the earth's crust. It is composed of relatively light rocks and varies in thickness. It is thickest underneath the continents, where it is some 20 to 30 miles deep, and thinnest under the oceans, where it is thought to be as thin as 7 miles in some places. This outer, rigid shell is very

140

sensitive to any changes in the earth's interior, and, therefore, the exterior features which are visible, e.g., the mountains, reflect the forces which are at work deep in the sima, or the nife, layers.

The Sima

This layer, sometimes called the *mantle*, is separated from the sial by the Moho discontinuity. This is the point at which earthquake waves begin to bend, indicating a change in the density, or weight, of the rock. It has been determined scientifically that the rocks of the sima layer weigh twice as much per cubic foot as those above it. This layer is roughly 1,800 miles thick and the material in it may be solid, but the intense heat and pressure at that depth could render it somewhat plastic.

The Nife

According to the density of the rock this core area can be subdivided into the outer, and the inner, core. The outer core is thought to be 1,300 miles thick and the inner core to be 1,800 miles in diameter. The density of the rock in these two layers ranges from twice to four times that of the rocks at the surface. The condition of the material cannot be completely determined. The intense heat and pressure may have liquefied the core. However, there are some indications that it may be plastic, or even solid. It is generally thought to consist of a mixture of 90% iron and 10% nickel since the density of the core corresponds to the density of this alloy.

The composition of the earth cannot be accurately determined, but it appears to have the features indicated here.

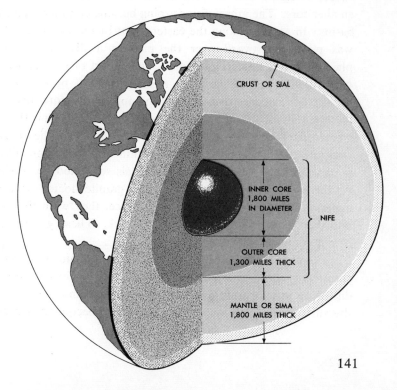

CRUST OR SIAL

INNER CORE
1,800 MILES
IN DIAMETER

NIFE

OUTER CORE
1,300 MILES THICK

MANTLE OR SIMA
1,800 MILES THICK

This distribution of rock layers may have come about while the earth was cooling and the heavier metallic material sank towards the centre leaving the lighter rock near the surface. On the other hand, the composition of the earth's material substance may remain the same throughout and the change in density may be due to the increase in pressure. At a depth of about 20 miles the pressure is nearly 15,000 pounds per square inch. At the earth's centre it approaches a pressure of 50 million pounds per square inch. Just what effect this pressure might have has not been determined, but it is of such a magnitude that pressure alone might be responsible for the high density of the nife layer. Until we are able to reach the earth's core or recreate in the laboratory the conditions that exist there, it would seem that we can only speculate or surmise as to what materials exist beneath our feet. At this point the student may be able to advance some theories of his own regarding the composition of the earth and the means of determining that composition.

The Origin of The Continents

The origin of such features as continents and ocean basins, has long been the subject of conjecture, and many theories have been advanced in attempts to explain them. Perhaps the simplest theory to understand is the *thermal contraction* theory. This states that the earth shrank or contracted as it cooled from a molten to a solid state. When temperatures became low enough, the exterior solidified but the interior remained molten. Further cooling and contracting of the interior caused buckling and warping of the outer shell so that it could conform to the smaller core. The areas of upwarping became continents and the downfolds became basins. In an area along the eastern part of the Canadian Rockies a mass of rock was pushed eastward over the prairies a distance of about 15 miles. This phenomenon is offered as evidence in support of this theory, for the circumference of the outer shell of the earth appears to have been shortened by that distance. What other evidence can you find to support or refute this idea?

In view of the fact that the rocks which make up the continents are, for the greater part, granitic and, therefore, lighter than the dense basalt rocks which compose the floor of the oceans, continental formation may be due to *magmatic segregation*, that is, the heavier materials separated by sinking towards the centre. As the earth cooled, masses of lighter granite floated on a sea of heavier molten material or magma. Being on the surface, they were the first to cool and harden and thus remained above the denser rock. These granitic masses are thought to be our continents of today.

Another theory which attempts to explain this phenomenon deals with *convection currents*, which are thought to exist in any molten mass owing to the difference in temperature between the surface and the interior. The material near the surface contracts on cooling and thus, becoming denser, sinks. This sinking forces up the lighter material, which, in turn, cools and sinks again. As the entire mass cools, the current slows down, and bulges occur over the area of rising currents; meanwhile depressions are created over the area of sinking currents.

A closely related explanation is the *continental drift* theory, which states that the lighter, granitic material solidified first but was concentrated in one continuous mass. Subsequent action of convection currents in the earth's interior caused this mass to break up and the fragments or pieces drifted apart. Further cooling resulted in the entire outer crust's solidifying and fixing the positions of the continents. It is interesting to fit the various continental outlines together to see how closely their coastlines are related.

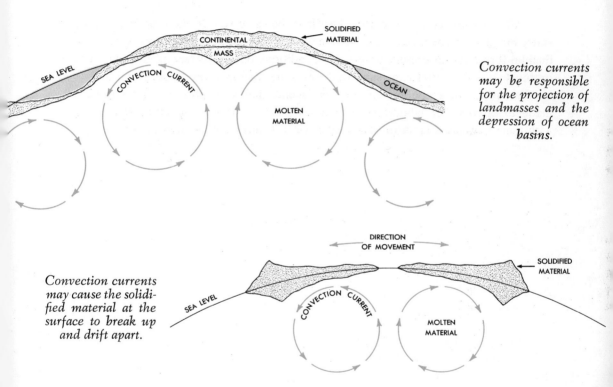

Convection currents may be responsible for the projection of landmasses and the depression of ocean basins.

Convection currents may cause the solidified material at the surface to break up and drift apart.

One final theory, which has many exponents, is that of *isostatic readjustment.* After the solidification of the outer crust, a state of balance was set up between the oceans, mountains, and plains and this balance is maintained by movements within the earth's interior. When sediments are removed from the mountains by erosion and deposited in the sea, two adjustments occur. The weight of the sediments forces the crust to sink slowly while the release of weight in the mountainous area causes the mountain regions to rise. By this method of adjustment the oceans retain their depths while the continents remain above sea level. As this is a widely accepted theory, it should be carefully studied and critically analyzed.

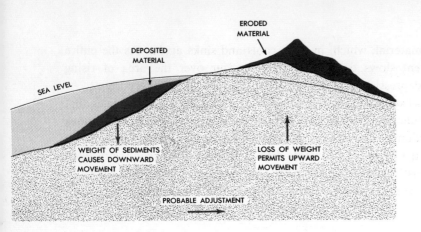

Adjustments in the earth's interior maintain a balance among the features of the earth's crust.

SEA LEVEL

ERODED MATERIAL

DEPOSITED MATERIAL

WEIGHT OF SEDIMENTS CAUSES DOWNWARD MOVEMENT

LOSS OF WEIGHT PERMITS UPWARD MOVEMENT

PROBABLE ADJUSTMENT

All of these theories accept the idea that the earth was at one time in a molten state, but it is interesting to note that none of them has attempted to relate continental formation to present observable conditions on the surface of the sun. The outbursts of solar activity, or sunspots, may some day give rise to solidified masses on the surface of a cooling sun. It also seems that very little attempt has been made to discover by laboratory techniques whether or not miniature continents, with their associated landforms, will form on the surface of molten material.

2 STRUCTURE OF THE CONTINENTS

In order to understand the environment in which we live, it is necessary to study the topography of the land. The total relief of the world from the highest peak, Mt. Everest, to the lowest depths of the ocean, the Marianas Trench, is just slightly over 12 miles. The aspects of this relief with which we are mostly concerned are mountains, plateaus, plains, and continental shelves. This chapter is devoted to the study of these general features.

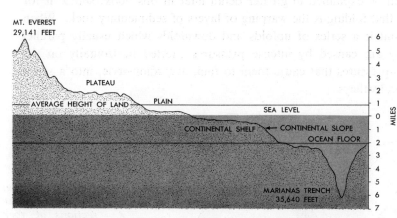

The total relief of the land (about 12 miles) is very small when compared with the earth's diameter.

THE TOTAL RELIEF OF THE EARTH AND ITS RELATIONSHIP TO STRUCTURAL FEATURES

Mountains

The term mountain usually conjures up a picture of breath-taking beauty, of sharp peaks, extensive snowfields, and rugged terrain. It is, however, somewhat difficult to define this particular term, for if we consider only elevation above sea level, we would have some plateau areas classed as mountains and some mountainous areas classed as plains. On the other hand, if we consider only the elevation from the base of the slope to its peak, we may have higher and steeper slopes in a dissected plateau than we have in an elevated area 10,000 feet above sea level. It is, then, exceedingly difficult to arrive at an acceptable definition of a mountain. Accordingly, we must accept certain distinguishing characteristics such as: mountains have a minimum elevation of 3,000 feet; they are usually steep and rugged; they have a high local relief which is usually over 2,000 feet; etc.

Mountains occur in many shapes and sizes and one method of classifying them is by their appearance. For instance, a single isolated mountain is often referred to as a *peak*. Examples of this are Mt. Assiniboine in the Canadian Rockies and Pike's Peak in Colorado. When a number of these peaks forms a continuous ridge, they are called a mountain *range*, e.g., the Monashee, Selkirk, and Purcell ranges. A mountain chain is a number of ranges which run, roughly speaking, in the same direction, e.g., the Columbia Mts. A number of parallel chains such as the Rockies, Coast Mts., and Insular Mts. is called a *cordillera*.

Another method of classifying mountains is by their origin. In this classification we have several types; namely, fold mountains, block mountains, volcanic cones, and dome mountains. A study of this grouping is particularly interesting because it gives us an insight into, and an understanding of, geological formations.

Fold Mountains

To understand the formation of this type of mountain we must understand the term *fold*. This will be explained in greater detail later in this book; suffice it for the moment to say that folding is the warping of layers of sedimentary rock. When this occurs the result is a series of upfolds and downfolds which usually parallel one another. They are caused by intense pressures exerted horizontally on the sedimentary beds—pressures that cause them to fold, accordion-style, into a series of parallel ridges and valleys.

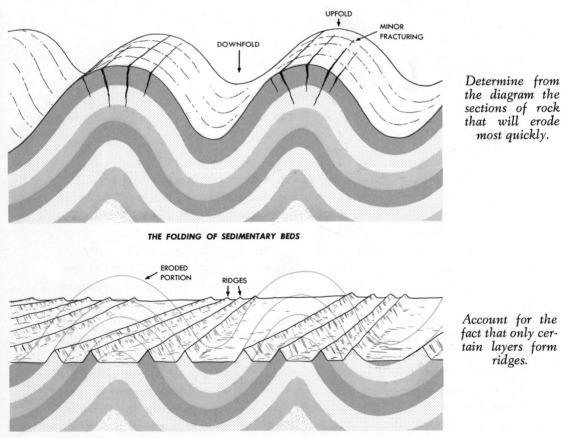

Determine from the diagram the sections of rock that will erode most quickly.

THE FOLDING OF SEDIMENTARY BEDS

Account for the fact that only certain layers form ridges.

THE GEOLOGICAL STRUCTURE AND SURFACE FEATURES OF TYPICAL FOLD MOUNTAINS

146

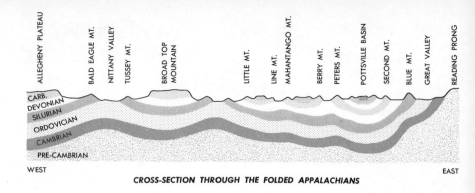

Which section of the Carboniferous layer will contain (a) bituminous coal (b) anthracite coal?

CROSS-SECTION THROUGH THE FOLDED APPALACHIANS

Because layers of rock are quite rigid, the folding action causes fissures to appear on the tops of the ridges, whereas the rocks at the bottom of the valleys are compacted and may change to hard, crystalline metamorphic rock. Owing to this difference the tops of the ridges are more easily eroded than the valleys and, therefore, quickly wear down to expose several underlying layers. The harder, more resistant layers form ridges and the softer rock is worn away to create valleys. Typical of this type of mountain formation is the Appalachian system of eastern Canada and the U.S.A. A most remarkable man-made feature of this area is the Blue Ridge Parkway, which for over a thousand miles winds along the crest of a ridge in the Central Appalachians. From this vantage point, the Great Valley and the ridge and valley section to the west can be seen spread out in a magnificent panorama.

Block Mountains

This mountain formation is caused by fracturing or *faulting* of the earth's crust. These faults are cracks in the earth which penetrate very deeply into the interior. Instead of the horizontal pressure, which causes fold mountains, block mountains are subjected to vertical pressures. These vertical pressures result in large sections of the crust being thrust up, or occasionally, forced down. Moreover, unlike the fold mountains, block mountains may form in either sedimentary or igneous rock. Their formation is accompanied by large-scale faulting of the earth's crust.

This diagram represents a cross-section through the Range and Basin region (after Lobeck) of the U.S.A. Note the numerous faults.

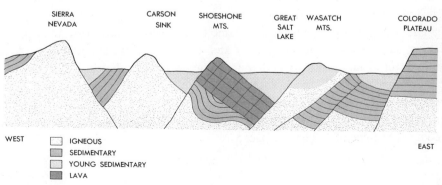

147

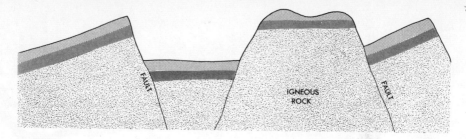

The formation of block mountains is due to severe faulting or fracturing of the earth's crust. These mountains may, or may not, be capped by sedimentary beds.

In appearance block mountains differ from fold mountains as they do not have any particular pattern. They usually present very steep slopes and may extend over a much wider area than fold mountains. They are not particularly subject to erosion and, therefore, may after a long period of time develop a normal or glacial landscape. An example of this type of mountain formation may be studied on Canada's west coast, where the Coast Mountains rise abruptly from the ocean to elevations exceeding 10,000 feet. This solid block of igneous rock (granite) has been forced up by internal pressures. Other examples are the Sierra Nevada and Wasatch ranges, as well as those of the Great Basin in the U.S.A.

Dome Mountains

Dome mountains are usually formed in sedimentary rock and have a circular or oval shape. They are caused chiefly by the intrusion of lava or salt between the layers of rock, thus forcing the overlying beds to warp upwards. The force which causes the lava to uplift the dome is described in an earlier part of this book. It is more difficult to understand the creation of a dome by salt, but it appears that salt will concentrate in an area when it begins to crystallize. Whatever the mysterious force is that causes this, it is sufficient to warp the sedimentary layers.

Domes formed by igneous intrusions are quite common and many of these have their cores exposed owing to rapid erosion of the higher, fractured, rock. The Henry Mts. of Utah, the Black Hills of South Dakota, and the Adirondacks of New York were formed in this manner. These are all well known because they cover wide areas and present some true alpine scenery. The summits of the mountains are much more rounded than those of fold mountains and usually are not as highly elevated. Most domes are surrounded by a series of *hogback* ridges which are the remnants of resistant sedimentary layers.

There are many small domes formed by igneous intrusions but, generally speaking, salt domes are much smaller and do not cover such wide areas. Indeed, it is doubtful in many cases whether they should be included in a discussion concerning mountains. In appearance they resemble igneous domes, but the salt core is not resistant to erosion. Consequently, when the sedimentary layers have been worn away, the salt core quickly dissolves and leaves a depression surrounded by concentric rings of hogback ridges.

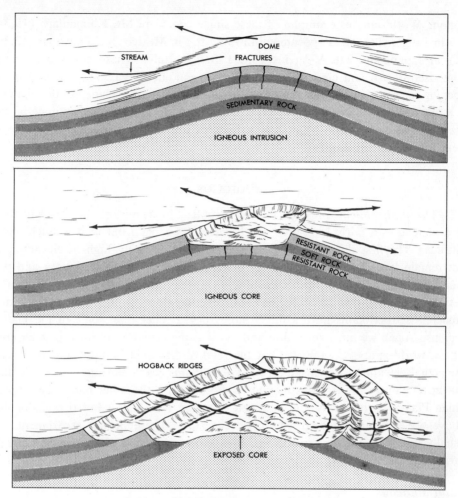

STAGES IN THE DEVELOPMENT OF A MATURE DOME

Volcanic Cones

Volcanism is a principal factor in mountain building. Volcanic activity may be localized or widespread, prolonged or intermittent. Where it is localized it usually results in the formation of a symmetrical cone, but where it is widespread it may result in the building of an entire mountain range. When the activity is prolonged it may result in the building up of peaks to 12,000 feet in elevation; when it is intermittent the peaks are not usually so high, but violent eruptions may occur owing to pressure building up beneath the cone.

The mountains which are formed in this manner are often strikingly beautiful in appearance and are in marked contrast to the topography of the surrounding region. World-famous examples of these single cones are Mt. Kilimanjaro (19,340 ft.) in Tanganyika, Mt. Popocatepetl (17,887 ft.) in Mexico, Mt. Fujiyama (12,390 ft.) in Japan, and Mt. Vesuvius (3,891 ft.) in Italy. These cones are usually composed of ash and cinders intermixed with solidified lava. The material in the opening, or neck, of the volcano often solidifies and forms a plug. As this material is more resistant than the cinder core, it may remain after the softer material has been eroded away. The Monteregian Hills of the Eastern Townships of Quebec were formed in this manner.

Plateaus

The term *plateau* presents another problem in definition. We usually think of a plateau as a fairly level area which resembles a plain but is at a much higher altitude. The first difficulty we face is that plateaus, being high in elevation, do not remain level for long as they are quickly attacked by erosive forces and thus many plateau areas become very hilly. On the other hand, if we distinguish between plain and plateau on the basis of elevation alone, we might find that certain areas classed as plains have a much more rugged relief than some of the plateau regions. Again we must generalize and say that the elevation of most plateau areas of the world is above 2,000 ft.; but the relative elevation is more important than the actual elevation. For instance, the Great Plains reach elevations of 6,000 feet, but in relation to the Rockies they are quite low. On the other hand, the Appalachian Plateau is relatively low in actual elevation (4,000 ft.) but rises 2,000 feet above the surrounding land on its eastern side. These abrupt escarpments are usually deeply carved by streams and appear as mountains when viewed from the lowland areas.

Fault Plateaus

Commonest are the fault plateaus formed by broad uplifts over a large area. This uplifting is usually accompanied, or followed, by vertical breaking or faulting along the edges. As this usually occurs in sedimentary rock, the result is an elevated tablelike structure with a relatively flat surface. The subsequent landforms which develop on these plateaus depend greatly on the climate of the area. In humid regions, gulleys and valleys quickly form and the plateau surface becomes hilly or dissected. In more arid regions the landforms tend to retain their blocklike shape, and where rivers traverse the area, they cut almost vertical canyons in the blocks. This is due to the fact that the layers of more resistant rock protect the softer, more easily eroded, layers. Other results of this protective action are the flat-topped features known as mesas and buttes. These are remnants of sedimentary layers. On the whole the surface of plateaus in arid regions is much smoother than those in humid areas. A comparison of the Appalachian and the Colorado plateaus will serve to illustrate this point.

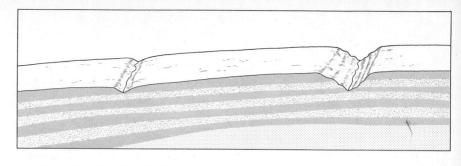

These uplifted series of sedimentary beds are just beginning to experience erosion.

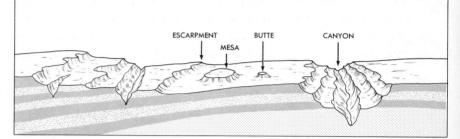

Plateaus in dry regions develop their own peculiar landforms such as canyons and escarpments.

ESCARPMENT   BUTTE   CANYON

MESA

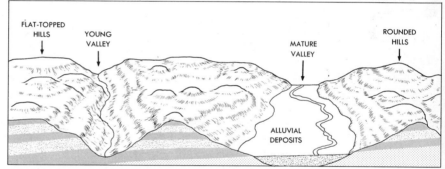

Plateaus in humid regions are usually dissected by streams and are quite rugged in relief.

FLAT-TOPPED HILLS   YOUNG VALLEY   MATURE VALLEY   ROUNDED HILLS

ALLUVIAL DEPOSITS

Lava Plateaus

Lava plateaus are similar in appearance to fault plateaus in dry areas. They have the deep canyons with vertical walls but usually lack the escarpments of resistant rock. Over a period of many years they are built up by extensive lava flows, one on top of the other, interspaced with old lake beds and alluvial deposits. Because the lava hardens quickly, these flows do not have a level surface but, rather, they present a surface with rounded features and deep canyons due to the columnar structure of lava. In Canada, lava plateaus can be found in the highlands of New Brunswick and central British Columbia, while in the United States the Columbia plateau is composed of a series of lava and alluvial layers.

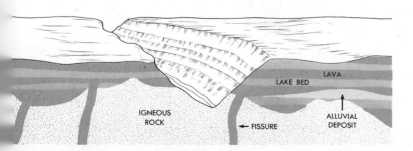

IGNEOUS ROCK   ← FISSURE   LAKE BED   LAVA   ALLUVIAL DEPOSIT

This diagram shows a lava plateau with lake beds and alluvial deposits interspaced with volcanic deposits.

151

Shield Areas

According to some geological definitions shield areas should not be classified as plateaus because of their low actual relief and their complex structure. On the other hand, they cannot be classed as plains because of their high local relief and variety of geological formations.

Shields are very complex, being made up of very old, igneous, metamorphic, and sedimentary rocks which have undergone faulting, folding, and *peneplanation*. This means that the surface has been worn down to a level which is almost a plain but that it still maintains considerable local relief. Because of their age and the pressures which they have endured, shield areas contain the hardest and most resistant of rocks. Shields are found in northeastern Canada, Finland, north central U.S.S.R., the Brazilian Highlands, most of Africa, and western Australia.

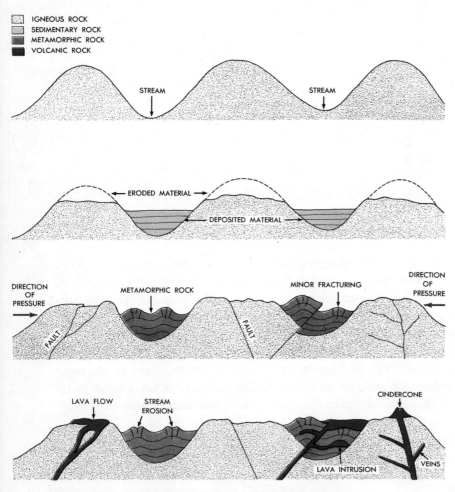

IGNEOUS ROCK
SEDIMENTARY ROCK
METAMORPHIC ROCK
VOLCANIC ROCK

STREAM
STREAM

A normal landscape is formed by stream action.

ERODED MATERIAL
DEPOSITED MATERIAL

The landscape undergoes change during a long period of stream action.

DIRECTION OF PRESSURE
METAMORPHIC ROCK
MINOR FRACTURING
DIRECTION OF PRESSURE
FAULT
FAULT

Great pressure can fracture or fault the igneous rock and change the sedimentary to metamorphic.

LAVA FLOW
STREAM EROSION
CINDERCONE
LAVA INTRUSION
VEINS

These complex-structure and surface features make up a typical shield area.

THE FORMATION OF A SHIELD AREA

152

Plains

Plains are composed for the most part of sedimentary rock or unconsolidated material lying in a more or less horizontal position. They have a low local and actual relief. They range in elevation from sea level to 6,000 feet but are classed as plains at this height only if they are low in relation to neighbouring mountains. In general, however, they are below 2,000 feet; because of this, many feel that shield areas should be grouped in with plains. Throughout this text, however, shield areas will be classified as plateaus.

Similar to mountains and plateaus, plains are of many different types. Classifying them according to their formation, we can distinguish marine, lacustrine, coastal, and till plains.

Marine plains are the result of the deposition of sediments in shallow salt-water seas, which from time to time inundated vast continental areas. Subsequent elevation of the land or a drop in sea level, has revealed these plains. In many cases, inundation of the same region several times created a thick layer of deposits which became compacted into sedimentary rock. In other cases, the thickness of the sediments was not enough to form rock layers. Evidence of the marine origin of these plains can be clearly detected in the fossils which are to be found, often in large numbers, in such areas. Examples of marine plains are the Great Plains of North America, the Argentine pampas, western U.S.S.R., northern Europe, and the Great Basin of Australia. Most of these plains consist of beds of relatively undisturbed sedimentary rock.

The St. Lawrence Lowlands are unique in that the sedimentary rock is covered by a thick deposit of Leda clay which was laid down in the Champlain Sea after the last ice age. Uneven uplift or subsequent uplift often alters the even, regular surface of the plain.

Lacustrine plains are similar in many respects to marine plains. They are beds of sediments, usually unconsolidated, which have been deposited in fresh-water lakes. Subsequent drainage of the lake has exposed these flat expanses of fertile soil. Sometimes a lacustrine plain will form on top of a marine plain. In this case, the lacustrine plain is distinguishable by its very flat, unbroken surface in contrast to the gently rolling topography of the marine plain. Glacial Lake Agassiz once covered a wide expanse of southern Saskatchewan and Manitoba as well as parts of North Dakota and Minnesota, all of which are underlain by marine sediments. As the ice retreated northward the lake gradually drained, and lakes Winnipeg, Winnipegosis, and Manitoba are all that remain of that much larger body of water, Lake Agassiz. In the basin and range area of western U.S.A. many lake plains fill the basins between the ridges. The best known of these is the Lake Bonneville plain, which is centred on Great Salt Lake.

Coastal plains, as the name implies, are located along the margins of continents. Although similar in appearance to other types of plains, they are usually narrower and have a somewhat different history of development. They are composed of sediments brought down by the rivers or eroded from the shore by wave action. These are deposited in the sea and distributed fairly evenly along the coast by the wave motion. On emergence, either by uplift or by a lowering of the water level, the broad flat expanse that is exposed is known as a coastal plain. The part that is not exposed is called a *continental shelf*. Between the coastal plain and the shelf are the *tidal flats*. These are areas which are covered with water at high tide but are exposed at low tide. Because much of the plain is very flat, wide marshy areas such as the Everglades of Florida often border the ocean.

Changes in sea level give a complicated structure to these coastal plains. An area which was undergoing sedimentation may emerge and experience active erosion. This region may again be submerged and covered with more layers of material. Since uplift and depression are usually not regular, the younger beds of sediments may lie at an angle different from that of the previously deposited layers. This is called *crossbedding*. Depending on the amount of sedimentation and the movements of the earth's crust, the plain may be wide or narrow. The east coast of Canada has a very narrow coastal plain; indeed, in some places, owing to subsidence, it is nonexistent. As a result, the wide continental shelf thus created has provided the world with one of its best fishing grounds.

Till plains are found in glaciated regions and may be formed on a base of sedimentary or igneous material. The till, or material deposited by a glacier, may be spread quite evenly over wide areas if the glacier retreated at a uniform rate. The material itself is a mixture of clay, gravel, and boulders, and is usually bumpy in appearance when viewed from ground level. The ability of the glacier to smooth over the projecting rocks and to fill in the depressions leaves an area of low relief. The term, *till plain*, is applied to an area only when the material covering it consists of the finer-textured deposits.

What agencies were at work to create the markedly different types of topography of the Canadian Shield and the St. Lawrence Lowlands?   R.C.A.F.

What features of glaciation are apparent in this photo of the Canadian Rockies?   R.C.A.F.

3 LANDFORMS AND THEIR RELATIONSHIP TO HUMAN ACTIVITY

Now that we have some knowledge of the structural features of the land-masses, let us turn our attention to a more detailed study of landforms and their relationship to human activity. Although landforms may not have as great an effect on man as climate or vegetation has, they influence his daily life and work in many ways. For example, igneous rock formations may provide man with certain valuable minerals, while loess, a wind-deposited soil, may be of great agricultural importance. Man, in his turn, may greatly influence his environment; more specific-ally, he may modify the landforms. He may remove hills to build roads, divert streams for hydroelectric power, tunnel into mountains in search of minerals, cultivate the soil for crop raising, or build cities which extend over wide areas, thereby obliterating all but a few of the surface features. It is this interrelationship between man and his environment which makes geography interesting and it is the purpose of the following chapters on landforms to point out as many aspects of this relationship as possible.

Volcanism

The following exercises should be completed before a study of this chapter is undertaken.

1. Determine the summit elevation of this landform.

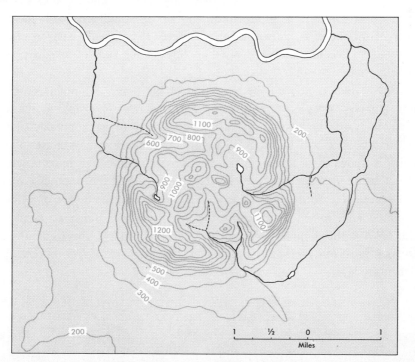

2. How many feet does it rise above the surrounding plain?

3. Draw a cross-section from northeast to southwest to determine the shape of the hill.

4. Determine the width of the landform along your cross-section. (Use the 300-ft. contour as the base of the hill.)

5. Explain how you think this landform might have been formed.

6. Compare your explanation in question five with that given on page 24.

7. Is this area covered with soil? What evidence supports your conclusion?

8. Note the difference in contour interval. What additional information can be gained from the map because of this?

9. What resources and uses might such a landform have?

The term *volcanism*, derived from Vulcan, the name of the Roman god of fire, includes all types of volcanic activity from the movement of molten rock deep within the earth's interior to the violent eruptions which sometimes shake the earth's outer crust. The term used to describe the molten material when it forms below the earth's surface is *magma*. It is generally known as *lava* when it makes its way to the surface.

Just why certain portions of the earth should liquefy is not clear, but it could be due to an increase in heat from radioactivity. Just as water will boil more easily at a high altitude than a low one, owing to a decrease in air pressure, so might the rocks liquefy and boil because of any sudden release in pressure. The magma, being liquid, works or melts its way upward to escape the great pressure of the overlying rock. It may find its way to the surface and solidify. In this form it is known as a volcanic *extrusion*. If the overlying rocks contain cracks or fissures, the magma may force its way into these and slowly solidify beneath the surface. This type of formation is known as an *intrusion*. It is usually easy to distinguish between the two because, owing to rapid cooling, the crystals of extrusive rock are much smaller than those of intrusive rock.

Intrusive volcanism, with the exception of the dome mountains described in an earlier chapter, does not create many forms which are visible at the surface. These structures may be highly mineralized and, therefore, economically significant; for this reason, they will be included here. The feature which causes the dome mountains is known as a *laccolith*. This is a mass of intrusive magma which has spread out between sedimentary rock strata and warped the overlying rocks upwards. Because of its formation in this way, it usually rests on a base of sedimentary rock. Subsequent erosion may expose the upper part, or bulgelike dome, of the laccolith. When this happens we call the exposed part of the laccolith a *boss*; this igneous intrusion is usually surrounded by *hogback ridges* or escarpments of sedimentary layers.

N. H. Darton, U.S. Geological Survey

Bear Butte, South Dakota is an exposed dome of volcanic rock that intruded sedimentary beds. To the left is a diagram to illustrate this formation.

Similar in formation and structure to laccoliths are *batholiths*. These are large irregular masses of intrusive rock which have forced or melted their way into the overlying rock formations. They are generally thought to be formed by the enlarging of faults or fissures in the earlier rock formations. The distinguishing characteristics of these are their unfathomable depths and their ability to intrude any pre-existing rock formation. Batholiths may undergo uplift subsequent to their formation and they, too, may be exposed by erosion. The Coast Range of British Columbia, the Sawtooth Range in Idaho, and the Sierra Nevadas in California were all formed in this manner.

In its upward movement, the molten material may force its way between layers of sedimentary rock to form *sills*. Though these may be quite extensive in area, they are thin and sheetlike in appearance. A similar thrust of molten matter, known as a *dike*, finds its way along lines of weakness, and because of this kind of progress, has no characteristic appearance or shape; yet it can be readily distinguished from the surrounding rock by the difference in its colour and structure. When molten currents intrude igneous rocks, they are usually referred to as *veins*. Some veins are mineralized and may contain such valuable elements as gold, silver, and cobalt. Many of the dikes and sills are harder than the rocks they intrude and may remain projecting above the surface after the softer material has been removed by erosion.

Extrusive volcanism is a term used to describe all volcanic activity, together with the landforms created by this activity, insofar as the effects of such activity are apparent at the earth's surface. The most common feature, or landform resulting from this activity, is the volcanic cone, of which there are several types. The

157

cinder cone is a pyramid of *scoria*, that is, solidified lava fragments which were thrown from the central vent. This action occurs when the magma has a high proportion of gases which are ejected at a pressure great enough to carry the particles with them. As man's technology advances, he is finding more and more uses for these extruded products.

The build-up of the cinder cone usually slows down as the heat of the volcano is dissipated. Eventually the lava solidifies in the *neck*, or *vent*, of the volcano, and activity ceases. When this occurs the loose scoria is quickly removed by erosion and only the solidified *plug* is left. This is usually a very striking feature, for it may rise several hundred feet above the surrounding terrain.

A *composite* cone is similar in appearance but different in structure. In it, layers of cinders and ash alternate with lava deposits. Such cones differ in shape depending on the type of material in the lava. If the lava contains much silica, it is very viscous and does not flow readily; hence, a steep-sided cone develops. If there is little silica present, the lava flows more readily and a broad-based, gently-sloping cone is formed.

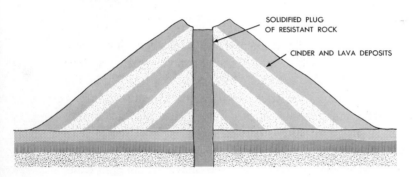

SOLIDIFIED PLUG OF RESISTANT ROCK

CINDER AND LAVA DEPOSITS

A typical volcanic cone mountain is composed of a mixture of lava and cinders.

The neck of a volcano may be closed by a plug leaving a *crater* where the vent once spewed forth its fiery blasts. If pressure builds up beneath the plug, a new vent may form on the side of the cone at its weakest point. This results in the build-up of a *subsidiary* cone. The main cone may be surrounded by several smaller cones. However, the build-up of pressure may be released in another manner. It may become so great that it will blow the entire top off the volcano and thus leave a large depression where the peak of the volcano once stood. This depression is known as a *caldera*; it may be more than a mile in width and well over 3,000 feet in depth. Both the crater and the caldera may become filled with water to form a *crater lake*.

Many explosions such as this have been recorded in history. Mt. Vesuvius, in Italy, exploded in 79 A.D. and buried the cities of Pompeii and Herculaneum under tons of ash and cinders. Mt. Etna, in Sicily, exploded in 1693 and over 60,000 lives were lost as a result of the eruption and the earthquakes caused by the explosion. Mt. Krakatoa, situated between Java and Sumatra, erupted with tremendous violence in 1883 and the ensuing tidal waves, or *tsunamis*, destroyed 36,000 people on the two islands. Other less spectacular and destructive explosions have occurred; however, it would seem that man has not yet learned his lesson, for the suburbs of Naples crowd the shadow of Mt. Vesuvius.

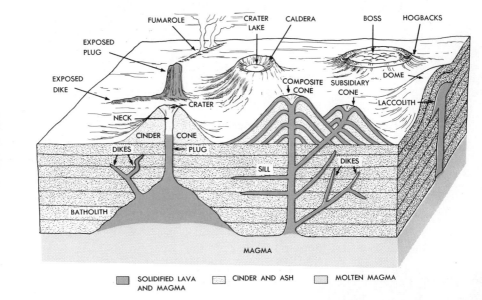

Intrusive and extrusive forms of volcanic activity create many different types of landforms, as can be seen by the diagram.

An activity which is closely related to volcanism is that of the emission of steam and other gases from fissures or *fumaroles*. Some of the steam comes from water that seeps down to areas of hot rock, but most of the steam and the other gases appear to come from the magma itself. In some instances, as in the Valley of Ten Thousand Smokes in Alaska, deep fissures in the rock extend to, or very near to, the magma. The gases and steam given off are extremely hot (1,200° F.).

In contrast to this activity, the steam given off by a *geyser* is just above the boiling point (212° F. at sea level) and all of its steam comes from water that has seeped down from the surface. The fissures in geyser areas are not as deep as fumaroles and the water is vaporized by heat conducted through several thousand feet of rock from deeper-lying magmas. Because the rocks are hotter at the bottom of a fissure than at the surface, the water boils at that point first. Steam pressure is built up beneath a column of water which acts as a lid to hold the steam in. The column of water is gradually raised by the expanding steam until it overflows on to the surface. This reduction in pressure is sufficient to allow the steam to send the remaining water skyward in a roaring column of boiling water and steam. The eruption continues until the underground cavities are almost empty. Then it subsides and ground water begins to filter into and collect in the cavities; the process thus begins all over again. Small cones of minerals are formed around the upper end of the tube of a geyser by material precipitated from the cooling water.

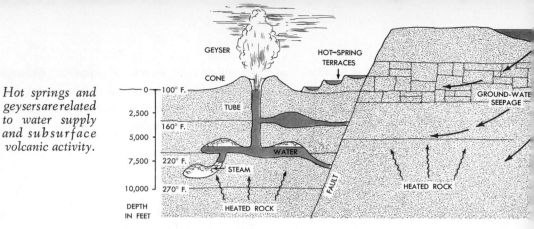

GEYSER

HOT–SPRING
TERRACES

CONE

0 — 100° F.

2,500

160° F.

5,000

7,500 — 220° F.

10,000 — 270° F.

DEPTH
IN FEET

TUBE

STEAM

WATER

FAULT

HEATED ROCK

HEATED ROCK

GROUND-WATER
SEEPAGE

Hot springs and geysers are related to water supply and subsurface volcanic activity.

Geologically speaking, *hot springs* are the last stage of volcanic activity. Here the heating is not great enough to create steam so the water is merely heated as it circulates underground and reappears on the surface as hot or warm springs. Because hot water dissolves minerals more readily than cold water, most hot springs build up terraces of precipitated material. Such formations are caused by the rapid cooling of the water as it comes in contact with the air. Yellowstone National Park, in Wyoming, is an ideal place to study hot springs and geysers as there are several thousand of them in this area.

Old Faithful is the best-known geyser because of the regularity of its eruption. What factors combine to create this regularity? Estimate the height of the eruption from the people in the picture.

U.S. National Park Service

Volcanism and Man

Although reference has been made to the destructive force of volcanoes, not all volcanic activity is detrimental to man. Dependent on the mineral content of the parent material, soils derived from volcanic rock may be the most fertile and productive in the world. The island of Java, which has an agrarian economy, is, perhaps, the best example of this, as it supports over 850 persons per square mile. There are some 30 active volcanoes here and the soil is almost all derived from volcanic extrusions. Another factor which increases the soil fertility in such a region is the fallout of fine ash which rejuvenates the soil. Other examples of rich agricultural extruded soils are found in the volcanic areas of Hawaii, Guatemala, El Salvador, and the Columbia Plateau of the U.S.A.

160

Perhaps, economically speaking, the most significant feature of volcanic activity is the mineralization which accompanies volcanism. There are four generally recognized types of such mineral deposits which are useful to man: namely, magmatic deposits, pegmatites, hydrothermal deposits, and replacement deposits.

Magmatic deposits are usually mined in areas where batholiths or laccoliths have been exposed by erosion. Iron, titanium, nickel, chromium, and platinum are often found in these formations. These minerals may be widely scattered throughout the enclosing igneous rock. At Bingham, Utah, an enormous mountain is being torn down in order to extract copper which assays at only 1.07% metallic copper. Because of an incompletely understood process, however, minerals tend to concentrate in a particular section of the magma as it cools and a valuable ore deposit may result. These magmatic segregations, as they are known, account for the vast iron deposits at Kiruna in Sweden, where the mineral content sometimes exceeds 65%.

Pegmatites are deposits of material which solidify more slowly than the rest of the magma. Because there are only a certain number of elements which react in this manner, pegmatite deposits are usually greatly concentrated. They are found in pockets in the surrounding rocks; or, where fracturing occurs, they may flow out along lines of weakness to form mineralized veins. Mica, feldspar, and quartz are concentrated and deposited in this manner. Tin and tungsten deposits may also occur in pegmatites.

Hydrothermal deposits, usually found in veins, make up the greater part of the gold and silver deposits in northern Ontario and Quebec. These deposits are similar in formation and appearance to veins of pegmatite, but, unlike these, the minerals are thought to have been dissolved in a solution and precipitated when the solution cooled. A number of veins in a restricted area constitutes a *lode*. Many veins do not contain material which is of use to man and many more are only slightly mineralized. The valueless material is known as *gangue*.

A *replacement deposit* is a modification of a vein formation. Sometimes the material which enters a fracture may be hot enough to melt the surrounding rock. In this manner the vein may be considerably widened and mineral ores can replace the former rock structure. The iron deposits at Marmora, Ontario, were formed in this manner.

Volcanic plugs do not often contain minerals, yet diamonds are found in such a formation in the Union of South Africa. The almost vertical plugs or pipes are congealed lava, and the diamonds are scattered through it. This is actually a form of magmatic deposit.

Extrusive forms of volcanic material do not provide the wealth of minerals that are found in intrusions. However, some deposits of sulphur are being mined in Italy, Japan, Mexico, and Chile and of increasing importance are the hot gaseous materials which arise from the fumaroles. These gases contain steam, which can be converted into electricity. This is being done near Rome and San Francisco today by tapping the source of steam and piping it to generators. In Iceland a similar method is used to heat homes and buildings.

Certain other products such as helium, sulphur dioxide, and ammonia, may be separated from the steam. Helium, a noninflammable gas, is used in making sulphuric acid, and ammonia is used in manufacturing fertilizers. It is sometimes advantageous to prevent these gases from escaping as some of them are poisonous to human beings and injurious to crops.

As well as providing important tourist attractions and mineral baths, the hot waters of geysers produce ammonium carbonate, sodium carbonate, borax, and alum. Certain forms of lava rock are also used industrially. *Pumice*, a light, hard stone is used for polishing and grinding. *Tuff*, a medium hard rock, can be quarried easily and is used for building stone.

Professor John A. Shimer

A lava tunnel recently carried molten rock over a mile and threatened native villages in Hawaii. The U.S.A.F. bombed the tunnel and diverted the flow. Explain how this phenomenon could occur.

W. C. Mendenhall, U.S. Geological Survey

This pahoehoe lava flow is very viscous and does not advance quickly. It "freezes" in peculiar formations. What chemical material in the lava causes it to solidify rapidly?

4 DIASTROPHISM— FOLDING AND FAULTING

Diastrophism, in its broadest sense, includes all movements of the earth's crust. The causes of diastrophic movements have been explained to some extent by the theories of isostatic readjustment, thermal contraction, and convection currents, all of which have been described in an earlier chapter. Evidence of diastrophism is present in several forms.

Marine fossils found in many places throughout the continents indicate that certain land areas have undergone *uplift*; that is, they have been pushed up from beneath the oceans. Evidence of *subsidence*, or sinking, is found in Nova Scotia, where coal seams, formed from land plants, run underneath the waters of the Gulf of St. Lawrence. By studying the rock strata and the fossils in them, geologists have been able to determine that some areas have undergone several periods of uplift and subsidence.

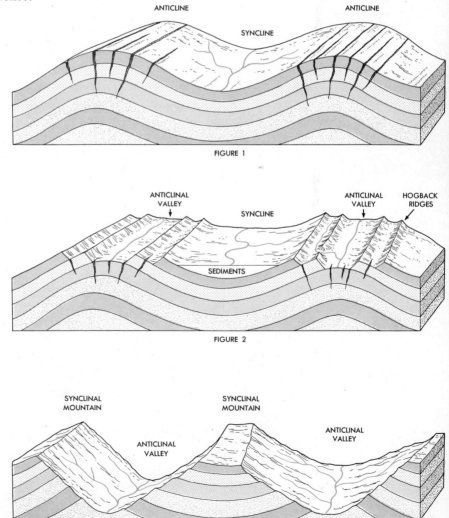

During the initial folding (Fig. 1) the rocks are broken at the summits of the anticlines and compacted in the synclines. Subsequent erosion (Fig. 2) removes the broken rocks and fills the synclines with sediments. Further erosion (Fig.3) will reverse the original land features by carving valleys out of the weaker anticlines and leaving the more resistant synclines projecting as mountains. Note the reversal of drainage accompanying this type of erosion.

FIGURE 1

FIGURE 2

FIGURE 3

Crustal movements are also apparent along seacoasts. Old beaches and wave-cut terraces are often evident several hundred feet above the present shore-line. There may be, as in the case of the coast at Nome, Alaska, a number of these beach lines, one above the other. Each of these represents an interval of stability in the land during a longer period of uplift. Other coastal areas indicate subsidence as long arms of the sea penetrate and drown river valleys. A highly indented and irregular coastline is usually indicative of subsidence, although similar features may be formed by glacial action.

As the landforms which are to be found along coastal areas are formed by wave action, a description of these features will not be included here. Instead, our study will include only the actual deformation of the rock itself and the landforms created by this phenomenon. The most common type of deformation to be found is known as folding. *Folding* is the bending or warping of rock by severe pressures. The displacement of rock created by these pressures may be upwards to form an *anticline* or *dome*; on the other hand, the rocks may be forced downwards to form a *syncline* or *basin*. Where the magnitude of folding is great, a number of parallel folds may form *fold mountains*. These mountains are among the highest and most rugged in the world. The Rockies, Swiss Alps, Caucasus, and Himalayan mountains were all formed in this manner.

As folding is more common and evident in sedimentary rocks, the illustration used here will be of folds in stratified material. Igneous rock is usually much harder and resists folding. It is more liable to break or tilt en masse than to warp.

A fold cannot continue indefinitely and it usually terminates by apparently sinking beneath the rock strata. Where this occurs, *a pitching fold*, surrounded by oval shaped *cuestas*, or hogbacks, results. The pitch of the fold or slope of the rock is described in degrees by measuring the angle between the horizontal and an imaginary line running along the top of the fold. This line is known as the *axis of the fold*.

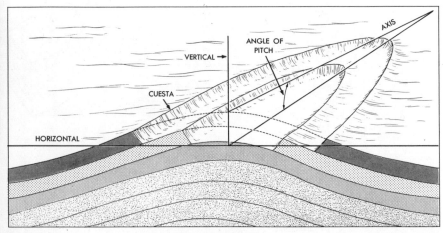

Many anticlines are cigar-shaped and have their axes slanting downwards at each end.

A PITCHING FOLD

164

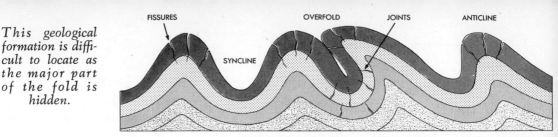

FISSURES OVERFOLD JOINTS ANTICLINE

SYNCLINE

This geological formation is difficult to locate as the major part of the fold is hidden.

AN OVERFOLD IN INTENSIVELY FOLDED STRATA

Occasionally, the forces which create folding are so intense that an *overfold* may result. Where this happens one anticline is forced against another and may even override it if the pressure is great enough. Joints and fissures are very evident where overfolding has taken place. *Joints* are cracks in the rock which occur without displacing the rock. Near the surface, where there is less pressure, the joints may widen out to form *fissures*.

Where the diastrophic forces are greater than the rocks can withstand, faulting occurs. *Faulting*, to distinguish it from jointing, is accompanied by displacement of the rocks along the line where the earth's crust breaks. Several types of faults have been observed and classified according to the movement which occurs in the rock. A *normal fault* is caused by tension on the rock strata. The stress is relieved by breaking and the rocks on one side of the break are displaced downwards in respect to those on the other. In a *reserve fault*, compression forces the rock to ride up along one side of the fault line. A *thrust* fault is also due to compression but here the rocks which are forced up actually override those on the other side of the fault.

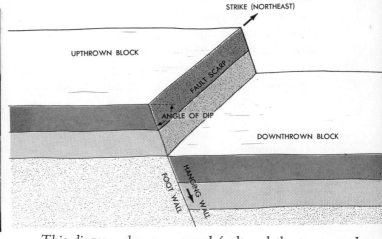

STRIKE (NORTHEAST)

UPTHROWN BLOCK

FAULT SCARP

ANGLE OF DIP

DOWNTHROWN BLOCK

FOOT WALL

HANGING WALL

This diagram shows a normal fault and the terms used to describe it.

The Mazinaw Lake fault in Ontario created this beautiful lake. Explain how this occurred.

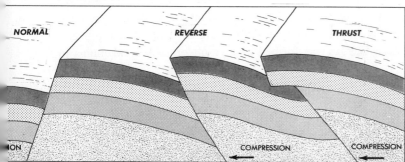

NORMAL   REVERSE   THRUST

...ION   COMPRESSION   COMPRESSION

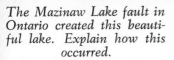

The accompanying diagram shows faulting in sedimentary strata. The long arrows indicate force, while the shorter ones show the nature of the displacement.

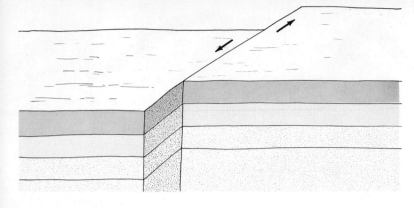

Here are rock strata illustrating horizontal displacement.

In the foregoing illustrations, the rock displacement has taken place in a vertical direction. Occasionally horizontal displacement will occur. In this case the break is known as a *horizontal fault*.

In discussing a fault, certain terms are commonly used in order to provide a more precise description. The *strike* of a fault is the compass direction which the break in the earth's surface follows. The *dip* is the angular direction which the fault assumes as it penetrates the earth. The abrupt cliff, often formed by vertical displacement, is a *fault scarp*. One side of the fault, or *foot wall*, supports the other, which is known as a *hanging wall*.

It is relatively easy to determine the movement of rock where single faults occur, but often there may be several faults in the zone of fracture. In this case the region must be carefully surveyed in order to determine the nature of the faulting.

In certain places on the earth, huge parallel faults have occurred and have created a set of landforms peculiar to faulting. Where two parallel faults have allowed a large section of land to drop, a deep valley *rift* or *graben* develops. Examples of these rift valleys are to be found along the upper Nile River in Africa, the upper Rhine in Germany, and the lower Ottawa in Ontario.

Here are shown block mountains formed from a number of horsts and grabens.

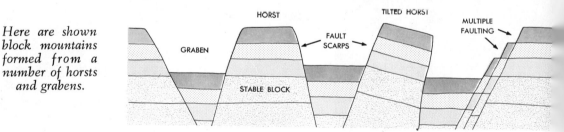

A *horst* is a block or section of rock which has been forced up and which is flanked by parallel faults. This same feature may be produced when two parallel rift valleys have sunk down and left the section of land between them undisturbed in a relatively elevated position. A number of horsts and rifts may occur when the earth's crust weakens. In this manner *block mountains* are formed. The basin and range section of the western U.S.A. was formed as a result of such weakenings in the earth's crust.

166

The Coast Range of British Columbia owes its existence to faulting as it is a huge horst of granite. Farther south this same Coast Range in the U.S.A. is flanked by the San Andreas fault on its seaward side. Slippage along this fault has caused severe earthquakes. The most violent of these brought severe damage to the city of San Francisco in 1906.

Economic Aspects of Diastrophism

If we are to follow to its conclusion our primary assumption that diastrophism includes all movements of the earth's crust, we must include in our study a discussion of the effects of subsidence and uplift.

One of the most notable effects of subsidence is the creation of a deeply indented coastline. The numerous harbours thus formed have provided the Canadian Maritime Provinces with some of the best fishing ports in the world. The British Isles have benefited greatly from subsidence because their drowned river valleys have provided excellent ports for their import-export trade. Emergent or uplifted coastlines are usually very smooth and the surrounding seas are shallow. In such coasts inlets are few and silting is prevalent. The cost of maintaining a harbour under such conditions is prohibitive.

As most sedimentary rocks owe their existence to diastrophism, they, too, deserve mention here. Much of the material which goes to make up sedimentary strata is laid down in the sea during a period of subsidence. By studying the fossils associated with sedimentary rock, we can determine the age of the material. Many valuable minerals are also found in sedimentary rocks. Common salt and gypsum are two of the most frequently found compounds. These salts are precipitated from sea water and are preserved by the overlying beds of sediments. Manitoba and Nova Scotia are Canada's leading producers of gypsum; and salt is found in southern Ontario and Nova Scotia.

Sulphur is sometimes deposited in workable beds as a by-product of gypsum (calcium sulphate). It is mined in the Gulf of Mexico region of the U.S.A. and is chiefly used for the production of sulphuric acid.

Potash and phosphorus, two of the leading mineral fertilizers, are also found in the strata of sedimentary rocks. Germany and New Mexico are the main suppliers of the former, while North Africa and Florida produce the latter. Dolomite, from which magnesium is extracted, and coal are widely mined throughout the world. Because they are relatively soft and easy to quarry, limestone and sandstone are used extensively for building stone. Chalk, another useful sedimentary deposit, is found in England, France, and southern Scandinavia.

Many rocks undergo structural change, or *metamorphism*, when they are subjected to the pressures of faulting and folding. Limestone is changed to a valuable ornamental building stone, marble, whereas shale is compacted to form a very hard slate. Several compounds containing silica undergo change to produce mica, asbestos, and garnet.

Of all the metamorphic rocks, coal has the most interesting history. It is deposited in marshy areas as peat. Drying out and settling produces a low-grade coal called *lignite*. If sediments are deposited over these coal seams, the lignite is further compacted to form *bituminous coal*, the most commonly used type today. Folding of these strata produces a very hard metamorphic rock called *anthracite coal*. In some cases all the organic elements, other than carbon, have been driven off by heat and pressure. Where this occurs, *graphite*, rather than anthracite, is the result of the folding. As this material is slippery and heat resistant, it is used for coating foundry molds so that the molten material will not adhere to the surface. It is also used as a lubricant and a paint pigment, as well as a conductor in dry-cell batteries. Extreme pressure on graphite will produce diamonds.

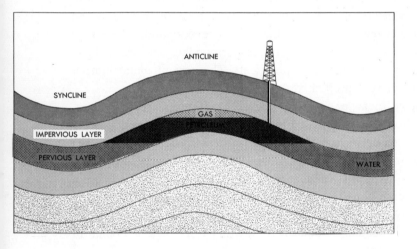

The impervious layer prevents the escape of the lighter gas and petroleum. The well is not drilled through the gas-bearing rock but into the pervious layer containing the petroleum. In this way the pressure exerted by the gas may be utilized to force the petroleum up the drill hole.

Certain rock formations act as traps for petroleum and gas. Porous, or pervious, rock usually contains water. If petroleum or gas is present, it floats on the top of the water and tends to work its way to the surface. When the overlying rock prohibits further upward migration, the petroleum products collect in anticlines or in upward sloping strata along fault lines. The pressure of the rock closes the fault and seals the petroleum in. Under certain circumstances, petroleum may be sealed in reservoir rock by the clogging of the pores with asphalt left behind by the escaping petroleum.

The water is carried through the porous layer from the wetter mountains to the dry basin in the interior. The impervious layer prevents the escape of the water.

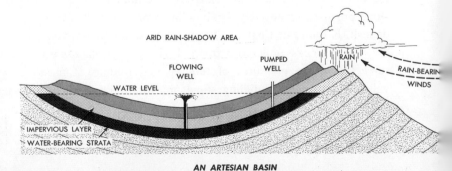

AN ARTESIAN BASIN

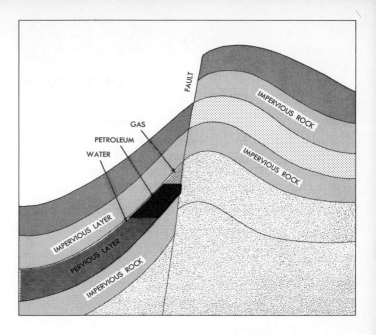

The pervious, or reservoir, rock has been sealed off by impervious rock. The beds are offset due to faulting action.

Another important economic aspect of sedimentary beds is their ability to carry water underground over long distances and thus bring water to arid regions. The interior basin of Australia is supplied with water in this way. The particular rock structure which performs this function is referred to as an *artesian basin.*

Volcanic action often accompanies faulting because the magmatic material can work its way to the surface along the lines of weakness. The mineralization which occurs has been described in an earlier chapter.

Not all diastrophic action is beneficial. Faulting can make it extremely difficult to follow a vein of ore or a bed of coal. Time and money are lost when a coal seam comes to a dead end along a fault line. Block and fault mountains often present serious obstacles to transportation routes. Slippage along fault lines causes earthquakes. These, in turn, may cause great loss of life, as well as economic loss, owing to falling brick and building material. Recent earthquakes demolished large portions of the city of Agadir in Morocco, while frequent minor quakes indicate instability in the earth's crust along the west coast of the Americas, southwestern Asia, and the East Indies.

These gently folded strata are exposed at Hog's Back near Ottawa. What geological formation is represented by this upfolded strata? Account for the different types of rock as shown by the darker shades of strata.

169

UNIT REVIEW

Vocabulary Review

Match the phrase in the left column with the correct word or phrase in the right column. Do not write in this book.

1. A pair of companion stars
2. Area where shock waves are faint
3. The earth's crust
4. Rocks on the ocean floor
5. The Central Appalachians
6. The Coast Mountains
7. Dome mountains
8. Monteregian Hills
9. The Canadian Shield
10. Deposition in salt-water seas
11. Fine-textured glacial deposits
12. Molten material within the earth
13. Cinder cones
14. Emission of volcanic gases
15. Mineralized deposits within batholiths

(a) basalt
(b) volcanism
(c) magma
(d) pegmatite
(e) binary
(f) folding
(g) fumarole
(h) sial
(i) shadow zone
(j) faulting
(k) peneplanation
(l) gangue
(m) marine sediments
(n) till plain
(o) scoria
(p) dome

Questions

1. Explain why the same material may have different properties in the earth's crust and in the core.

2. How could thermal contraction form ocean basins and continents?

3. What is meant by continental drifts? Use a diagram in your answer.

4. Use diagrams to explain the formation of a dissected plateau in a humid region.

5. What surface features distinguish block mountains from fold mountains?

6. Distinguish between marine and lacustrine plains.

7. Define the following terms: geyser, gangue, pegmatite, sill, boss, crater, tsunami, vein, tidal flat, isostatic readjustment.

8. How is extrusive volcanism different from intrusive volcanism? Explain how you might identify a rock sample of each.

9. Illustrate the difference in structure between block mountains and fold mountains.

10. Show how faulting and earthquakes are related.

11. Explain the differences between faults, fissures, and joints.

12. Why is folding more commonly found in sedimentary rocks than in igneous formations?

13. Show diagrammatically the different types of folds.

14. Give the distinguishing features of a laccolith, a batholith, and a boss.

Research Assignments

1. Find some of the industrial uses of the following materials: ammonium carbonate, sodium carbonate, borax, alum, sulphuric acid.

2. "Lava will weather to form fertile soil." Discuss this statement in the light of what you have studied.

3. "The destructive force of volcanism is offset by the benefits which man derives from it." In a carefully reasoned answer, attack or defend this statement.

4. Study a world map in your atlas. Where do extensive areas of relatively undisturbed sedimentary beds occur?

5. Refer to a geological of structural map of the world to determine the relationship between recent volcanic activity and physical features.

6. Endeavour to find other theories which explain either the origin of the earth or the formation of continents.

The Changing Face of the Land

1 GLACIATION AND ASSOCIATED LANDFORMS

Moving ice can play a part in the creation of landforms. Such movement produces two distinct agents of change, erosion and deposition, each capable of creating its own particular landform features. This movement of ice, plus the work which it does, is called glaciation and the moving body of ice is known as a glacier. Most glaciers may be classified as either alpine or continental. The smaller alpine type is found in high mountainous areas such as the Canadian Rockies, e.g., the Columbia Icefield, whereas the continental type covers much larger areas such as Greenland or Antarctica.

Formation and Movement of Glaciers

Glaciers are formed in areas where the average yearly temperature is near, or below, freezing or wherever more snow falls in the cold months of the year than melts in the warm season. As a result, the glacier receives an additional layer of snow each year. The older layers become buried and are compacted by pressure into ice crystals that eventually become transformed into a solid mass of ice. In time the weight of the accumulated ice becomes so great that the entire mass begins to move. How this actually happens is not fully understood, but it appears that the ice becomes more plastic, or softens, under pressure and acquires a slow, creeping motion. Another theory is that the weight of the glacier itself causes a rise in temperature in the underlying part of the ice. As the melting point approaches, the ice softens and movement occurs. In the case of alpine glaciers, snow accumulates at higher elevations and movement occurs down the slope following the path of least resistance. Continental glaciers, on the other hand, move out in all directions from the centre, oftentimes moving up and over former topographical features or formations. The ice continues to advance until the rate of forward movement equals the rate of melting. At this point the ice front becomes stationary. Owing to fluctuating temperatures, the ice front may retreat or advance, thus giving us an indication of warming or cooling trends in our climate.

Alpine Glaciation

There are three closely related types of alpine glaciers, viz: icefields, cirque glaciers, and valley glaciers. Icefields and cirque glaciers are found at, or above, the snow line, that is, the elevation above which snow remains all year. This line is located at an elevation of about 18,000 feet in tropical areas and 10,000 feet in such temperate areas as southern British Columbia. Valley glaciers may develop from either an icefield or a cirque glacier and move downwards towards temperate or even tropical regions.

Icefields are the largest of the alpine glaciers and usually are formed in an area lower than the surrounding mountain peaks or on a high plateau of low relief. Because of the area's physical features, the adequate precipitation, and the low temperatures, snow accumulates and gradually builds up until it covers the region. When the ice begins to move, it seeks outlets through the valleys or places of lowest relief, thus giving rise to valley glaciers which take the excess ice down the mountain to be melted at lower elevations.

Cirque glaciers are smaller since they develop in depressions, or cirques, on the sides of mountains or at the heads of mountain valleys. As the ice builds up, it enlarges the depression in which it was formed and eventually spills over the edge of the cirque to flow away as a valley glacier.

Valley glaciers are literally rivers of ice which move slowly and ponderously down slope to be melted by the warmer temperatures of lower elevations. Similar to rivers, they have many tributaries from both cirque glaciers and icefields. Unlike them, however, the ice fills the greater portion of the valley, whereas a river occupies only the lowest part of the valley's floor. The rate of movement of such a glacier depends primarily on the slope of the land and secondly on the rate of snow accumulation. The glacier may progress anywhere from a few inches to a hundred feet per day.

In order to understand more fully the work done by glaciers let us examine a representative area, namely, Mt. Waddington, British Columbia. This mountain, the highest in B.C., is located in the Coast Mountains some 180 miles northwest of Vancouver. Its sides are covered perpetually by an icefield that gives rise to several valley glaciers. The surface of the ice is covered with light drifting snow.

Underneath this is a compacted layer of ice crystals called *névé*. This in turn gives way to solid, bluish-coloured ice below it. Many cracks or crevasses traverse the icefield, hidden in some cases by only a few inches of drifted snow. These crevasses are found most often where there is a distinct break in the slope of the land or where the glacier rounds a sharp bend in the valley. During the summer months these cracks often act as water courses for melting snow on the surface.

This type of glacier does not perform a great amount of work as it moves very slowly. It does, however, provide the cutting tools for valley glaciers by picking up rocks on its underside. These rocks, broken off from the mountain sides, become imbedded in the ice. As the weight of deposition at the centre forces the ice to move outward, these rocks become effective cutting tools to scour and grind up the bedrock. By this method, usually referred to as *abrasion*, an icefield enlarges its own bed. The mass of unconsolidated material is carried along with the ice to be deposited along the front of the glacier when it melts. Such deposits constitute a *moraine*; moraines will be discussed later in this chapter.

Valley Glaciation

One of the most striking forms of glacial erosion is the U-shaped valley (See Rocky Mountain map—Robson Glaciers). As the valley glacier moves along a typical V-shaped valley formed by river erosion, it widens and deepens the valley, cutting off or *truncating* any protruding *spurs*. This action produces the rounded profile which is so typical of glaciated regions. In some cases later deposits of alluvium have flattened the valley floor, giving the profile a boxlike appearance.

Tributary glaciers do not enter the main stream at the base level of erosion, that is, at the elevation of the valley's floor. Instead, owing to the resistance of ice in the main valley, they enter at a considerable height above the main floor.

Explain how these valley glaciers in the Coast Mountains sculpture the landscape.

R.C.A.F.

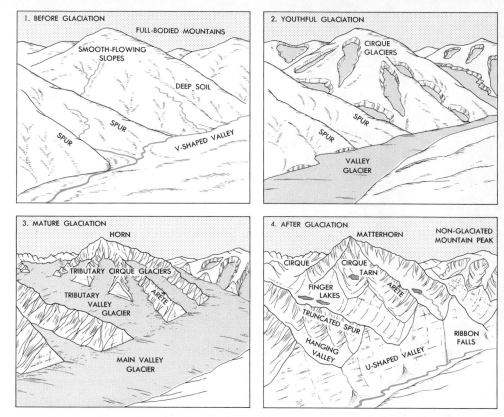

1. BEFORE GLACIATION

FULL-BODIED MOUNTAINS
SMOOTH-FLOWING SLOPES
DEEP SOIL
SPUR
SPUR
V-SHAPED VALLEY

2. YOUTHFUL GLACIATION

CIRQUE GLACIERS
SPUR
SPUR
VALLEY GLACIER

3. MATURE GLACIATION

HORN
TRIBUTARY CIRQUE GLACIERS
TRIBUTARY VALLEY GLACIER
ARETE
MAIN VALLEY GLACIER

4. AFTER GLACIATION

MATTERHORN
NON-GLACIATED MOUNTAIN PEAK
CIRQUE
CIRQUE
TARN
FINGER LAKES
ARETE
TRUNCATED SPUR
HANGING VALLEY
U-SHAPED VALLEY
RIBBON FALLS

THE CYCLE OF ALPINE GLACIATION AND THE DEVELOPMENT OF GLACIAL FEATURES

When the glacier retreats, this leaves a hanging valley some distance above the elevation of the main Channel. Quite often such tributary valleys are the beds of post-glacial streams and the lowest areas are occupied by finger lakes, such as Lake Louise. At the point where the valley enters the main channel, beautiful ribbon falls cascade down hundreds of feet. The two best examples of this are Bridal Falls in Yosemite National Park, California, and Takkakaw Falls in Yoho National Park, British Columbia.

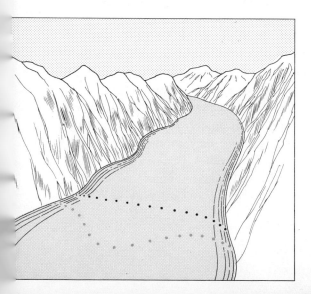

The movement of different parts of a valley glacier can be measured if stakes (dots) are driven into the ice. The coloured dots show the positions of the stakes at a later time.

175

*Takkakaw Falls is an outstanding example
of a ribbon falls tumbling from a hanging
valley. Why has the stream not cut down
through the rock? What can you learn
of the rock structure by studying the outcrop? Why are there no trees on the slope
at the bottom right?*

Cirque Glaciation

The term *cirque* is derived from a French word meaning *circus* and, in the
present context, refers only to the stadium or amphitheatre from which the
spectators were wont to view the circus acts. Owing to the shape of the depressions
formed in isolated pockets on a mountain side, the term has now been applied to
both the glacier itself and the landform it creates. This rather unusual shape is
caused by the movement of the glacier, which tends to rotate about its centre of
gravity and thus creates a bowl-shaped depression deeper in the centre than at
the rim. This movement tends to pull the ice away from the rock wall at its head
and to leave a deep crevasse known as a *bergschrund*. The rock basin thus formed
usually contains small lakes or *tarns*, such as Lake Agnes, which are left after the
glacier has disappeared. Sometimes a number of cirques may form, one above the
other; this is due to a changing snowline. The resultant series of tarns is known
as *paternoster* lakes because of their resemblance to beads on a rosary.

Several notable land features are formed by cirque action, namely, arêtes,
cols, and horns. *Arêtes* are sharp knifelike, serrated ridges. These are formed by
glaciers' eating away at both sides of a mountain range or spur. When the two
glaciers have eroded the bedrock on either side of the spur to a point where they
are almost meeting, the result is a sharp ridge of protruding rock. Then further
erosion unites the glaciers and the arête is worn down quickly to produce a low
rounded gap called a *col*. Occasionally, valley glaciers may produce the same
result by building up and overflowing the sides of the valley. Occasionally, too,
owing to their inability completely to erode the bedrock, a number of cirque
glaciers eating away at the sides of a mountain may create a sharp peak or *horn*.

176

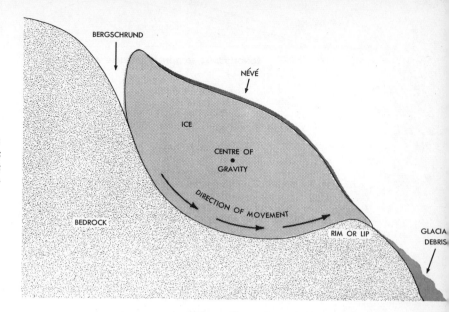

A typical cirque glacier abrades its bed and carves out the "amphitheatre".

As the sides of the peak become steeper as a result of erosion, the ice tends to move down slope and leave a very sharp projection. These peaks are often called *matterhorns* because of their similarity to the mountain of that name in the Alps. A number of cirque glaciers eroding a range of mountains of uniform elevation may produce a series of horns and cols which is known as *biscuit-board topography*. A number of the above-mentioned features can be identified on the topographical sheets and the accompanying photographs.

Continental Glaciation

The glaciers that come under the general heading of continental glaciers are those that are found today in Greenland and Antarctica. As the average temperatures of these areas are very low, most of the snow that falls remains to create a huge ice sheet which covers most of the land surface. The Greenland icecap reaches a depth of 8,000 feet, and 14,000-foot depths have been recorded in Antarctica.

Because of their great thickness and weight, these continental glaciers create a set of landforms very different from those created by alpine and cirque glaciers. Instead of the sharp peaks and arêtes of alpine glaciation, continental glaciation tends to round and smooth landforms by overriding them. It removes the existing soil, grinds the surface of the bedrock, and deposits great quantities of material *detritus* at its farthest point of advance as well as along its line of retreat. An occasional mountain peak, by virtue of its height and steep sides, manages to remain above the ice sheet and, therefore, retains its sharp angular form or outline. Such a feature is known as a *nunatak*.

177

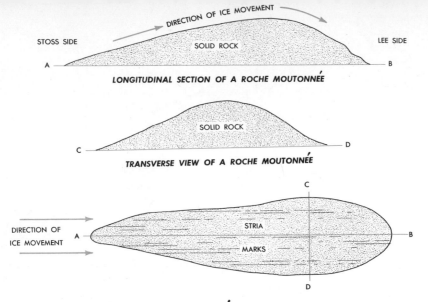

DIRECTION OF ICE MOVEMENT

STOSS SIDE

LEE SIDE

SOLID ROCK

A   B

LONGITUDINAL SECTION OF A ROCHE MOUTONNÉE

SOLID ROCK

C   D

TRANSVERSE VIEW OF A ROCHE MOUTONNÉE

C

DIRECTION OF
ICE MOVEMENT

A   STRIA   B

MARKS

D

TYPICAL SHAPE OF A ROCHE MOUTONNÉE VIEWED FROM DIRECTLY OVERHEAD

As the ice moves out radially from the centre, it scours the underlying bedrock, leaving it scraped bare of soil; indeed, it oftentimes cuts into the rock itself. Scratches made by the stones imbedded in the ice are called *stria marks*, while deep cuts are referred to as glacial *grooves*. Many rock formations are modified by this abrasive force and are worn down to form rounded humps of rock or *roches moutonnées*. This French term meaning *rock sheep* is used because of the striking similarity of these rock outcrops in the Alps to flocks of sheep grazing on alpine pastures. The outcrop itself is usually rounded and elongated with a smooth surface on the side from which the ice came, but often rough and broken on the opposite side. This broken lee side appears to be caused by the stress and the freeze-thaw, plucking action of the glacier. Such rock outcrops are often striated or grooved. Another feature, called a *chatter mark*, occurs on some of them. These marks are crescent-shaped cracks in the surface of the rocks caused, apparently, by the pressure and the motion of the ice. Such cracks are small, about 6 inches in length, and 2 or 3 inches deep, and the horns of the crescent indicate the direction of the ice movement.

How have these glacial grooves been formed?

Ohio Historical Society

R.C.A.F.

What features of alpine glaciation are shown by this photo of Victoria Glacier?

Glaciation Deposition

Generally speaking, glacial deposits may be classed as either till or drift. *Till* refers to a mixture of sand, clay, angular stones (called *erratics* when they are boulder sized), etc., which were scraped or ground off the bedrock, and which, after being thoroughly mixed, were deposited by the glacier. *Drift* has basically the same composition but has been sorted and worked over by meltwater from the glacier. It can be readily distinguished from till as it is a stratified deposit; that is, it has definite layers of clay, sand, or gravel. This is typical of all water-worked material.

Glacial deposits may also be classified by the landforms they create. At the point of farthest advance of a glacier, considerable mounds of debris are heaped up as the ice front usually remains stationary for some time. Such a roughly semi-circular ridge of hills is known as a *terminal moraine*. In the case of a valley glacier, it is sometimes referred to as a *horseshoe moraine*, whereas in the case of a continental glacier, it is called the *lobate moraine*.

When warmer temperatures prevail or the glacier receives insufficient nourishment, it begins to retreat. The material which was being carried forward is then dumped over the region formerly occupied by the ice. In this form it is known as *ground moraine*. During the time of retreat, the front may remain stationary for long periods. This enables the ice to form another ridge of hills to those found in the terminal moraine. To distinguish between the two, the term *recessional moraine* has been applied to this deposit. *Lateral moraines* are deposited along the sides of valley glaciers and these form a *medial moraine* when a tributary joins the main valley glacier.

Relate this photograph to the picture of Victoria Glacier on page 178. Locate a lateral moraine, a pro-glacial lake, and a cirque glacier.   National Film Board

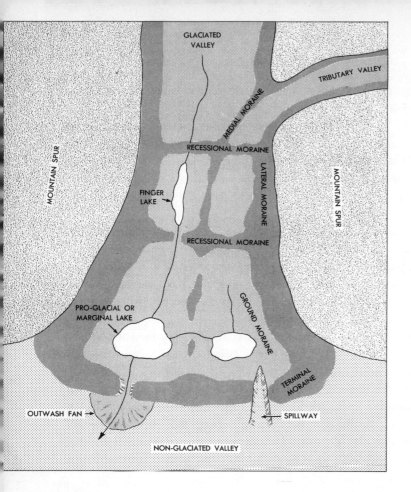

There are many features of glacial deposition associated with the retreat of a valley glacier.

A continental glacier usually advances over a wide area at one time and forms several larger lobes. Sometimes two lobes meet and a huge mass of material, known as an *interlobate moraine*, is built up between them. An example of this formation can be found running from northwest of Toronto to Trenton in the Bay of Quinte area.

After the terminal moraine has been built up and the glacier begins to retreat, the meltwater becomes trapped between the ice and the morainic deposits. This *pro-glacial* or *marginal* lake continues to grow until an outlet stream breaks through the moraine and quickly lowers the level of the lake. In so doing, it often forms an *outwash fan* of stratified deposits on the outer edge of the terminal moraine. Because of the large amounts of glacial debris in the area, these outlet streams often change their course, leaving dried-up *spillways* where the stream once flowed. Meltwater running off the glacier, underneath it, or alongside it, carries considerable amounts of sediment. These are deposited in *lacustrine beds* in the pro-glacial lake.

Drumlins, eskers, and kettle holes are other features of deposition. Just exactly how drumlins are formed is not clear, but it seems that they develop under-

Identify the long sinuous ridge lying just north of highway 7 to the east of Peterborough.

neath a continental glacier where there is an excessive amount of debris. A *drumlin* is an oval-shaped mound of glacial till, similar in shape to a roche moutonnée, but lacking the solid rock core. Drumlins are usually found in groups scattered over a wide area which has become known as a *drumlin field*. Examples of these can be studied in the Peterborough and Belleville areas of southern Ontario.

Eskers are stratified deposits laid down in the beds of glacial streams which ran underneath or through the ice itself. As these deposits are held in on both sides by the ice, they stand out as a ridge snaking across the country after the glacier has retreated. Because of the sorting action of the water, eskers usually contain deposits of sand and gravel which are very useful for road construction. In the Canadian North the roads often run across the top of the esker in order to take advantage of the better drainage and the firmer base.

When a glacier is retreating, large blocks of ice are often left in depressed or protected pockets. These blocks become covered with a mantle of ground moraine and thus do not melt for a considerable length of time. When the ice eventually disappears, a depression or *kettle hole* is formed. Numerous kettles or sloughs can be found in the Canadian West. Many of these fill with water in the spring and act as reservoirs during the summer. Others dry up after each rain and, as a result, have become quite salty or alkaline.

This typical drumlin lies off the coast of Nova Scotia. Account for the fact that it is surrounded by water.   R.C.A.F.

This drumlinized plain is located in Manitoba. What economic activities might be carried on in such an area?

The Dummer Moraine lies northeast of Belleville, Ontario. Much of the finer material has been washed out, exposing the limestone erratics. Suggest a use for such an area.

The Glacial Periods

There have been at least four glacial periods in the history of the world and within each period considerable fluctuations of the ice front have taken place. During the last period, called the Ice Age, the glaciers covered most of Canada, the northern U.S.A., and northern Europe. This period began approximately one million years ago and lasted until about 20,000 years ago. The Ottawa area has been free from ice for some 15,000 years while the Labrador region lost the last remnants of the glacier 7,000 to 8,000 years ago. Today the actual ice front itself may be studied at the Columbia Icefield, only 150 miles from Calgary. By studying these recently ice-freed areas, as well as existing glaciers, we can determine how landforms were created and we can also formulate theories about the causes of the glacial periods.

Basically, ice ages can be brought about by either one of two causes. First, the land may cool because of several factors or, secondly, more snow may fall in winter than can be melted in the summer. The amount of heating of the earth's crust is directly related to the amount of sunlight which reaches the earth. Cooling can be brought about by any factor which reduces the amount of energy received by the earth or given off by the sun. It has been suggested that slight changes in the inclination of the earth's axis could cause the direct rays of the sun to fall within 10° or 15° of the equator instead of the present 23½°. This would leave the polar regions with less insolation and an ice age could result. However, the glaciers were not centred about the polar regions during the Ice Ages.

Another theory involves the slight wobble which the earth's axis makes and the irregularity of the earth's orbit around the sun. The amount of sunlight received by the earth is slightly reduced when the earth is at its greatest distance from the sun and the earth's axis has assumed its most vertical position in relation to the plane of the earth's orbit. Some contend that this combination of circumstances is enough to create glacial conditions, but this theory is undermined by the fact that these conditions occur at regular intervals and glaciation does not.

The land surface may also be cooled by mountain building. Large areas may be uplifted, with a consequent drop in temperatures. Volcanic activity is usually associated with mountain building; such activity produces large amounts of dust which would shade the earth's surface from the sun's radiation. Either one or a combination of both these conditions could result in a glacial period.

Perhaps the most popular theory is associated with an increase in precipitation, for such a theory does not necessitate any basic changes in the conditions on the earth's surface. In its simplest form the theory states that precipitation could be increased to the point of building up masses of snow and ice if more water were available for the air to evaporate. At present this water is said to be locked in the Arctic, Greenland, and Antarctic icecaps. This could be freed by warm water from the Atlantic pouring into the Arctic, but at present it is prevented from doing so by an underwater mountain ridge dividing both oceans. The level of the Atlantic is slowly rising at the present time, perhaps because of increased radiation, as fewer clouds obscure the earth. Some of the existing glaciers are melting and the Atlantic may rise enough to pour its waters into the Arctic. This would melt the Arctic icecap, raise the sea level some 100 feet or more, increase precipitation, and allow an ice sheet to form on the landmasses adjacent to the Arctic. Eventually the sea level would drop as the ice sheet expanded and the Atlantic and Arctic oceans would be separated once again. The Arctic ice cover would be restored and the continental glaciers disappear as their supply of snow became locked up once again. The cycle would then recommence with the rising of the waters of the Atlantic.

The factor or combination of factors that initiates a glacial period is not fully understood. The fact remains, however, that glaciation has occurred in the past and is likely to occur again in the somewhat distant future.

The Belleville, Ont., area also possesses s o m e fertile drumlinized a r e a s. These two d r u m l i n s have been cleared for cultivation. Account for the difference in the soil here and that shown in the photo on page 182. These areas are within 20 miles of each other.

Present Climatic Trends

This leads us to take a closer look at the present changes in our climate. According to H. C. Willett of the Massachusetts Institute of Technology, the climate of Canada and the U.S.A. has warmed up appreciably during the last fifty years, but the trend has halted and will in all probability be reversed during the next ten years. This distinguished meteorologist bases his remarks and forecasts on his study of past climatic conditions and their relation to outbursts of solar energy, or sunspots. He goes further to say that the temperature fluctuations thus caused differ only in degree and duration from the climatic changes which brought about the Ice Age.

Willett claims that not all types of solar outbursts produce the same quantity or quality of radiation. Certain types of radiation are absorbed more readily by the earth's atmosphere, thus raising the temperature of the outer air. Owing to the earth's magnetic field, this radiation collects over the polar regions and creates atmospheric disturbances. Recently, confirmation of this theory, at least in part, has been added by the recording of a 76° F. rise in temperature during a period of 24 hours in the air over Berlin. Subsequent study showed that this event coincided with one of the most severe solar disturbances of the season and was followed by violent atmospheric storms and heavy precipitation. However, further study must be made before a positive relationship between climatic changes and sunspot radiation can be established. It may even be necessary to wait until a solar observatory is orbited above the earth's atmosphere before Willett's theory can be either refuted or verified.

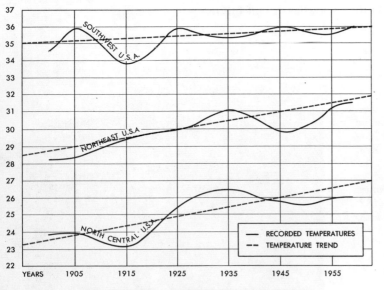

TEMPERATURE TRENDS IN VARIOUS REGIONS OF THE U.S.A.

Temperature trends in various regions of the U.S.A. indicate a gradual warming up of our climate.

184

2 THE NORMAL LANDSCAPE

The Changing Face of the Earth

Landscapes formed by running water are usually so common to man that he seldom takes time to study their formation. These normal landscapes, as they are called, are most frequently found in humid regions and thus coincide with the areas of greatest population density. Consequently, most of the landforms familiar to us are the result of this very active erosive agent, running water.

The source of water is the apparently inexhaustible supply stored in the oceans. This is evaporated by the air, carried over the land, and precipitated as rain, hail, snow or sleet. Some of the precipitation falling on the land is evaporated again, but a great amount of it runs back into the ocean by way of rivers and streams to begin the *hydrologic cycle* again.

During this process, the erosive force of water comes into play and attacks the landscape. Regardless of how the landscape was formed or shaped originally, running water tends to wear down high areas and deposit sediments in the lowlands. Three stages in this process have been classed as youth, maturity, and old age. The term *youth* applies to mountainous areas, *maturity* to a subdued, but hilly terrain, and *old age* to a peneplain, that is, an area worn down to almost a plain. *Rejuvenation* may occur and result in the peneplained area's being uplifted to form mountains a second time. Erosion again becomes most active in the higher areas and the *cycle of erosion* has completed one full revolution.

This limestone area in the Alps has been dissected by a youthful stream. Why is limestone eroded so easily? Why does the highway (upper right) not follow the valley floor?

The erosion, or wearing down of the landscape, is aided by weathering. This is the process whereby the rocks of the earth are broken up into smaller pieces and particles. Wind abrasion, chemical action, frost wedging, and differential heating are some of the forces at work on the parent rock. Occasionally, the roots of plants will penetrate small crevices and force the rock to split. Abrasion, the action of sand on rock, has been discussed in the chapter on aeolian features. In chemical weathering, water combines with other elements to form acids. These attack and destroy rock surfaces. Frost wedging is the action of water in freezing and expanding to widen cracks in the rock. Differential heating may cause the outside layer of rock to break away because, owing to the heat of the sun, it has expanded more than the interior of the rock. This is also called *exfoliation*.

This weathering action provides the material which is carried away by the rivers and streams. The amount of material, or load, transported by the water varies with the quantity of weathered material available, the slope of the land, and the volume of run-off. The material may be moved by being rolled or slid along the stream bed, by *saltation*, that is, by its being lifted and carried for short distances at intervals of time, by *suspension* or being borne along while suspended in the water, and by *solution*, which entails a dissolving of the material in the water itself.

The material which is transported by the streams may come from several sources. During a heavy rain a thin layer of soil may be removed from the surface of fields by the rapid run-off. This *sheet wash* can be almost wholly prevented by a good covering of vegetation. *Gullying* provides another source of material. When the surface vegetation is destroyed in areas of thick soil, rapid vertical erosion occurs. This forms a stream channel, which is widened and deepened with each successive rainfall. More material is added through abrasion and cave-ins of the banks. As the gully widens and deepens it also increases in length by extending its source farther inland. This *headward erosion* is very difficult to stop; indeed, tributaries to the main gully may develop, the total effect being the destruction of several neighbouring fields or even farms. Some of the load which a stream carries may come from glacial debris. In arid regions, weathered particles tend to collect in mountain valleys and await the flash floods which transport them to lower elevations.

Deposition of the material results principally from a decrease in the velocity of the stream. This slowing of the current may be caused by a decrease in the steepness of the slope, a decrease in the volume of water, or an increase in load. Decrease in gradient or slope occurs where mountain streams emerge on to plains or where a river approaches its mouth; decrease in volume is usually due to evaporation; and an increase in load is caused by sediment-filled tributaries' entering the main stream. A certain amount of deposition also occurs in lakes and along continental shelves. The deposits in fresh water are known as *lacustrine* beds, whereas those in salt water are termed *marine* sediments. A characteristic of all water deposits is *stratification*. As the flow of water in a stream is subject to change in volume and velocity, deposits usually occur in layers. Thus the spring flooding of most streams could form a deposit which differs in amount and material from the one deposited the spring before.

In the process of deposition, sorting takes place. Finer-grained materials, such as clay and silt, are carried long distances and make up the majority of lacustrine and marine deposits. Sand, which is heavier, is dropped sooner and is more commonly found in stream beds, along river banks, and at river mouths. Farther upstream, coarser gravels are found. Some mountain-stream beds are floored, in their upper reaches, by pebbles and stones sorted according to size.

In a youthful landscape, mountains are prevalent, slopes are steep, and streams are rapid. During this period the streams are said to have a *torrent* course and to follow the shape and slope of the land. The *interfluves*, or land areas between streams, are influenced very little by the erosive force of the water and, therefore, retain their original configuration. The water begins its work by cutting down or *degrading* its bed. This action produces steep-sided V-shaped valleys, canyons, and gorges.

The stream is said to be attempting to cut down to its *base level*, i.e., to the elevation of the point where the stream enters another body of water. During the early stages of this process, resistant rock formations in the stream beds cause lakes and swamps to form on the upstream side of the formation and *waterfalls* and *rapids* to flow on the downstream side. These *temporary base levels* disappear when the resistant formation is cut through and the lake is drained.

In areas where two different rock structures, such as igneous and sedimentary formations, meet, a *fall line* may develop. The softer rock will be eroded faster and an escarpment occurs. In humid areas, many waterfalls and rapids tumble over such a formation. Fall lines of this sort are found at the edge of the Appalachian Piedmont and along the southerly boundary of the Canadian Shield.

After many years of stream action, the stage known as *maturity* is reached. The mountains are now lower and rounder owing to almost continuous weathering action and erosion, and the streams are said to have entered a *valley course*, as they have widened and deepened their valleys to the point where their V-shape has almost disappeared. Lateral, or sideward erosion, aided by deposition, has flattened the valley bottoms to form *flood plains*. These long narrow plains which border the river for many miles are formed by stream meandering. A *meander* is a semicircular bend or loop in a river. Where an obstruction is encountered by a stream, the water is deflected laterally. It will continue to flow in this direction until another obstruction deflects it back again. In this manner the stream widens its bed and creates meanders. The flat flood plain is created by deposition of material on the upstream side of the meander as it migrates downstream.

In any meander, the bank which deflects the current will undergo active erosion, while the opposite bank, where the current is slower, experiences deposition. The undercut bank moves slowly downstream under the erosive force of the water, while the slip-off slope follows it closely owing to the continual addition of sediments.

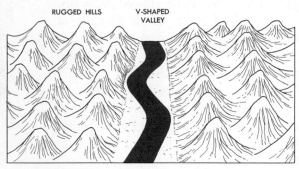

Youthful stream begins lateral development of a flood plain.

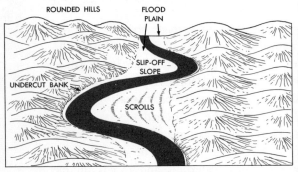

Mature stream, with a well-developed flood plain, begins to meander.

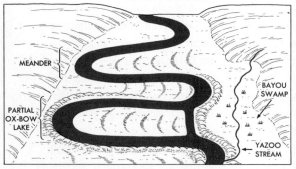

An old-age stream with meanders shows the initial stage of an ox-bow lake.

R.C.A.F

These scrolls were left on the landscape the meandering of Pasquia River near T Pas, Manitoba. At what stage of developme is this area? Account for the location of T Pas. How was the lake formed?

The Red River at Winnipeg has flooded its banks several times and caused extensive damage. Judging from the photo, can you explain why flooding is prevalent? What could be done to prevent such a disaster?

Old age is reached when the stream has cut down almost to the base level of the sea. The flood plain has been widened greatly and the interfluves are very low and subdued. The area may now be said to have been peneplained. The landforms which were begun in maturity are enlarged and improved upon. Many great meanders are to be found. Sometimes a meander will become cut off from the main stream to form an *ox-bow* lake. When these lakes dry up or become filled with sediments, they leave on the land horseshoe-shaped scars which are termed scrolls.

The river is now in its *plain course* and several new landforms are to be found here. Because of the great amount of sediments which have been brought down through the years, the stream bed is choked with sandbars. The river may, therefore, break up into several smaller streams to by-pass these obstacles. It is now said to have a *braided* channel. The great amount of sedimentation may cause the stream bed to be elevated above the surrounding land. Its waters are then held in by *levees* or banks which build up along the sides of the stream where the current is weaker and deposition is greater. If the river should happen to breach these levees, extensive flooding and great damage may occur. Such floods have been experienced along the Hwang Ho in China and the Mississippi in the U.S.A.

Along the lower reaches of the Mississippi, annual flooding and water seepage through the levees have created huge marshy areas known as *bayou* swamps. In this area also, the Yazoo River, which lends its name to many streams, parallels the Mississippi for many miles before it can effect entry to the main stream. Similar tributaries, which are kept from entering the main channel by the levees, have become known as *yazoo* streams.

As old-age streams can do very little vertical erosion, they deposit, sort, and shift the sediments in their bed many times. Eventually this material is transported to the mouth of the stream, where it is deposited in a huge arc on the continental shelf. In this manner a *delta* of sand, clay, and silt is built up. As the delta enlarges, the sediments may choke the river mouth and cause the stream to change course several times. Because of this, most deltas are laced with several stream channels, or *distributaries*, of the main stream. Deltas are classified according to their shape as arcuate, bird's foot, or estuarine. The *arcuate* delta, as the name implies, is roughly triangular in shape; the *bird's foot* has several long spines protruding along the distributaries; while the *estuarine* delta is usually long and narrow, as it is deposited in a drowned river mouth.

To complete the *cycle of erosion*, the land must be *rejuvenated*, or uplifted, again. According to the theory of isostasy, the removal of a large quantity of material by erosion lightens the load on the earth's crust at a specific point and uplift occurs. At the same time, the area where the deposition of the eroded material has occurred, sinks down; thus a balance is maintained. This sinking action may occur suddenly and create new fold mountains, or it may be slow and intermittent. Rejuvenation may occur, and often does, before a landscape is peneplained.

A rejuvenated area can be recognized by its characteristic landforms. Where an area undergoes uplift after old age has been reached, the streams retain their meandering course and cut their way down towards the newly established base level. In this manner *entrenched* meanders are created. If the uplift is intermittent, the river will experience stages of rapid downcutting interspaced with periods of lateral erosion and deposition. During each of these periods a new flood plain is built up. Remnants of these old flood plains can be found along many streams and are called river *terraces*. Another feature of a rejuvenated area is flat-topped mountains and hills. These eventually disappear as erosion continues and rounds them off. Where many flat-topped landforms occur with their summits at, or about, the same elevation, an old *erosion surface* is said to exist.

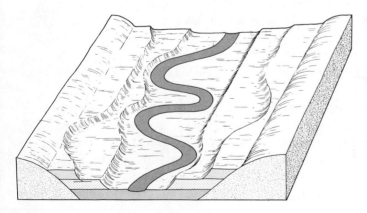

A rejuvenated stream, with several terraces, indicates intermittent uplift. What evidence is there to show that the stream was approaching old age when uplift occurred?

Classification of streams according to their origin provides us with an interesting study of the relationship between stream patterns and geological structure. In its initial stage of uplift, a syncline is drained by *consequent* streams, that is, streams which follow the slope of the land. As the summit of the syncline becomes eroded, *subsequent* streams develop as tributaries to the main stream. These usually run at right angles to the general slope of the land. Such tributaries may eventually develop their own tributaries. When this occurs, the streams are termed *obsequent* if they flow opposite to the general slope and *resequent* if they revert to following the original land slope.

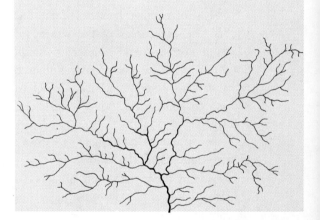

Tilted sedimentary beds create a trellis drainage pattern. In this diagram, consequent (C), subsequent (S), obsequent (O), and resequent (R) streams can be determined.

Right: A typically dendritic drainage pattern develops on a uniform slope with a uniform geological formation.

Below, left: The radial drainage pattern, which develops on youthful domes, is composed mainly of consequent streams.

Below, right: A maturely dissected dome usually develops an annular drainage pattern. The subsequent streams in this case are controlled by the circular rock escarpments surrounding the dome.

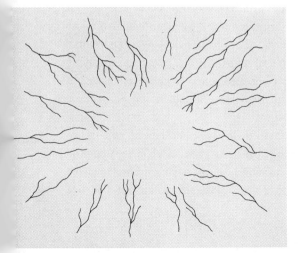

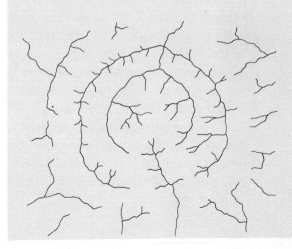

191

Drainage patterns also make an interesting study. If a stream develops on a relatively uniform slope and is not impeded by resistant geological formations, it will develop a *dendritic* pattern. This closely resembles the silhouette which the bare branches of a maple tree would make against the evening sky.

Trellis drainage develops in strongly folded regions such as the Appalachian Mts. and in tilted sedimentary beds. Because of the parallel ridges and valleys of such an area, most tributaries enter the main stream at right angles to its course. This produces the trellis shape from which this pattern derives its name.

A third pattern which is easily identified is the *radial*; this develops on domes and synclines. In this pattern all streams are consequent and flow outwards from the height of land. *Annular* drainage is very similar. When a dome becomes maturely dissected, the consequent streams often follow a circular pattern around the dome. Through careful study, many geological structures may be determined by the drainage pattern which develops on the landscape.

Running Water and its Effects on Man

Most of us have been fortunate enough to have escaped the ravages of flood waters. In some areas of the world, however, thousands of people live in dread of the flood season and wonder how high the waters will rise next time. China and Southeast Asia are particularly vulnerable to annual flooding when the monsoon rains strike. Other areas are subject to flooding owing to the melting of winter snows. In either case, flood waters can be very destructive and are expensive to control.

Dams may be constructed to store the excess water and allow it to run off at a later date when the waters subside. Artificial levees aid in controlling some streams, but these are often breached by flood waters. To avoid this, we may construct gates in the levees; at high water these gates are opened to allow flooding of only the poorest land.

Not as spectacular, but often more devastating, is the slow erosion of valuable farm land. In humid areas, great quantities of soil are removed from the fields by sheet wash. This may continue unnoticed for years and by then it may be too late to do anything, for the valuable top soil will have disappeared. Gullying is more noticeable, but is very difficult to stop because, once a gully is started, it acts as a funnel where run-off is collected, and by virtue of the increased volume of the run-off, erosion is speeded up.

To combat sheet wash farmers are advised to husband their soil more carefully. Such practices as contour ploughing, crop rotation, and strip farming, tend to retard the run-off and decrease the erosion. In monsoon areas, terraces built into the hillside perform the same function and retain the water for the rice crops as well.

Gullying can be prevented, or at least slowed down, by building small dams to obstruct the flow of water. Planting of grass or shrubs along the natural course of the run-off, is also helpful. These areas should never be ploughed, as one heavy rain could create a gully three or four feet deep. This type of erosion is common in loess belts and areas which receive infrequent but torrential rains.

Not all aspects of the erosive work of rivers is detrimental to man. The material which is eroded must be deposited eventually. The *alluvium*, or water-deposited material, provides us with some of the most fertile areas in the world. The deltas of the Nile, Ganges, Mekong, and Irrawaddy rivers support millions of people on an agricultural economy. Some of these areas produce two and three crops a year without any noticeable loss of soil fertility.

The annual flooding which occurs in these areas has been used to advantage by the people. The waters are allowed to flood the fields and thus aid in the production of the rice crop. This annual flooding also serves to enrich the soil with a fine deposit of silt.

Another aspect of stream action which is beneficial to man is the sorting of material which gives rise to beds of sand, gravel, and clay. Sand, which has a high silica content, is used for making glass. Optical glass requires a silica content of 99.8 per cent. Metallic impurities add colour to the glass, and hence we get glass of red and yellow colours from iron that is present; similarly, we get amber glass from manganese, red from selenium, green from copper, and blue from cobalt. Sand is also used in the preparation of concrete and mortar, as well as in asphalt road surfacing and for molds in iron foundries.

Gravel, a much coarser-textured material, is the main additive to cement in the production of concrete and is also used for surfacing secondary roads. A mixture of sand and gravel is used as a filter for most of our drinking water.

There are many types of clays and they have different uses. Kaolin, a fine-grained clay, is used for making expensive dinnerware, such as china. It is also used as a filler in paper. Coarser clays produce pottery, porcelain, and tile. Clay, which fuses at a temperature of about 1000° C., is used in manufacturing common brick. Higher-fusing clays produce a heat-resistant brick which is used to line blast and refractory furnaces.

Alluvial deposits are the basis of all sedimentary rock. The commercial uses of sedimentary rock are many and varied; these have been discussed in an earlier chapter. Among the mineral deposits which are of use to man are the tin-bearing sands of Malaya and the gold-enriched alluvium found along the Klondike and Yukon rivers.

Rivers and streams themselves have played an important part in human history. As transportation routes, they served to open up the North American continent. Today rivers are used throughout the world to transport freight and passengers. In some areas rivers have provided the only possible route through mountainous terrain.

In their youthful stages, rivers are usually not too satisfactory as transportation routes. In such stages, we find them being used to generate electricity, to float logs to mills, or to provide salmon for the canning industry.

Water for irrigation of arid regions is playing a more important role than ever before as the world's expanding population seeks new areas to cultivate. Industry, too, is expanding and competing for its share of the water. At present, the use of Lake Michigan water by the city of Chicago is creating an international problem. More water is required for sanitary purposes, drinking water, and industry, than can be supplied without lowering lake levels and thus endangering lake shipping. Stream pollution by an excess of industrial waste must be guarded against if man is to derive the full benefits from that greatest of all resources, water.

Embassy of Iran

The snows of the Elburz Mountains in Iran supply much-needed water for irrigation and city usage. Why is there vegetation only in the foreground of this photo?

A ditch digger brings water to the semi-arid steppes of the U.S.S.R. Where, in Canada, are similar projects carried on? What is meant by a high saline content in the soil?

194

Embassy of the U.S.S.R.

3 KARST LANDSCAPE

Some landforms owe their shape and formation—indeed their very existence —to solution by running water. In some areas, particularly limestone regions, great quantities of rock are dissolved by the slightly acidic waters which run over, and percolate through, the material. Carbonic acid, formed from carbon dioxide in the air, and acetic acid, picked up from decaying vegetable waste, are two of the acids which attack the rock. Removal of material occurs both at the surface and underground along the cracks and joints which are common in most crustal rocks. Areas where the landscape has been affected greatly by solution are known as *karst* regions. The name is derived from the Carso plateau of Yugoslavia where solution has been very active. Other noted areas are the Yucatan Peninsula of Mexico, Carlsbad Caverns of New Mexico, Shenandoah Caverns of Virginia, and Mammoth Cave of Kentucky.

For the sake of convenience, the study of karst areas can be done under the headings of youth, maturity, and old age. It should be borne in mind, however, that the process of solution is gradual and usually continuous. Therefore, many landforms of stages intermediate to the three noted, can be found; such forms are not described in this text.

Limestone is a sedimentary rock which can be formed in two ways. When igneous rock, such as granite, is weathered, the water which carries away the weathered particles usually contains carbon dioxide. This forms carbonic acid, which combines with the calcium in the rock to form calcium carbonate. This is carried in solution to the ocean, where the addition of other minerals affects the ability of the water to hold the calcium carbonate in solution or where the evaporation of water concentrates the solution to the point where precipitation will occur. Beds of calcium carbonate, which harden into limestone, are deposited in this manner.

The formation of limestone can also be brought about by the plant and animal life of the sea. Certain animals, such as the polyp, remove the calcium carbonate from the water and use it to form shells or skeletons. As the organisms die, layer after layer of calcareous material is deposited to build up vast beds of limestone.

Eventually, uplift elevates these beds and they appear above sea level. This time the moving water has almost pure limestone to work on, and as a result, the dissolution of the rock takes place much faster. The consequence is that many features are created which are peculiar to limestone areas.

In youth, shortly after uplift, the surface may be a plain, a plateau, or fold mountains. Influenced by the topography, normal drainage will result, but downcutting through solution is quite rapid. The channels which develop are similar in appearance to normal V valleys; yet considerable water may be lost from the streams through seepage into the joints in the rock. On the surface, water lying in pools will enlarge their beds by dissolving the limestone and disposing of the material by run-off after each rainfall. In this manner are formed *solution basins*, which vary in size from a few feet in diameter to several hundred.

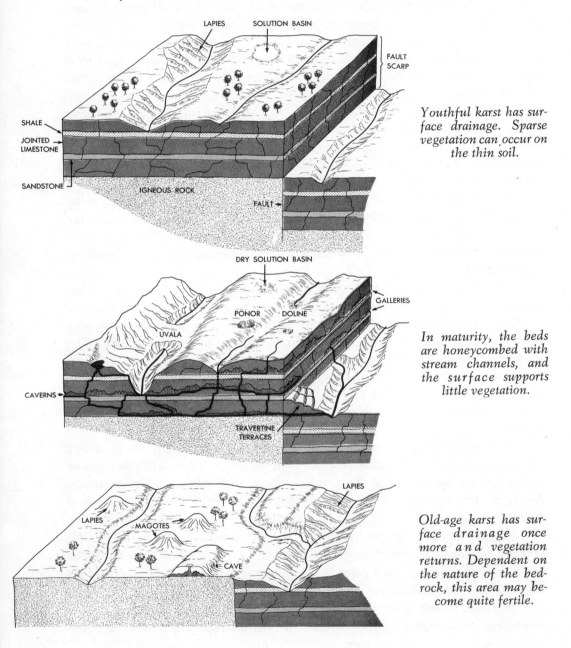

Youthful karst has surface drainage. Sparse vegetation can occur on the thin soil.

In maturity, the beds are honeycombed with stream channels, and the surface supports little vegetation.

Old-age karst has surface drainage once more and vegetation returns. Dependent on the nature of the bedrock, this area may become quite fertile.

196

As maturity approaches, the joints in the rock are enlarged to form *solution channels* and drainage disappears underground. Solution basins are drained and even large streams are diverted underground. In places where the rock is more soluble or where subterranean streams converge, the channels widen out to form *caverns* or *caves*. If the limestone happens to be interbedded with a more resistant rock, caverns develop at two or three different levels. The term *gallery* is used to denote a line of several consecutive caves.

Through time, the roofs of these caverns collapse and depressions, called *sinkholes*, appear on the surface. If the sinkhole is funnel-shaped, it is called a *doline*. If it has steep, straight sides, it is known as a *ponor* or *cenote*. A long, narrow depression, formed from the collapse of the roof of an underground stream, has been termed a *uvala*. The term originally referred to a spring, part of the underground stream, which entered the trenchlike depression. Today it is commonly used to denote the entire depression whether or not it has a stream running through it.

A unique feature of underground waterways is the deposition of calcium carbonate in crystalline forms on the roofs and sides of the caverns. Water seeping into the cave from above will normally contain much dissolved limestone. As the water drips from the ceiling, evaporation takes place and some of the calcium carbonate is precipitated. If the water drips continuously from the same spot, a long iciclelike deposit is built up. The water may continue to drip from the end of this *stalactite* and a reverse image, called a *stalagmite*, will grow up from the floor. Eventually these two combine to form a *column* of glittering calcite crystals. Impurities in the precipitate often lend colour and brilliance to the crystals.

These streams must emerge from the earth eventually; this emergence usually occurs along fault lines or escarpments or where the limestone abuts upon an insoluble rock formation. If the outflow is slow, travertine terraces of calcium carbonate, similar to those found in Yellowstone Park, build up. If the outflow is rapid, these do not occur as most of the dissolved material is carried away.

A sinkhole in Wyoming is a natural danger for grazing cattle. Explain how this feature is formed. Why is such a feature common in limestone areas?

N. H. Darton, U.S. Geological Survey

Owing to constant solution, cavern collapse, and removal of the material by the water, the layers of soluble material can be almost entirely removed. In this old-age stage, the landscape regains the pattern which it had in youth, except that the entire area has been lowered somewhat. Drainage reappears on the surface, soil begins to build up again, and the general appearance of the land is flat or gently rolling. Some remnants of the limestone rock may be in evidence as small irregular hills that are honeycombed with solution channels. These *magotes* may have very sharp, knife-like ridges, called *lapies*, running up their sides. These are the interfluves of the rivulets which occur after each rainfall.

Karst and Man

In the early stages of karst development, water is usually abundant and drainage is on the surface. Limestone soils, however, are usually quite thin and infertile. As a result, many youthful karst areas have been left in pasture, and beef cattle provide the main source of income. Some areas, such as the limestone plains near Belleville and Ottawa, are very fortunate because thick deposits of glacial debris have covered the bedrock and serve to protect it from erosion. Mismanagement of such soils would soon expose the limestone, and karst drainage would develop.

By the time sinkholes and caverns have developed, conditions have changed greatly. Any precipitation that falls on the land drains quickly underground. The soils become dry and dusty. Vegetation is sparse and cultivation of the land is almost impossible except along the sunken streams or in depressions where water is available. Irrigation, while almost essential to such an area, is next to impossible, for the streams are so far below the general elevation of the land that the cost of pumping it up to the fields is prohibitive.

Sinkholes, particularly ponors, are a blessing and a curse. They can provide water for the stock but it is too stagnant and mineral-filled for human consumption. They interrupt the pattern of roads and railways and often must be fenced off to prevent livestock from falling in. Dolines have more gently sloping sides and are often used for pasture or cultivation.

When old age is reached, the landscape may be said to have returned to normal. Drainage is again on the surface and water is in plentiful supply. The underlying bedrock may contain the necessary minerals to form a fertile soil. In this case, agriculture takes over, interrupted by the occasional remnant of limestone rock which time and solution will dispose of in due course.

One of the important functions which underground water performs is that of cementation. *Cementation* is the process involved in the formation of sedimentary rock from unconsolidated material. Calcium carbonate is precipitated between grains of loose material and acts as an effective binding agent. Some unusual formations can result from this process. Cementation can begin at some central point and spread out in all directions. In this way a sphere, or *concretion*, results.

198

This limestone q u a r r y is located near Hull, Quebec. What use could be made of the material removed from the quarry?

The large, oval-shaped stones composing concretions are often to be seen exposed along beaches and are sometimes called *kettles*.

A *geode* is a smaller spherical stone which forms in small underground cavities. The cavities become lined with deposits and when erosion uncovers the geode, it appears as an egg-shaped stone. Such stones, or geodes, are usually hollow, because they are actually just the lining of the cavity.

Many fossils are found in limestone. This is because of a process called *petrifaction*, which preserves the shape of most organisms. Water percolates into the cells of vegetable and animal material. Precipitation of mineral deposits within the cell causes the shape of the organism to be preserved in the limestone.

Speleology

Spelunking, the colloquial term for cave exploring, is not highly developed in Canada owing to the lack of caves of any great size. In other areas of the world, however, cave exploration is a popular sport for the tourist, a source of information for the historian, and a subject of scientific interest to botanists, biologists, geologists, and geographers. Much of the history of mankind has been recorded and preserved in the caves of Europe and southwest Asia. The blind fish, the colourless crayfish, and the almost sightless bat lend credence to the scientist's theories of evolution.

Those of us who live in the St. Lawrence Lowlands are fortunate to have caves which are readily accessible. These are concentrated in three areas: Ottawa, Guelph, and Owen Sound. The majority of the caves of southern Ontario are associated with the geological structure known as the Niagara escarpment. This is, in actuality, the edge of a sedimentary bed of limestone.

Just east of Guelph, in the Rockwood area, there are at least ten caves worthy of consideration. Here the Eramosa River has cut a gorge 40 to 50 feet in depth through an anticline. Tributary streams along this gorge have succeeded in hollowing out several fairly long caves. Rockwood, Richardson's, and Pierre's caves all contain passageways large enough for human exploration.

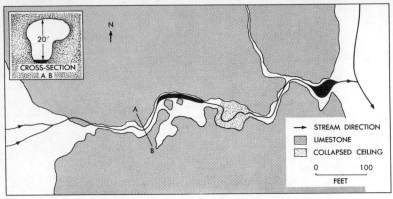

CROSS-SECTION A B

N

→ STREAM DIRECTION
▨ LIMESTONE
▨ COLLAPSED CEILING

0   100
FEET

Caves, sinks, and underground drainage are all features of karst topography.

MAIN CHANNEL OF LUSK CAVE, NEAR WAKEFIELD, QUEBEC

At Smithville, an opening 2 feet by 2 feet at the bottom of a doline leads to an underground stream. This appears to have carved a tunnel some 1,300 feet in length. Much of this is not fully explored owing to the depth of water usually found in the cave.

Most of the caves along the Bruce Peninsula are sea caves which were hollowed out of the escarpment by wave action. North of Ottawa, several pockets of limestone have been preserved in the Canadian Shield. Streams have carved Lusk Cave and Laflèche Cave from these formations. Lusk Cave is reached by travelling to Lac Phillipe and taking the footpath around the southern end of the lake to the cave entrance. Here a small stream has carved its way through 700 feet of limestone, all of it passable in dry weather. Laflèche Cave on the eastern side of the Gatineau River, is easily reached by car and is only 20 miles from Ottawa. Here we find some stalactite and stalagmite development.

The accompanying map shows the chief caves of the St. Lawrence Lowlands. Many others, no doubt, are to be found throughout Canada. A little research by an industrious student could provide the necessary information for an exciting field trip.

What does the distribution of these caves tell of the rock structure known as the Niagara Escarpment?

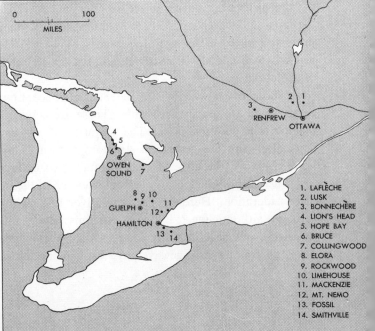

0   100
MILES

1. LAFLÈCHE
2. LUSK
3. BONNECHÈRE
4. LION'S HEAD
5. HOPE BAY
6. BRUCE
7. COLLINGWOOD
8. ELORA
9. ROCKWOOD
10. LIMEHOUSE
11. MACKENZIE
12. MT. NEMO
13. FOSSIL
14. SMITHVILLE

ST. LAWRENCE LOWLAND CAVES

4 COASTAL FEATURES

The Action of Waves

The shape and character of coastlines are of great importance to man and no study of our physical environment would be complete without reference to these features. First, however, it is necessary to understand that coastlines can be very complex and usually are the result of the operation of many different natural agents.

Sea level may change because of an increase or decrease in the amount of water in the oceans. Uplift or subsidence of the land will also change the water level. This change may be sudden, slow, or intermittent. The age of the landscape which is undergoing movement will also have an effect on the coastal features. It is obvious that the subsidence of a mountainous area will create very different landforms than will that of an old-age landscape. The hardness of the rock along the coast will vary and react differently to wave action. Heavy rainfall will result in a great amount of eroded material's being brought down by the streams. This may be deposited or carried away depending on the strength and direction of the ocean currents.

It can be easily seen, then, that many different landforms may appear along a short distance of shoreline. Because of this, it is very difficult to classify coastlines. An attempt will be made here to describe the evolution of a coast from youth to old age and to explain the meaning and use of terms pertinent to the forms evolved.

For a coastline to be classified as young, it is necessary for the water to be deep and the shore steep. The waves, which are the chief erosive force, are then able to wash away rock fragments or use them as a cutting tool to hurl against the rock. This action produces steep, vertical *sea cliffs*. The less resistant rock is eroded to form *sea caves*, while the more resistant material remains as small off-shore islands or *stacks*. All three of these features can be readily observed along the Bruce Peninsula, the Gaspé Peninsula, or the southeast coast of Nova Scotia. Sometimes, wave action will attack both sides of a headland and eventually create a tunnel through it. The arch thus formed will collapse as the shoreline recedes.

Why has the central part of this stack been eroded more quickly than the remainder?

Embassy of the U.S.S.R.

As the waves cut into the cliffs, they create a slightly submerged *wave-cut bench* or platform. The material removed from the land is deposited to create a *wave-built bench*. The two combined are referred to as a *marine terrace*. This is distinguished from the continental shelf as it rarely extends more than a few hundred feet offshore. The sea cliffs slowly recede under the pounding of the waves and a sandy *beach* develops at the base of the cliffs.

As maturity approaches, the sea cliffs become rounded and lose their steepness, the beaches become wider, and the landforms which are created are those of deposition rather than of erosion. Several types of sand bars are created by the action of the waves. After a marine terrace has been built up, the waves will begin to break as they enter the shallow water. These *breakers* expend their energy by advancing up the beach. Some material is brought forward by this action, known as the *send* of the wave, but much more is carried seaward by the *backwash*, or *undertow*, as the wave recedes.

This material is deposited some distance out at sea to create an *offshore* bar. Such an offshore bar may become elevated above the water and join other similar bars to create a long, narrow island. A body of water is often trapped behind these bars to form a *lagoon*. Some of these lagoons later become accessible to boats as the tide may breach the sand bar and provide an inlet for ships.

In areas where peninsulas or promontories interrupt the seacoast, pools of relatively calm water are to be found on the side of the projection which is leeward to the wave action. Here sand bars are created. If the bar runs approximately at right angles to the coastline, it is called a *spit*. If it is curved, it is termed a *hook*. If it joins an island to the mainland, it is known as a tombolo. Occasionally, two bars projecting from the coast will meet at their tips to form a *cuspate* bar. Some bars do not fit neatly into any category and hence are called complex spits, hooks, etc. Bars are often classified as bay-mouth, mid-bay, and bay-head bars, in accordance with their position in the bay.

This sorting and shifting of the eroded material continues until the bays have been filled and the headlands have been straightened out. This stage of smooth, unindented coastline is known as old age. During this time the shore is said to have developed a *slope of equilibrium*; that is, the amount of material brought forward by the send of the wave is equal to the amount removed by the backwash. Little erosion is carried on here; the beaches are wide and sandy, and the land itself has subdued relief.

This coastline will change only slightly in outline unless rejuvenation takes place. This can be accomplished by a change in sea level, by subsidence of the land, or by uplift. If the land subsides or the water rises, a coastline of *submergence* is said to exist. This is, in effect, a youthful coast, and active erosion begins almost immediately.

If, however, the land rises, or the sea lowers, an *emergent* coastline develops. This has many of the characteristics of an old coast for the gently sloping marine terrace will be exposed. If the uplift of the land is great, the marine terrace may be completely exposed and the seacoast now exists where the edge of the terrace formerly stood. In this case youthful landforms will develop. If the uplift is intermittent, several small beaches, one above the other, will form. By studying these *raised beaches* the nature and amount of uplift can be determined.

Seacoasts may also be described in another manner. If we disregard the developmental factors and look at the coastal features as they presently exist, we can distinguish fault, estuarine or ria, fiord, deltaic, coral-reef, and compound shorelines.

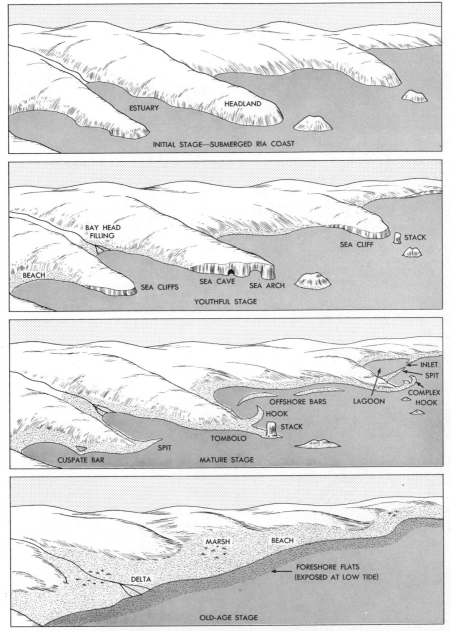

DEVELOPMENT OF A SHORELINE OF SUBMERGENCE

203

A *fault coast* is one where the shoreline is very abrupt. In this case, the down-thrown block has subsided below sea level and the shoreline meets the fault scarp. A *ria* coast occurs where many drowned river valleys, or *estuaries*, enter the sea. If these valleys have been rounded by glacial action, the shoreline is referred to as a *fiord* coast. *Deltaic* coasts are those where rivers have dumped great quantities of sediment into the ocean to build up a series of deltas. Occasionally, in tropical areas, marine organisms build up *coral reefs* from their shells and skeletons on the offshore bars. When many agencies have combined to create a shoreline, it is termed *compound*.

A CORAL ATOLL

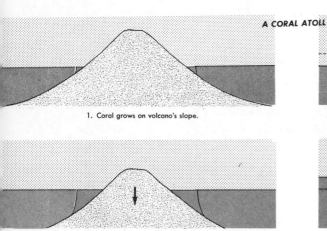

1. Coral grows on volcano's slope.

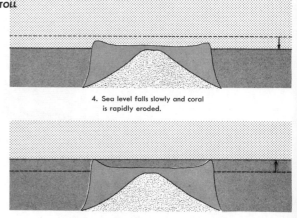

4. Sea level falls slowly and coral is rapidly eroded.

2. Coral increases as volcano sinks.

5. Sea rises again and coral begins rebuilding around edges.

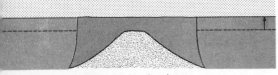

3. Sea rises slowly and coral grows above volcano.

Find the areas in the world where coral reefs and atolls are most common. What characteristics do these areas share in (a) temperature (b) depth of water?

Coral coastline such as we see here is a common sight in Bermuda and the Bahamas.

ahamas News Bureau Photo

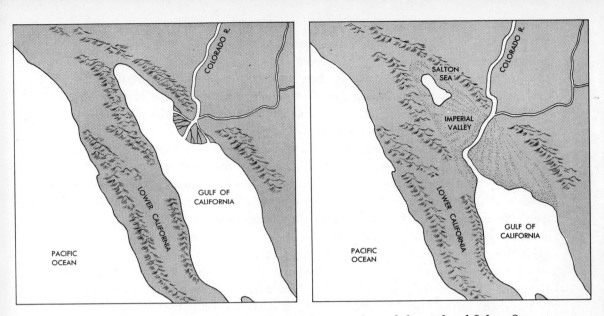

Delta formation by the Colorado river has now formed the enclosed Salton Sea.

Economic Aspects of Shorelines

Should you have ever sat and watched the ships of the world as they ply their way up the St. Lawrence Seaway, you would have missed an important geographical relationship if you did not form a mental image of the countries from which these vessels came. The first picture to enter the mind is usually one of the map outline of the country involved.

It is interesting to note that most of the ships come from countries with greatly indented coastlines. Trim, stately cargo ships arrive from the fiords of Scandinavia; freighters and steamers churn their way upstream from the estuaries of the Rhine, the Thames, the Seine, and the River Plate; oriental vessels arrive from as far away as the ria coasts of the Philippines and Japan.

These coastal features provide excellent harbours for shipping, and if the country has the necessary raw materials, shipbuilding is usually one of its main industries. Good harbours also foster a thriving fishing industry. In the case of ria and fiord coastlines, access to the interior is usually limited owing to the steepness of the sea cliffs. Such areas often produce hydroelectricity and may become the centres of the forest industries.

Most ria and fiord coastlines have a very high tidal range because the incoming tide is trapped or confined in the narrowing estuaries and fiords. The result is that the water can go only one way and that is up. Several schemes have been proposed to tap the tides of the Bay of Fundy and Passamaquoddy Bay in order to produce electricity; indeed, several pilot plants are already producing power from the tides along the coast of France.

Agriculture is, of necessity, limited along very steep coastlines. However, where a shoreline of emergence exposes the marine terrace, broad coastal plains provide space for agriculture. The people of Virginia, Georgia, Alabama, and Mississippi do not look to the sea for their livelihood, but use it mainly to export their agricultural produce. Because of the amount of sedimentation in these and similar areas, harbours must often be artificially created and constantly dredged; thus they are a very expensive undertaking. There is, however, a notable exception to this circumstance, for tidal action often keeps an inlet to a lagoon dredged so that ships may enter in safety. A unique feature of the south and southeastern coast of the U.S.A. is the long, narrow, offshore sand bars which act as a breakwater and allow ships to sail in the calm waters between the bar and the mainland. So extensive are these bars that the Intracoastal Canal has been partly constructed by connecting lagoons from the Chesapeake Bay area to Key West, and from Tampa to Brownsville on the Mexican border.

Of greatest significance to earliest man were the deltaic coasts. Here the Egyptians, Thais, and Chinese made use of the deltas and the annual flood waters of the rivers in building their ancient cities and civilizations. East and southeast Asia are still very greatly dependent on these landforms for their livelihood.

The fiord coastline of Norway does not provide much land for agriculture. What type of vegetation covers the hillsides? What material is used for insulation of the roofs? Why do fiords make good harbours?

5 AEOLIAN LANDSCAPE AND LANDFORMS

Aeolus, according to Greek mythology, was a subdeity who controlled the winds. He restrained the wind by keeping it in large bags and could greatly influence man and his voyages by presenting him with a favourable or an unfavourable wind. Today, no less than in ancient times, the wind plays an important part in our lives. Our climate, crops, clothing, houses, etc., are all affected in some way by the rain, snow, or arid conditions which the wind may bring.

In this chapter we shall deal with the work of the wind in carving landscapes and landforms. These *aeolian* features, as they are known, are of great significance to man. In some areas, where winds deposit fertile soil, man is attracted to settle there, but in other regions shifting sand dunes invade fertile oases and drive out the inhabitants.

In mountainous areas winds play an important part in the *denudation* of the higher areas. Little soil ever collects here because weathered particles either fall from the peaks by the force of gravity or are picked up by the wind and transported to lower areas. This action permits little vegetation to grow and hence the term denudation is used to describe the rocky outcrops of mountainous areas.

Where the mountains are high enough to experience glaciation, much rock is ground up and deposited along the front of the glacier. The wind carries the finer particles some distance and may deposit them in beds covering a wide area. These *loess* beds, as they are known, are also deposited along the margins of desert areas.

This complex of dunes is located in central Asia. Why are such soils usually fertile if irrigated?

Embassy of the U.S.S.R.

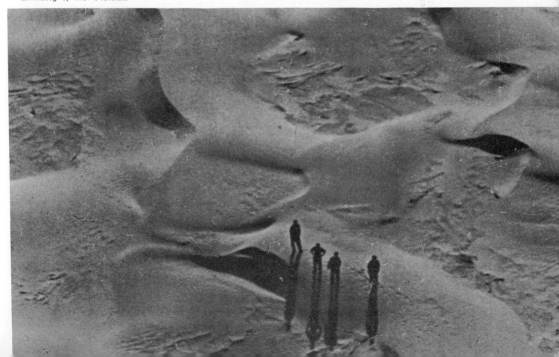

Winds play an active part along coasts where wave action has exposed a wide expanse of sandy material. When this material becomes dried out, the winds begin to move the sand. Soon *dunes*, curiously-shaped sand hills, are created, and these may begin to move slowly inland, influenced by the direction of the prevailing wind. In humid areas such dunes quickly become covered with vegetation and stagnate to become *sand hills*. Active dunes are to be found along the eastern shores of Lake Michigan, the southern part of the Atlantic Coast of the U.S.A., and the north coast of Europe. Sand hills are located along the north shore of Lake Erie in the Port Colborne area.

The wind has its greatest effect on desert areas. Here the weathered particles are not bound together by moisture or vegetative cover and the wind is, consequently, able to transport and deposit the sand particles freely. As there are many types of these in desert regions, an attempt will be made to classify them.

The *barkhan* is the simplest dune type to describe as it is usually isolated and has a characteristic crescent shape. The horns of the crescent point downwind and indicate the direction of movement of the dune. Where sand is abundant, however, the dunes will coalesce to form wavelike landforms separated by troughs. These *traverse* dunes are at right angles to the direction of the wind and may cover a wide area. This sand sea has been termed an *erg*.

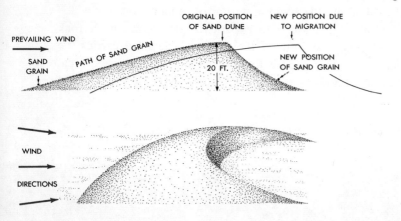

A sand dune moves slowly, grain by grain, in its migration across the countryside. These dunes create an almost irresistible force and can encroach on fertile farm lands.

The typical barkan dune is found in most desert areas.

Where the wind is very strong and blows mainly from one direction, long narrow dunes develop parallel to the wind direction. These *siefs* may run for many miles across the countryside. Where some obstacle prevents the free drifting of the sand, long tapering dunes will form in the lee of the obstacle. If the wind is strong and the obstruction formidable, these longitudinal dunes may reach up to two miles in length.

The source of most sand is desert bedrock, which is weathered by a force called *abrasion*. This is a sandblast action wherein the wind hurls previously weathered sand grains against the solid rock. By this method the weaker rock is removed first and rock sculpturing occurs. In sandstone the looser material is usually held together by the silica which permeates the rock. When the wind removes this looser or weaker material, a lattice-work of the harder silica may remain to form peculiar shapes and patterns.

Because the abrasive force is strongest near the surface, many landforms are undercut. The *pedestal rock*, balanced on a thin stem, is an example of this. If there are several layers of sedimentary beds exposed, the wind will remove the softer material and a *fluted* surface will develop. This action makes the more resistant beds stand out very prominently.

Another source of sand is provided by intermittent streams which follow the torrential rains that occasionally occur in desert areas. Between rains, a mass of weathered material collects and is carried into desert regions by fast-flowing streams. Where mountain valleys emerge on to desert plains, huge *alluvial fans* of sand and pebbles may build up. Other, and finer, sediments may be carried farther, only to be dumped unceremoniously into some arid basin as the water disappears into the parched sands or is evaporated by the searing sun. In these basins, or *bolsons*, small lakes may form. When evaporation occurs, a wide flat expanse of silt is exposed. This *playa*, or dry lake, may contain salts, which cement the silt together to form a concrete-hard, erosion-resistant surface. The dry ditches carved by the streams are called *wadis* or *arroyos*.

In semi-arid areas, the weathered material is usually held in place by vegetation. When this protective covering is broken through, or removed by over-grazing, etc., *deflation* occurs. This is the removal by wind of the finer particles from a large oval-shaped area. The surface level may be lowered several feet and the resultant depression is called a *blowout*. The finer material may be carried some distance, but the coarser material is heaped at the edge of the hollow to form a sand dune.

This canyon in Iran is the site of a hydro-electric dam. What caused the pitted indentations in the canyon wall?   Embassy of Iran

Why do artificial lakes in semi-arid regions become filled with silt so quickly?

How do you explain the fact that this now-barren area of Iran once supported a prosperous civilization?

Where the drifting sand becomes trapped by vegetation, the taller brush may not be entirely covered and will continue to grow. The new growth traps more sand and then grows on top of this. In this fashion a small *hillock* dune is formed. These dunes closely resemble stooks of corn and reminded one traveller so much of this fact that he named such an area in Death Valley, California, The Devil's Cornfield.

Not all desert areas are covered with sand dunes; we must, therefore, look at the areas from which the sand particles were removed if we are to get a true picture of aeolian landscapes. Some regions are swept clear of unconsolidated material to reveal the unbroken bedrock. This rock desert may undergo weathering to such a degree that the bedrock breaks up. A *hamada* or *stony* desert of sharp angular stones may thus develop. These stones are a serious hindrance to transportation, for camels and other beasts of burden often cut their hoofs on them as they attempt to cross such deserts.

Another feature of desert areas is the *desert pavement*. When alluvial deposits dry out, the finer particles may be carried away. Then salts precipitated from the evaporating water cement the gravelly material together. A wide expanse of this type of erosion-resistant surface is called a *reg*.

Economy of Aeolian Regions

The wind affects all people and all areas in some way; but as its effects are more noticeable in drier areas, the study of the economy of such an area, is, of necessity, the study of the economy of arid and semi-arid regions. Most of us are familiar with certain aspects of desert regions. Much of what we know is related to the hot, arid conditions, which make these areas difficult to live in. That deserts present great hardships to man is true, but they do have some aspects which are beneficial to him.

The loess material blown out from deserts or moraines produces some of the best farm lands in the world. Since this material retains most of its minerals, it needs only water to become productive. Fertile loess covers much of Kansas and Missouri. In Europe, the Central Depression of Germany is floored with loess, while the upper Hwang Ho in China cuts through a great thickness of these sediments.

The loess clay of some regions is sometimes mixed with straw, hair, or grass to form building bricks. In other areas, e.g., China, where there are steep cliffs, dwellings are carved out of the soft material. Evaporation from the walls forms a deposit of lime on the interior—a deposit which serves to hold the loess in place.

As loess deposits are usually found in marginal areas, especially between deserts and tall-grass prairies, they have a number of drawbacks. Destruction of their vegetation may start the material drifting again. Small streams may carve the area into a maze of gullies and ridges. South Dakota's Bad Lands illustrate this point remarkably well. Constant travel over the same route churns up the fine particles and the wind carries them away. As a result, the road slowly sinks below the level of the land. Owing to the nature of the loess deposits, the road banks remain almost vertical. In periods of drought, dust drifts into these depressions and obstructs traffic. During a heavy rain, the road beds become stream channels and an unwary traveller may find himself hemmed in by fifty-foot-high walls with a torrent of water bearing down on him.

In desert areas, oasis agriculture is carried on wherever water is available. These areas may be very productive; often, however, the farmer finds himself locked in a losing struggle with the wind. Sandstorms may destroy his crops by dumping great quantities of material on his fields. The slow march of the dunes may engulf his crops, buildings, and even the oasis itself. This encroachment of dunes is not confined to arid areas only, but may occur in any region where wide expanses of sand are exposed.

Irrigation of the desert has long been practised by man in such places as Egypt, Iraq, and southwestern U.S.A. Recently, huge new dams and reservoirs are turning desert areas into fertile farmlands. The Aswan Dam in Egypt will soon turn millions of acres of wasteland into productive fields. In California, the Great Valley and the Imperial Valley have already been extensively irrigated as a result of the construction of the Shasta, Friant, and Imperial dams.

The constant search for water has given rise to nomadic herding in North Africa, central Asia, and Saudi Arabia. Here, nomads follow their flocks of sheep, cattle, camels, etc., as they migrate long distances in an effort to take advantage of the seasonal rains.

In most aeolian areas, evaporation exceeds precipitation. This gives rise to salt water lakes, playas, and inland seas. Salt is sometimes extracted from these bodies of water by pumping the water into diked fields and allowing it to evaporate. This process is repeated several times until a bed of salt is built up. The residue is then collected and purified; calcium, sodium, magnesium, chlorine, etc., can be obtained from it.

In earlier times many salt-water lakes and seas dried up and the salt deposits so formed were preserved either by continuing arid conditions or by a covering of sedimentary materials. The nitrate deposits of the Atacama Desert in Chile are the result of ages of such surface evaporation.

Potash beds have been preserved in sedimentary rock in Germany, France, Russia, and the U.S.A. At present shafts are being sunk (in Saskatchewan) to the rich deposits which underlie the Canadian Prairies. Florida and North Africa have similarly formed deposits of phosphates. Salt is mined very extensively throughout the world. Huge beds are found in the U.S.A., Austria, Nova Scotia, and southwestern Ontario. These salts, nitrates, and phosphates, together with potash and common salt, supply the majority of the mineral fertilizers of the world, as well as providing the chemical industry with its basic raw materials.

Thus we can see that not all aspects of desert areas are unfavourable to man. Arid areas act as a storehouse for soluble minerals, as a source of mineral-rich soil, and as pasture land for herds of livestock.

SALT

↓

Elements

Sodium ← → **Chlorine**

Compounds							
Sodium Hypochloride	Sodium Hydroxide	Sodium Carbonate	Sodium Cyanide	Hydrochloric Acid	Calcium Chloride	Chlorine	Potassium Chlorate
Uses							
Antiseptics

Cleaning fluid | Lye

Petroleum refining

Soap

Wood pulp

Paper

Cellophane

Viscose | Glass

Soap

Tanning fluid

Water softener

Cleaning powder | Gold refining

Insecticides

Electroplating | Cleaning metals

Textiles

Dyes

Synthetic rubber

Glue

Glucose | Dust preventive

Refrigerating brines

Drying agent

Calcium metal | Water purification

Bleaching

Plastics

Insecticides

Solvents

Dyes

Medicines

Antifreeze

Poison gas | Matches

Fireworks

Explosives

Source of oxygen |

212

UNIT REVIEW

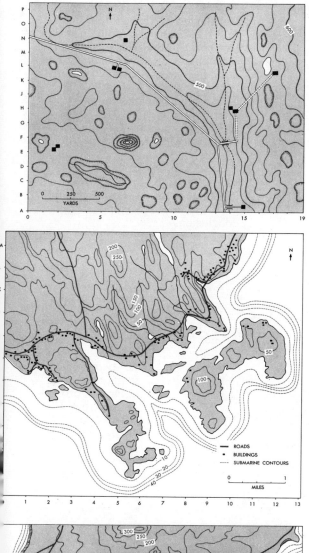

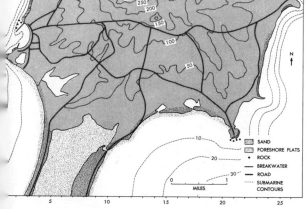

MAP OF KARST AREA

1. What is the difference in elevation between the buildings at 15-A and 17-L? 2. What do the closed hachured contours signify? 3. Identify the features at 5-D, 6-F, 8-A, and 3-H. 4. How deep is the depression at 6-F? 5. Account for the broken lines in the valley bottom. 6. How has the drainage pattern affected (a) settlement, (b) transportation? 7. Why is there no road into the buildings at 2-E?

TANGIER, NOVA SCOTIA

1. At what stage of development is this coast? 2. Account for the population pattern. 3. What landform is located at 9-K, 5-H, 7-C? 4. Account for (a) the change in contour interval and (b) the peculiar distribution of the submarine contours. 5. On paper, trace the outline of the coast if the land were to rise (a) 10 ft., (b) 30 ft. 6. What difference would you then note in the landforms created? 7. Trace the outline of the coast if the land were to sink (a) 50 ft., (b) 100 ft. 8. At which of the four elevations stated in 5 and 7, could the shore line be classified as one of old age?

GRINDSTONE ISLANDS, MAGDALEN ISLANDS, QUEBEC

1. Indicate an area which shows features of (a) youth, (b) maturity, (c) old age. Identify the features of each area. 2. Account for the peculiar formation of the sand bars in the southwest. 3. Identify the features found at 9-E (2 features), and 17-J. 4. What additional information would you need before you could classify the landform at 21-G as a tombolo? 5. Why must you hesitate before calling the landform at 23-K a spit?

213

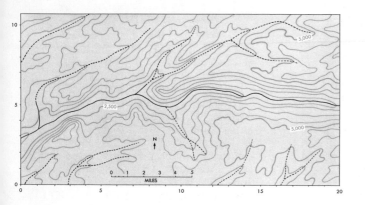

WESTERN SLOPES OF
SIERRA NEVADA

1. What is the contour interval? 2. State the difference in feet between the highest and lowest points. 3. In which direction does the stream flow? 4. How many feet does it rise in 24 miles? 5. Account for the number of intermittent streams. 6. Draw a cross-section from 15-3 to 15-7 (grid reference). 7. How high are the river banks at this point? 8. Where is the stream bank the steepest? (Give grid reference). 9. State the age of the stream and give evidence to support your conclusion.

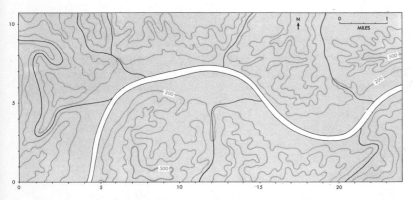

1. Which way is the river flowing? Why is it hard to tell? 2. Give the grid references for the two highest points of land. 3. Draw a cross-section from 17-0 to 17-6. 4. Compare this cross-section with that drawn for the previous map. Note the vertical difference in the scales you use. 5. What do you call the area along the river where there are no contours? 6. Why is the river not meandering? 7. Classify this stream as to age and justify your choice.

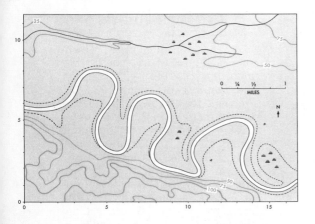

1. Which way is the main stream flowing? 2. What do the dotted lines indicate? 3. Why are these lines missing at 5-3 and 9-2? 4. What feature is shown at 10-10? 5. Draw a cross-section from the highest point to the lowest point. 6. Why does the river not flow to the lowest point of land? 7. Why does the tributary not enter the main stream at 5-8? 8. Would you classify this as a mature or an old river? Justify your answer.

PART THREE

THE WORLD'S CLIMATES

1. The Tropical Climates
2. Tropical and Subtropical Climates
3. Mid-Latitude and Polar Climates

	POLAR HIGH	POLAR VARIABLES		CYCLONIC STORM BELT
PREVAILING WINDS & CALMS			SUMMER RAIN	
PRESSURE BELTS	HIGH			LOW
CLIMATIC TYPE	ICE CAP	TUNDRA	SUBARCTIC	EAST-COAST CONTINENTAL WEST-COAST MARINE
VEGETATION				
SOIL	PERMAFROST		PODZOLIZATION	HUMUS LEACHED LAYER (IRON, ALUMINUM, SILICON)
LATITUDE	90°	REGOLITH	66½°	ZONE OF ACCUMULATION (SODIUM, CALCIUM, MAGNES
SOIL TYPE		TUNDRA	PODZOL	E.C.CONTINENTAL—BROWN PODZOL W.C.MARINE—BROWN FOREST
VEGETATION TYPE		TUNDRA BIRCH PARK	CONIFEROUS	E.C.C.—BROAD-LEAFED DECIDUOUS & MIXED W.C.M.—BROAD-LEAFED DECIDUOUS & CONIFEROUS
SPECIES OF VEGETATION		MOSS, LICHEN, GRASS, SHRUBS	SPRUCE, PINE, LARCH, HEMLOCK, BALSAM	E.C.C.—BEECH, OAK, ASH, ELM, MAPLE, BIRCH, PINE, CEDAR W.C.M.—OAK, ASH, BEECH, ELM, FIR, SPRUCE, PINE
ANIMAL SPECIES	PENGUIN POLAR BEAR	REINDEER, CARIBOU, ARCTIC FOX, HARE, SEAL, MUSK-OX, WALRUS	WOLF, BEAR, MOOSE, MINK, MARTEN, LYNX, SABLE, OTTER, WEASEL	E.C.C.—FOX, BEAVER, BEAR, DEER, RABBIT, WOLF W.C.M.—FOX, DEER, MT. LION
DOMESTICATED ANIMALS		REINDEER	HORSES, REINDEER	CATTLE, HORSES, PIGS, SHEEP, POULTRY
CULTIVATED VEGETATION			TREE FARMING	WHEAT, OATS, RYE, BARLEY, ROOT CROPS, FODDER, APPLES
TYPES OF ECONOMY		TRAPPING & HUNTING NOMADIC HERDING HUNTING & FISHING	MIXED LIVESTOCK & CROPPING, FORESTRY, TRAPPING, SUBSISTENCE & PARTTIME FARMING	E.C.C.—PEASANT, ROOT, LIVESTOCK & GRAIN FARMING ORCHARD, FISHING, FORESTRY, MANUFACTURING W.C.M.—PEASANT, GRAIN & ROOT FARMING, ORCHAR HORTICULTURE, FORESTRY, FISHING, MANUFACTURING
SAMPLE STUDIES FOR STUDENT RESEARCH	GREENLAND ANTARCTICA	ESKIMOS, LAPS YUKAGIR OR TUNGUS	COMPANY TOWN— PULP & PAPER TRAPPING— N. AMERICAN INDIAN	E.C.C.—MIXED FARMING—OTTAWA VALLEY, GUELPH W.C.M.—PEASANT FARMING—FRANCE, BRITISH ISLES —LUMBERING—BRITISH COLUMBIA

This generalized diagram shows some of the relationships existing within each of the world's climatic regions.

Classification of Climates

In order to facilitate the study of geography, man has grouped rocks, land-forms, etc., into various classifications. This is done so that similarities and differences will become more apparent and therefore can be more easily explained. However, the study of climate in this manner, is difficult, for there are so many variables that no classification is acceptable to everybody.

Climates may be classified on the basis of temperature, precipitation, latitude, or vegetation. For example, the world's climates can be grouped on the basis of

| WESTERLIES | SUBTROPICAL HIGH | | TRADES | | EQUATORIAL LOW |

Diagram labels: WINTER RAIN · HIGH · SUMMER RAIN · LOW

CHINA MEDITERRANEAN — SUBTROPICAL STEPPE — TROPICAL DESERT (MOISTURE DEFICIENCY) — TROPICAL STEPPE — SAVANNA — TROPICAL RAINFOREST

ZONE OF ACCUMULATION — (SODIUM) CALCIUM MAGNESIUM) — EVAPORATION — LATERIZATION — HUMUS — LEACHED LAYER (IRON, ALUMINUM, SILICON)

(IUM) · REGOLITH · REGOLITH · 23½° · 0°

CHINA—RED EARTHS MED.—RED & YELLOW TERRA ROSSA	RED-BROWN	RED DESERT	RED-BROWN	RED-LATERITIC	LATERITIC
CHINA—SUBTROPICAL EVERGREEN MED.—MEDITERRANEAN SCRUB	GRASS	DESERT SCRUB	GRASS	PARKLAND, THORN SCRUB	SELVA
CHINA—MAGNOLIA, CAMELLIA, CAMPHOR, S. PINE MED.—ACACIA, OLIVE, HOLLY, SAGE, MAQUIS, OAK	SAGE, GRASS, SALTBUSH	CACTUS, PRICKLY PEAR, MESQUITE	SPINIFEX, GRASS, SALTBUSH	ACACIA, THORN, EUCALYPTUS, GRASS	MAHOGANY, EBONY, LIANA, PALM, RUBBER, BAMBOO, MANGROVE
CHINA—BEAR, OPOSSUM, ALLIGATOR MED.—GOAT, WILD PIG, COUGAR	DEER, ANTELOPE, DINGO, HYENA	CAMEL, FOX, LIZARD	DEER, ANTELOPE, HYENA	GIRAFFE, LION, DEER, RHINOCEROS, HIPPO, ZEBRA, HYENA	APE, MONKEY, PANTHER, CROCODILE, SNAKE, DEER, ELEPHANT, LEOPARD
SHEEP, GOATS, OXEN, MULE, DONKEY	CATTLE, SHEEP, GOAT	CAMEL	CATTLE, GOAT	CATTLE	ELEPHANT
CHINA—MAIZE, COTTON, MILLET, TOBACCO, PEACHES, PEARS MED.—OLIVES, GRAPES, CITRUS FRUIT, WHEAT	FIGS, MAIZE, COTTON	DATES	FIGS, MAIZE	COFFEE, TOBACCO	RUBBER, CACAO, YAMS, BEANS, PUMPKINS, BANANAS, RICE
CHINA—PLANTATION, HORTICULTURE, FORESTRY, FISHING, MANUFACTURING MED.—VITICULTURE, ORCHARD, LIVESTOCK, FISHING, HORTICULTURE, MANUFACTURING	NOMADIC HERDING, IRRIGATION FARMING, OASIS AGRICULTURE, RANCHING	OASIS AGRICULTURE, NOMADIC HERDING	NOMADIC HERDING, OASIS AGRICULTURE, COLLECTORS & HUNTERS	HERDING, HUNTING, PLANTATION	PLANTATIONS, MIGRANT AGRICULTURALISTS, COLLECTORS & HUNTERS, FORESTRY
CHINA—HORTICULTURE—N. CAROLINA MED.—ORCHARD—S. SPAIN, CAPE PROV.	OASIS AGRICULTURE — EGYPT, MESOPOTAMIA	NOMADIC HERDING SAUDIA ARABIA —BEDOUINS	COLLECTORS & HUNTERS— ARUNTA—AUSTRALIA BUSHMEN—KALAHARI	PLANTATION— BRAZIL—COFFEE RHODESIA—TOBACCO MALAYA—RUBBER	MIGRANT AGRICULTURALISTS — MALAYA—SAKAI MEXICO—INDIAN

Because of their peculiar characteristics, monsoon and temperate-steppe regions are not included.

temperature into three main categories: tropical, mid-latitude, and polar and high-latitude. These three main groups are further subdivided on the basis of the vegetation found within each group.

Tropical climates include the rainforest, monsoon, savanna, tropical steppe, and tropical desert. Generally speaking, these climatic types experience no month cooler than 55° F. Poleward from the tropical climates lie the mid-latitude climates. China, Mediterranean, subtropical-steppe, west-coast marine, east-coast continental, and temperate-steppe climates are all included in this group. The polar and high-latitude climates include the subarctic, the tundra, and the icecap. This latter group experiences no month warmer than 65° F.

The Tropical Climates

1 THE TROPICAL RAINFOREST

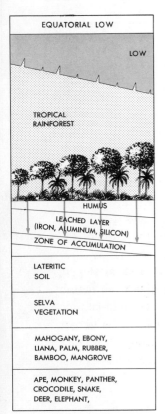

EQUATORIAL LOW

LOW

TROPICAL
RAINFOREST

HUMUS
LEACHED LAYER
(IRON, ALUMINUM, SILICON)
ZONE OF ACCUMULATION

LATERITIC
SOIL

SELVA
VEGETATION

MAHOGANY, EBONY,
LIANA, PALM, RUBBER,
BAMBOO, MANGROVE

APE, MONKEY, PANTHER,
CROCODILE, SNAKE,
DEER, ELEPHANT,

Embassy of Franc

*Typical selva vegetation is found along the Guinea
Coast of Africa.*

Tropical rainforests are generally located within 10° of the equator and owe many of their peculiarities to *insolation*, that is, to the amount of heat received from the sun. As the vertical rays of the sun are confined to an area between 23½° north latitude and 23½° south latitude, it follows that the greatest amount of heating will occur here. Within the region, there will be differences in the amount of insolation. A line connecting the points which experience the highest annual average temperatures has been termed the *thermal equator*. Owing to the effect of landforms and land elevations, and the distribution of land and water, this line does not always correspond with the latitudinal equator.

This graph shows the average temperature and precipitation conditions for Singapore. Locate this city and attempt to explain why these conditions exist. What is the relationship of the city to the thermal equator?

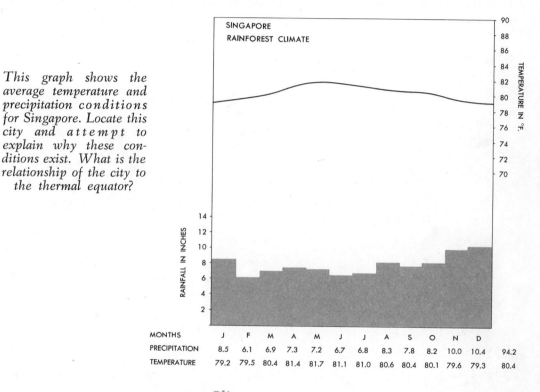

MONTHS	J	F	M	A	M	J	J	A	S	O	N	D	
PRECIPITATION	8.5	6.1	6.9	7.3	7.2	6.7	6.8	8.3	7.8	8.2	10.0	10.4	94.2
TEMPERATURE	79.2	79.5	80.4	81.4	81.7	81.1	81.0	80.6	80.4	80.1	79.6	79.3	80.4

Climate

The most notable characteristic of the climate of this region is certainly its uniformity. Study the graph for the climate of Singapore and determine the differences between the hottest and coolest months and between the wettest and driest months. How do these figures compare with those for your own area? Later, comparisons with other climatic regions will show that the rainforest has a greater degree of uniformity of temperature and precipitation than any other climatic region.

The factors which influence this type of climate are closely related to insolation. As the earth and the atmosphere above it are heated by the sun, the air expands to form a *low-pressure* area. Because the warm, light air of this low-pressure area does not weigh as much per unit volume as does the cooler air on the poleward sides of the equator, it is displaced by the cooler air. Displacement can occur only in one direction, and that is upwards, because the heavier air flows in from both north and south. When the displaced air reaches higher elevations, it cools and contracts and precipitation occurs. This type of precipitation is referred to as *convection rain*.

The sun cannot shine vertically on any more than one place at one time. It follows from this fact that clouds and precipitation will tend to follow the sun's vertical rays as they circle the earth. Another way of stating this same fact is to say that rain occurs daily at any particular spot in the rainforest shortly after the sun has passed overhead. To understand this more fully let us examine a typical day in a rainforest area.

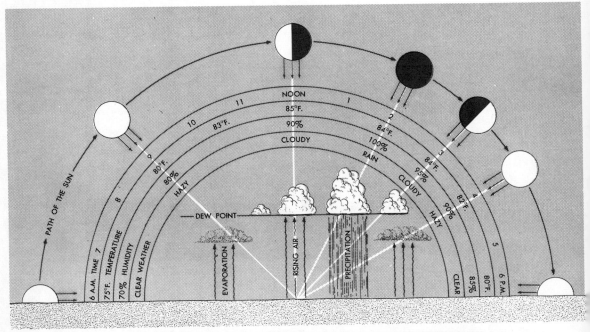

WEATHER PHENOMENA AS EXPERIENCED DURING A TYPICAL DAY IN A RAINFOREST REGION

The day dawns bright and warm, and because the humidity is low, this is the most enjoyable part of the day. As the sun climbs higher, the land heats up, evaporation takes place, and a haze may occur. By eleven o'clock the first clouds begin to appear as the air that was forced upwards begins to cool. The clouds gradually thicken and the sky becomes overcast. This clouding shuts out the sun's rays and aids in the cooling and condensation of water vapour. By approximately 1:30 p.m., the ascending air can no longer retain all its moisture and precipitation occurs. The ensuing rains are short in duration but torrential in force.

When the rain ceases, the sky slowly clears and allows the sun's rays to reach the earth once again. Here they find the moisture which was previously held in cloud formation. Evaporation recommences, and we may truthfully say that the forest steams. Not enough moisture can return to the air to cause precipitation before sunset, but there is sufficient water vapour present to reflect the rays of the setting sun. As a result, the tropics experience beautiful and spectacular sunsets.

Sunset usually occurs about 6 p.m. and darkness descends almost immediately. The temperature drops several degrees overnight. In fact, there may be a greater difference between night and day temperatures than between January and July average temperatures. These phenomena are caused by the fact that the sun drops away, so to speak, at right angles to any particular point along the equator. Because of this, there are fewer oblique rays to warm the atmosphere than there are in the higher latitudes.

Vegetation

Such a climate is certain to influence the vegetation and the soil, and indeed, all aspects of the earth with which it comes in contact. The *selva* vegetation which flourishes under the hot damp conditions of the rainforest is, perhaps, the most luxuriant forest type to be found anywhere in the world. Because of the continuous high temperatures and the abundant supply of moisture, growth can continue throughout the year. The type of trees which grow under these conditions is called *broad-leafed evergreen*. These trees do lose their leaves, but the new foliage grows so quickly that a tree is never completely devoid of leaves.

One of the characteristics of selva is its great variety of tree species. An examination of an acre of forest may reveal as many as 100 different tree species. In such a forest the general appearance is one of tiers, or layers, of vegetation. The first tier is one of *emergent* or giant hardwoods, such as mahogany, which reach to heights of 150 feet. These trees are isolated and project 25 or 50 feet above the second, or canopy, layer. In this second layer, the tops of the trees intertwine and may prevent the sun's rays from reaching the earth's surface. Such trees are mangrove, rubber, and some palms. Beneath these at heights of 40 to 60 feet are the bamboo and tree ferns that struggle upward in search of sunlight. If any sunlight is able to penetrate through this mass of vegetation, a ground cover of shrubs and ferns will develop. In most cases, however, the selva floor is amazingly devoid of vegetation because of the lack of sunlight. Lianas, giant vines such as the aroid, the strangler fig, and the palmetto, extend from the treetops to the ground, using the tree as their support. Only in areas where less rainfall hinders tree growth and the sun's rays penetrate to the ground does the underbrush, or jungle, develop.

Soil

Because of the constant loss of leaves throughout the year, a thick layer of decaying vegetation, or humus, develops on the forest floor. This is constantly being attacked by bacteria and fungus growth so that the minerals locked in the plant can be made available again for fresh growth.

The decaying vegetation, however, also produces several acids, such as carbonic and humic acid. These are picked up by the rainfall and carried down into the soil. Here they react with the chemicals in the soil to perform a process called *leaching*. By this action the more soluble minerals, such as calcium, sodium, and magnesium, are dissolved in solution. These are then carried away by the run-off or percolate downwards through the soil to be precipitated some 10 to 20 feet below the surface. By this process the soil develops a horizontal zonation: *humus*, *leached layer*, and *zone of accumulation*.

As the insoluble minerals in the leached layer do not provide nourishment for plants, soil of this layer is classed as infertile. One may well ask how this is possible when it supports such a dense vegetational cover. The truth is that the larger trees have roots deep enough to penetrate to the zone of accumulated minerals, and hence can obtain food. The smaller plants and trees live upon the supply of food stored in the humus layer. If man were to clear the selva for cultivation, the layer of humus would be washed away in a short time by the torrential rains and the roots of his crops would not grow deep enough to penetrate the mineralized zone. This, in some measure, explains the poorly developed economy of the rainforest region.

Fauna

The animal life, although not as well developed as the plant life, provides us with an interesting study of environmental conditions. For the most part, the ecology of animals is based on a food chain: the *herbivorous* animals feed on the vegetation and the *carnivorous* feed on the herbivorous animals; eventually, all are returned to the soil to provide more vegetation for more animals. Because of the great variety of tree species, the herbivorous animals must search widely for their particular food supply. This is the weak link in the food chain, hence, animal life is not abundant.

The life which has developed is closely associated with, and dependent upon, its environment. The treetops are the main habitat for the most abundant forms of animal life. Here, hundreds of varieties of insects abound, including the dreaded malarial mosquito. Birds of all sorts feed on the insects and vegetation, each species cultivating a taste for a particular plant or insect.

Other arboreal species that long ago forsook the dark humid selva floor for the more abundant food supply in the trees, are apes, monkeys, sloths, bats, and squirrels. Among the selva's denizens that commute between forest floor and tree-top are snakes, anteaters, panthers, and leopards. As a rule these animals are not numerous in true selva, and except for small deer, wild pig, and some varieties of anteater, very few ground-dwelling animals exist. In more lightly forested areas an occasional elephant or elephant herd may take up residence.

This, then, is the environment with which man must cope if he is ever to inhabit successfully the rainforest area.

Students of the Eastern Caribbean Farm Institute inspect native tropical cocoa plants on a plantation in Trinidad.

United Kingdom Information Service

Palm Orchards thrive in the selva regions of Senegal.

Embassy of France

2 THE MONSOON REGION

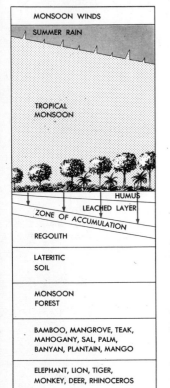

Miller Services

Months	J	F	M	A	M	J	J	A	S	O	N	D	YEAR
Temp.	77.8	79.8	81.6	83.6	83.1	78.5	76.7	77.4	78.3	79.1	79.5	78.3	79.5
Precip.	0.3	0.2	0.6	3.2	9.5	35.0	29.8	15.3	8.4	10.3	4.9	1.1	118.6

CLIMATIC DATA FOR KOZHIKODE, SOUTHWEST INDIA

1. Construct a graph to illustrate the climate of the monsoon area. Refer to the climatic graph for rainforest areas as a guide.

2. How does the annual range of temperature compare with that for rainforest areas?

3. How do you account for the drop in temperatures during July and August?

4. Describe the two distinct seasons which are indicated here and by reference to the diagrams of monsoon winds account for the difference.

Climate

The monsoon climate is influenced by the differential heating of land and sea, and hence is found only where the physiographic setting is right, mainly in southeast Asia. The monsoon influence extends northward along the Asiatic coast as far as Japan. It is also experienced in northern Australia, parts of Brazil, and Central America.

In southeast Asia, however, where the world's largest landmass, Asia, meets the earth's greatest expanse of water, the Pacific ocean, the conditions are such that they create a typical monsoon climate. When the sun apparently shifts northward in our summer, the greatest amount of heating does not occur along the Tropic of Cancer, but takes place over the Thar Desert of India and the Gobi Desert of China. This is largely due to the fact that the land heats up more quickly than the water.

The monsoon winds are related to heat and pressure. Note that in summer 30.0 inches is termed a high-pressure area in relation to the low of 29.4 inches. In winter, 29.8 is classed as a low in relation to the high of 30.4 . All temperatures and pressures should be observed in relation to neighbouring temperatures and pressures.

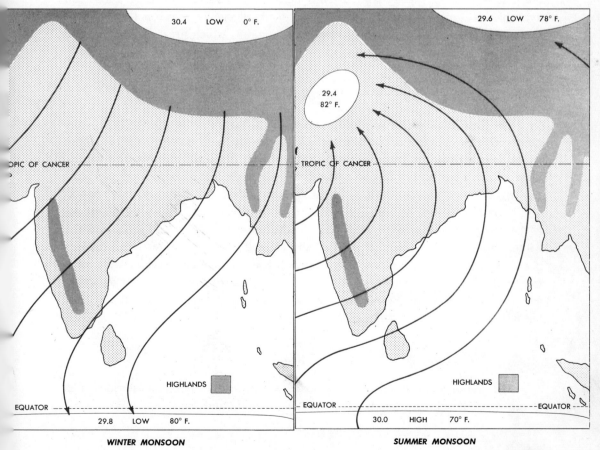

WINTER MONSOON   **SUMMER MONSOON**

The low-pressure areas which are formed over the land attract the winds which blow out from the high-pressure cells over the sea. Because of the rotation of the earth, these winds do not blow directly from high to low, but approach the continent in a huge *monsoonal curve*. The winds cross the southwest coast of India and travel northeastward over the subcontinent until they strike the mountain barrier of the Himalayas. Here they are deflected northwestward toward the low-pressure centre in the region of the Thar Desert. One of the important results of this deflection is the heavy rains which are brought to India and southeast Asia. Precipitation occurs when the winds rise over the Ghats of India, the Dawna Range of Thailand, and the Himalayas of India and Tibet. The cooling effect of the higher altitudes is the same as that described for rainforest climate. In this case, however, the relief of the land causes the air to rise; hence the increased precipitation on the uplands is called *relief rain*.

The winter monsoon of India is caused by conditions exactly opposite to those of the summer monsoon described above. In this season, the sun has apparently shifted southwards and the low-pressure area now exists over northern Australia and south-central Africa. The wind direction is reversed and a flood of cool, high-pressure air flows outward from central Asia. As this air descends from the mountains, it warms up rapidly and extends across the land, evaporating almost all available moisture and parching the land. Rainfall occurs only on the northern shores of such islands as Ceylon, Java, and Sumatra, which are fortunate enough to lie in the path of the wind.

Vegetation

The vegetation which is found in monsoon areas is very similar to that of the rainforest areas. Many of the tree species are similar to, if not the same as, those of the selva. However, because of the long periods of drought during the winter, most of the trees have adapted themselves to this desiccation by dropping most of their leaves to prevent drying out through transpiration. Owing to this adaptation, monsoon forests are often referred to as *semideciduous*. Another difference is the heavy growth of underbrush due to the more widely spaced trees and the winter drought. This forest is more easily cleared, and, therefore, more densely populated, than selva. Here, too, stands of an individual species are more frequently found. The Sunderbans, or mangrove swamps, along the Ganges delta, and the teak forest of Burma are dense, almost single-species, stands of giant hardwoods.

Soil

The soil of monsoon areas is the same as that of the rainforest-lateritic. The heavy rains of summer remove the soluble minerals and leave an impoverished soil, rich in iron and silica content. The period of winter drought is both a curse and a blessing. It allows the soil to dry out until it becomes as hard as pavement. Few crops can be grown in this season. On the other hand, this period of drought allows weathered rock particles to collect. These are carried down by streams and spread over the lowlands to enrich the soil again with the coming of the monsoon rains. With irrigation many areas can grow crops all the year round.

Fauna

Because of the lighter forest and the thicker underbrush, many more animals inhabit this area than the rainforest. Many of these range into the selva or the savanna, but a few have become particularly adapted to this environment. Elephants and rhinoceros are large, thick-skinned animals which feed on the foliage of the trees and shrubs. The water buffalo and various species of deer are found here as well. Among the carnivorous animals, lions, leopards, and tigers stalk this area, occasionally retreating into the selva or foraging out on to the savanna. Many species of monkeys inhabit the trees, sharing their refuge with birds and snakes alike.

Miller Services

The settlement of monsoon areas is clustered around the river valleys to ensure a supply of water in the dry season.

Rice-planting time comes to Shensi province, China. What animal is used for ploughing? Why are there so few trees in this humid area?

227

Eastfoto

3 THE SAVANNA REGIONS

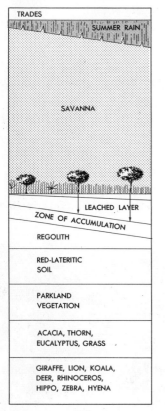

United Kingdom Information Service

Months	J	F	M	A	M	J	J	A	S	O	N	D	YEAR
Temp.	80.4	80.1	80.0	79.2	74.4	70.3	71.5	73.4	77.1	79.1	80.2	80.3	77.3
Precip.	6.4	6.7	4.8	5.0	3.3	1.9	0.3	1.3	2.3	3.9	6.0	7.4	49.3

CLIMATIC DATA FOR CORUMBA, BRAZIL

1. Locate Corumba and state its latitude.
2. In what season does the Corumba area receive most rainfall?
3. Construct a climatic graph using the data given above.
4. What aspects of this region are (a) similar to, and (b) different from, monsoon areas?
5. How is the amount of rainfall reflected in the above picture?
6. Has the above picture been taken near Corumba? Justify your answer.

7. What economic activity would you expect to find in the area shown in the photograph?
8. Is there much difference between the temperatures of the wet and dry seasons? Account for this difference.

Climate

The savanna regions are located on the poleward margins of the equatorial rainforest and the monsoon areas. They can be readily distinguished from either of these climatic types. To distinguish savanna from rainforest we can note the two distinct seasons in the former, whereas there is no such division in the latter. Monsoon areas also have two seasons, but the amount of rainfall which occurs in savanna areas is very much less. The areas where the savanna climatic type prevails are these: Brazilian and Guiana Highlands of South America; the regions north and south of the Congo Basin, as well as much of Kenya and Tanganyika in Africa; the northwestern section of the Deccan in India; the interior of southeast Asia.

The savanna climate owes its characteristics to the apparent shifting of the sun's rays. It receives convection rain as the sun appears to swing directly overhead in the hot season, and in the cooler months it has drought when the high-pressure systems take the place of the overhead sun. During this latter period the savanna comes under the climatic influence of the subtropical high-pressure cells. The trade winds normally blow from the high-pressure cells to the equatorial lows.

The two seasons which are experienced here are a hot, damp season and a warm, dry season. We must understand that these terms are relative and that a temperature which might seem warm to a Nigerian could be hot for a Canadian. The rain which falls in the hotter months, however, is not sufficient; accordingly, the savanna is generally thought of as having a transitional climate between that of the rainforest and the semi-arid steppes. It has, in fact, characteristics of both; for the hot, wet season reminds us of a rainforest, whereas the dry parching conditions are characteristic of semidesert areas.

Vegetation

Owing to the lack of rainfall and the high evaporation rate experienced in this climatic zone, there is not sufficient moisture in the soil to support dense stands of trees. Instead, we find semideciduous varieties of trees which are interspaced with areas of open tropical grasslands. The denseness of tree growth depends on its position in relation to the selva. As this is a transitional area, the densest forest growth will be found along the margins of the selva and the thinnest along the grassy tropical steppes. The chief species of trees found here are the acacia, eucalyptus, and thorn bush. This mixture of grass and tree growth has been variously called light tropical forest, thorn shrub, and *parkland*. The latter, being more descriptive of the area, is the term that will be used here.

The grass which we find in this area is very different from that which we are accustomed to seeing in Canada. When the rains occur, the land is carpeted with a dense cover of fast-growing grasses that may reach heights of 6 feet. In this period the grass is tender and is useful for grazing, but when the rains stop the grass quickly hardens and becomes woody. This change is an adaptation to the climate, as the plant is endeavouring to protect its moisture supply. In this state the grass is practically inedible and indigestible. This circumstance gives rise to a nomadic type of inhabitant, for the herders must move their flocks in order to follow the rain and obtain suitable forage for their animals.

Soil

The *red lateritic* soil of this area is potentially the most productive of the tropical soils. Because of the thick covering of grass, much of which dies during the annual drought, considerable quantities of humus are added to the soil each year. Owing to the smaller amount of rainfall, leaching of the soluble minerals is not as prevalent here as in the monsoon and rainforest areas. An examination of the soil profile will reveal that the zone of accumulation is close enough to the surface to supply the minerals necessary for plant growth. We might well ask ourselves, then, why these regions have not produced thriving agricultural economies.

Much of the agriculture which is carried on in the tropics is indeed done in this region. Brazil is world famous for coffee; rich crops of tobacco and cotton are produced in Tanganyika and Kenya; India supports many millions with the agricultural products of the Deccan. These, however, are the exceptions, for savanna soils are particularly susceptible to erosion and exhaustion. Where poor soil management or excessive cropping has destroyed the surface vegetation, the soil becomes powder dry in the dry season and much of it is carried off with the first rains. Another drawback to agriculture in this area is the hardness of the soil during the periods of drought as the excessive evaporation brings soluble salts to the surface and these cement the soil particles together. During this period it is almost impossible to use a plough on the land, for it will barely penetrate the surface. Judging from this, it seems likely that hoe cultivation, herding, and hunting are to be the chief occupations of the inhabitants of savanna regions for some time to come.

Fauna

At some time or other, most of us have seen films of the big-game country of Africa, or have journeyed in our mind's eye with some safari across the endless plains of Tanganyika and Kenya. Let us imagine for a moment that we are about to set out from Nairobi, Kenya, for a trip to Lake Victoria.

At the outset, we cross wide expanses of grassland. Trees are found along the streams and on the flood plains of rivers. These extensions of the tropical forests into semi-arid lands are called *galeria forests*. In this region we may see a great number of herbivorous animals: wildebeest, hartebeest, impala, gazelle, and buffalo graze contentedly on the open range. These animals prefer open spaces so that they can the better escape their predators. As we get farther inland, the vegetative cover begins to thicken and we can see giraffe feeding on the leaves of trees while zebra shade themselves from the sun by crowding under an acacia tree.

Deer are still numerous and we witness a sudden stampede among them as a lion attacks from ambush and succeeds in capturing his evening meal. As the lion dines, he is ringed about by hyenas and buzzards waiting for their share of the kill. Farther on, herds of elephant trumpet a warning and we give them a wide berth to avoid an attack. A short-sighted rhinoceros sniffs the wind and eyes us suspiciously before snorting off into the underbrush. Eventually, we reach Lake Victoria, and as we approach, a partially submerged hippopotamus disappears beneath the water and swims noiselessly away. He emerges some hundreds of feet distant and proceeds to feed on aquatic plants that grow along the shore.

This brief travelogue is intended to convey some information regarding the animal life in a savanna area. Such life is, however, no longer as abundant as the foregoing description might imply, nor are all the species mentioned here found in all savanna regions. In Australia, we find the koala bear, which feeds on the foliage of the eucalyptus tree, and the kangaroo, which is a grazing animal. The peccary, or wild pig, is found in the savanna areas of both South America and Mexico.

In conclusion, we may say that this area is a potential source of agricultural wealth. It will require careful conservation of its water supply and many irrigation projects if we are fully to utilize its resources. However, if the raisin-producing area of Australia, Sunraisia, is any criterion, we can expect the savanna region to become an extremely important agricultural area.

Imire Farm

Norman Travers went to Rhodesia from England in 1939 and immediately started work as a trainee-assistant on a farm. After service in World War II, he returned to Rhodesia in 1945, completed his farm training, and under a veteran's programme was allocated Imire farm by the government and given a loan of about

$6,000. This programme demanded that he pay back the loan in seven years; if, however, by that time, he had shown himself to be an efficient farmer, the land was to become his property without any further payment. Imire farm consists of about 3,000 acres situated ten miles away from the place where Mr. Travers learned farming.

At first many people advised him not to take Imire because the ground seemed to be very difficult to work and there appeared to be little possibility of developing any worthwhile water-conservation schemes. When he arrived, Imire was virgin land; it had no fences, no buildings, no roads. After building a pole and dagga (mud) house, which when whitewashed can be quite pleasant, Mr. Travers employed native help to put up other buildings and construct his first tobacco barn. That first year he grew 60 acres of tobacco and made enough profit to erect more barns and buildings and to construct a dam to provide water for his seedbeds. Since then Mr. Travers has turned most of his profits each year back into the farm—erecting fences, clearing and stumping fresh land, constructing dams, drilling bore holes, increasing simple irrigation facilities, planting shelter belts of gum trees, and carrying out a variety of other improvements.

The foregoing list of projects on which Mr. Travers has spent his hard-earned money includes several which indicate his deep concern with water supply.

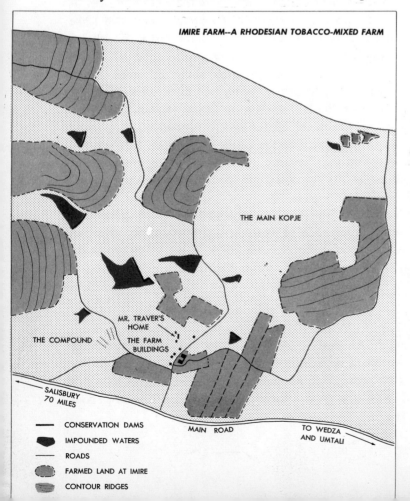

IMIRE FARM--A RHODESIAN TOBACCO-MIXED FARM

THE MAIN KOPJE

MR. TRAVER'S HOME

THE COMPOUND   THE FARM BUILDINGS

SALISBURY 70 MILES

CONSERVATION DAMS

IMPOUNDED WATERS

ROADS

FARMED LAND AT IMIRE

CONTOUR RIDGES

MAIN ROAD

TO WEDZA AND UMTALI

Having found Rhodesia on a good map of Africa, locate the cities of Salisbury and Umtali. You can tell a good deal about the relief of Imire by examining the contour ridges on the cultivated areas. Estimate what proportion of the whole farm can be classed as cultivated land.

Rainfall is by far the most important climatic concern of the people who live in this area; in addition, the elevation of the land is an important factor in determining how much rain any part of the African veld will receive. The rainy season is from mid-November to late March and all cropping takes place during that period. At times the rains may be late in starting or there may be an interruption in mid-season. Either of these occurrences can mean disaster unless a farmer has made adequate preparation. Imire averages about 36 inches of rain a year; but averages are particularly misleading in this part of the world, for Mr. Travers has experienced years with 55 inches and 12 inches respectively. One area not far away received only 12 inches of rain a year for four consecutive years.

Up here on the High Veld temperatures would be described as subtropical. Fresh, sunny mornings are followed by days which are hot from ten a.m. until about three p.m. and are then followed by delightfully cool evenings. The low humidity makes life particularly comfortable here and temperatures never become intolerably high. April to November is described as winter, but this term can be quite misleading in spite of the few nights in August when a ground frost may occur. During September and October temperatures rise fairly steadily, the land becomes parched, and dust prevails everywhere until the November rains bring welcome relief.

The land Mr. Travers found at Imire was a large area of flat-to-rolling country of essentially sandy soils, broken in many places by hilly granite outcrops called *kopjes* and by several *ruwares* (flat granite slabs). The land was covered by a variety of grasses (described as sweet, mixed, or sour depending on their quality). Standing out of the tall grass and above bare, rocky patches were acacia, msasa, and mnondo trees, which tend to be more stunted and closely packed together in the drier areas. Much of the land is still unaltered. Farmers in this part of the world take many years to organize their farms, but seldom a year

Below is a view of the main kopje today. Throughout Imire, a scene such as this confronted Mr. Travers on his arrival there.

Association of Agriculture, Great Brit

passes without a major addition to the farm. Already Mr. Travers has opened up 9 miles of sandy but well-drained road, and has fenced 9 of the 10 miles of boundary to his property; he has also built 21 more miles of barbed-wire fence within Imire itself. His water-conservation schemes provide a capacity of over 80 million gallons. He has contoured several large fields by building a series of small parallel ridges that prevent rapid run-off and either allow the rain water to soak into the soil or else lead it off to a selected area.

Imire is a tobacco farm. This statement requires some qualification, however, as only 200 acres are planted in tobacco each year. Such a figure may seem small, but in view of the enormous hand labour that it demands, it is really considerable. Planted in November and December in seed beds that have been treated with fertilizer and insecticide, the seedlings are shaded from the sun by cheesecloth and grass mulching. Through this they are watered 2 or 3 times a day for a few weeks. Gradually the covering is raised and watering reduced until the tobacco is ready for transplanting. The land to be used for the young plants has already been carefully fumigated and the transplanting is then done by hand. Various operations are completed as the young plant grows, until, beginning in January, leaves of uniform size and ripeness begin to be picked. These are then tied to sticks and placed in the barns for curing.

In the early days of growth, tobacco on Imire takes about 50,000 gallons of water per acre. Mr. Travers' irrigation pipes are such that they can be moved easily by tractor. In spite of all this work, occasionally a whole tobacco crop will be ruined by hail. Most of the farmers insure against this; sometimes they even get a bonus by *ratooning*, that is, by cutting off damaged leaves and allowing the tobacco still to grow—in addition to collecting insurance.

At one time, Mr. Travers also grew corn, but since he found that it was taking too much nutrition out of his soil, he has abandoned this crop. The rotation he follows is this: one year of tobacco, four years of improved pasture, then another year of tobacco. In order to grow 200 acres of tobacco each year, to how many acres of farm land must Mr. Travers give attention? The answer is concerned with those four years of pasture in the rotation cycle. The availability of so much pasture encouraged Mr. Travers to go into the livestock business. He now has 2 pedigree Friesian bulls and 80 medium quality Friesian milking cows; as a result, he is able to sell 180 gallons of milk a day to a company in Salisbury. Every week each of these animals is put through a *race*, or bath, to keep down ticks and other insects. The same treatment is given to beef cattle, which in this country take longer to reach maturity and to fatten than in the major meat-supplying regions of the world. Mr. Travers will buy approximately 100 ranch steers about 3 years old and merely fatten them for the market, thus easing the load of work that a full-scale beef herd would involve. All cattle are kept outdoors throughout the year. The best time to sell cattle is in October at the end of the dry season. Prices are lowest in March. Explain why this is so.

Most farmers on this part of the veld do not keep sheep because of the danger of ticks and other parasites that could easily contaminate the water supply. At Imire there are over 250 breeding ewes; about 120 6-month-old lambs are, therefore, sold each year. Merino, Dorset Horn, Blackhead Persian, and other breeds have been used by Travers to develop a breed adapted to the climatic conditions prevailing at Imire. So far he has had a measure of success in selling his male lambs in October each year and keeping the ewes for breeding. The chief grazing land for the sheep is the drier pastures where there is no danger of foot rot; however, by the use of electric fences they can also be grazed on the better pastures after the dairy herd has used them. Hitherto the sheep have been poor sources of wool, but the aim is still to have a dual-purpose animal on this farm. There is no law in Rhodesia compelling the regular dipping of sheep; nevertheless, on Imire they are all dosed for worms and fluke every month.

Imire has changed greatly since 1946. Formerly unclaimed and unwanted land, it now supports a native village or compound of nearly 150 workers. These have come from Nyasaland, Mozambique, or native reserves; some have come from other farms. All the machinery and equipment on the farm is administered by a coloured engineer who has special accommodation in keeping with his office. Most of the homes in the compound are now of brick, although some natives still prefer the dagga hut in spite of the fact that it seldom lasts more than 7 years. There is even a store in the compound. In addition to his wages, each worker in Imire receives a house, half an acre of land for his personal cultivation, rations, medical care, schooling, and clothes. At certain times of the year women and children will voluntarily accompany the men to the tobacco field; each of them is then paid his or her own wages. Mr. Travers also extends credit to his workers and many of them have thus been enabled to buy their own bicycles. Problems, of course, still exist. Most of the Africans have difficulty in settling down in one place and every year a very large number move off to another part of the country. Even improved conditions and higher wages are of no avail in inducing these people to stay.

The Travers family—there are two sons and one daughter—now occupy a brick bungalow, which has a pleasant stoep or verandah along the front. Their garden, with its lawn and flower beds, is very attractive; nearby stand two thatched rondavels (round houses) which are simply one-room guest units. All the buildings have been proofed against ants. Mrs. Travers is a very energetic Rhodesian, who, in addition to her household and gardening tasks, also teaches her children and supervises their correspondence courses every morning. When old enough, they will go to boarding school in Salisbury. Mr. Travers, his manager, and the other white workers begin work each day about 5 a.m. Their day is a heavy one, with all the farm activities to plan and supervise—particularly whenever a large number of women and children are required in the fields. Work on this scale would be impossible without mechanical help; accordingly, among the thousands of dollars of equipment on Imire there are now five tractors, one of which is of the heavy caterpillar type.

The pools created by the dams play a conspicuous role in the life of the farm. The purposes they fulfil include a supply of drinking water for cattle, irrigation water for crops, and water for the natives to bathe and wash clothes in. These pools also serve to raise the underground water table. However, in their relaxed moments Mr. Travers and his workers like to fish there for the bream and bass with which they have been stocked.

In spite of the drought, the rough veld bush can easily grow out of control and ruin good pasture. Periodic burning can control this threat, and it is also recommended as a precaution against veld fires similar to the wild forest fires that break out here in Canada. For this reason, a fireguard of burned land about 30 yards wide is usually kept clear around the edge of each farm and along the fringe of fields that are being cultivated.

This photograph of Sarowe, Bamangwato, shows that the meagre rainfall of savanna regions is insufficient to support a forest cover.

United Kingdom Information Service

4 THE TROPICAL AND SUBTROPICAL STEPPES

United Kingdom Information Service

Months	J	F	M	A	M	J	J	A	S	O	N	D	YEAR
Temp.	70	81	89	94	96	91	84	82	82	85	83	77	85
Precip.	0.0	0.0	0.0	0.0	0.6	3.9	8.3	8.3	5.6	1.9	0.3	0.2	29.1

TROPICAL STEPPE CLIMATIC DATA FOR KAYES, SUDAN REPUBLIC

Months	J	F	M	A	M	J	J	A	S	O	N	D	YEAR
Temp.	55	57	63	66	72	75	78	79	78	75	66	59	69
Precip.	3.7	1.8	0.7	0.1	0.1	0.0	0.0	0.0	0.1	0.3	2.1	3.1	11.9

SUBTROPICAL STEPPE CLIMATIC DATA FOR BENGHAZI, LIBYA

1. Construct climatic graphs for the above stations. Mark on them the latitude of each.

237

2. Compare the climate of the two stations under the following headings: temperature—annual range and annual average; precipitation—amount and distribution.

3. Consult the diagrams for the climatic types and attempt to explain the difference in precipitation distribution for the two stations.

4. Account for the difference in the annual average temperatures and annual range of temperatures.

5. With 29.1 inches for the year, Kayes appears to have a sufficient amount of moisture for agriculture. Explain why this rainfall is actually insufficient.

6. Explain the causes of the drought conditions in both climatic types.

7. In an atlas locate these climatic types and note their relationship to desert areas.

Tropical and subtropical steppes are areas of meagre rainfall, long periods of drought, and high average temperatures. They are located along the margins of tropical deserts, by whose arid climates they are greatly influenced. They are, however, different from desert insofar as they receive sufficient moisture to grow a sparse vegetation cover of grass and shrubs. This vegetation will support, at least in the wet season, herds of sheep and camels. To distinguish the steppes that lie on the equatorial side of the desert from those that are found on the poleward side, the term *tropical* is used to describe the former and *subtropical* the latter. Along the east coasts of some regions, these two types of steppe sometimes merge because of the influence of ocean currents and wind systems, e.g., Australia's easterly coastal areas.

These two climatic types are, accordingly, grouped together, for they are similar in many respects. Despite the fact that the tropical steppe has rain at a different time of the year, the net result is very much the same. In general there is an insufficient supply of moisture with the result the vegetation is sparse and the soil highly alkaline.

Climate

Because of its proximity to the equator, the tropical steppe has a higher annual average temperature than the subtropical. It receives its rain during the period of high sun largely because of convectional activity. The rainfall is usually heavier in the tropical steppe than the subtropical, but it is more quickly evaporated and, therefore, less able to support vegetation. The drought of summer is caused partly by the migration of the sun's rays, and consequently of the rainfall, towards the opposite hemisphere. The subtropical high-pressure cells migrate towards the equator as well, and hence extend their drought conditions into this area.

The subtropical steppe has a much cooler average temperature but the annual range is greater. This difference is due to its higher latitude, which also accounts for the difference in the seasons. The maximum of rain falls during the period of low sun as the westerlies blow over this area and bring cyclonic storms. During the period of high sun the westerlies migrate poleward and the shifting high-pressure systems extend their influence over the steppe. Owing to the lower annual temperatures, the rate of evaporation is not as great here, and plants can, therefore, grow with less precipitation than in the tropical steppe.

Vegetation

One of the results of the lack of moisture is the nature of the vegetation cover, which consists mainly of drought-resistant grasses and shrubs. The grasses of the steppes are coarse; moreover, along the margin of the true desert, they often grow singly or in clumps with considerable stretches of bare ground between plants. When the rains occur, they shoot up quickly to a height varying from a few inches to several feet; they rapidly mature, the blades becoming stiff and knife-edged. Then, as the dry season approaches, the grasses dry out, turn brown, and wither to the ground.

The shrubs which grow here are collectively known as *chaparral* and consist of a community of plants, both evergreen and deciduous, which seldom grow taller than two or three feet. The most commonly known species are sage, mesquite, buckthorn, and mallee.

Soil

The soils found here are of an intermediate type between the true desert soils and the laterites of the tropics. Because of the lack of moisture and sparse plant coverage, these soils are usually deficient in humus but high in soluble salts. The zone of accumulation is very close to the surface, and, in fact, appears on the surface, where water-filled depressions, or *sloughs*, dry up and leave a coating of salt on the ground. In some areas this accumulation of alkaline salts is so great that it destroys all but a few species of plants. When steppe land is irrigated, it usually produces good crops, but a constant vigil must be kept to see that the salinity does not rise above the danger level. This type of soil is known by several names: brown steppe, chestnut-brown, seirozem, and *red-brown*. The latter term is used here to indicate the presence of iron oxide (red) and a slight amount of humus (brown).

A feature of this soil which is similar to the red lateritic soil of the savanna region is the presence of *hardpan*. This is the accumulation of salts slightly below the surface in the dry season. These minerals cement the soil particles together and make it almost impossible to plant crops during the dry season. Most of this climatic region supports only migrant people who live off their herds. In some cases permanent settlement can be accomplished with the aid of irrigation.

Fauna

These steppe areas support some of the largest herds of grazing animals to be found anywhere in the world. The species which inhabit this area are essentially the same as those found in the savanna region, with the exception of the giraffe and other animals which live off the foliage of trees. Elephants and lions are not commonly found here either, but they are seen occasionally. The region is inhabited by several species of deer, by large birds such as the ostrich and the emu, by the hyena and the dingo, and also by that most peculiar of animals, the kangaroo.

As a result of the sparser vegetation a wide variety of small animals inhabits this climatic zone. The rabbit, when introduced into Australia, proved remarkably able to adapt itself to the conditions existing there. The fox, rat, wild pig, and badger are some of the other animals found in steppe areas. Most of the smaller animals have adapted their habits to suit their environment; thus, they burrow holes to protect themselves from the fierce sun and are mainly nocturnal. The larger grazing animals migrate across the steppe with the seasonal rainfall.

The tropical grasslands are often suitable for rough pasture. Here we see ranchers visiting a section of range in Western Bechuanaland.

United Kingdom Information Service

Tropical and Subtropical Climates

1 THE TROPICAL DESERT

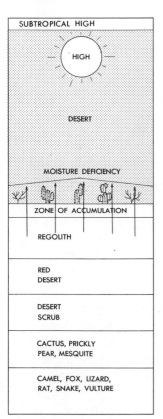

SUBTROPICAL HIGH

HIGH

DESERT

MOISTURE DEFICIENCY

ZONE OF ACCUMULATION

REGOLITH

RED
DESERT

DESERT
SCRUB

CACTUS, PRICKLY
PEAR, MESQUITE

CAMEL, FOX, LIZARD,
RAT, SNAKE, VULTURE

U.S.D.A. Photo

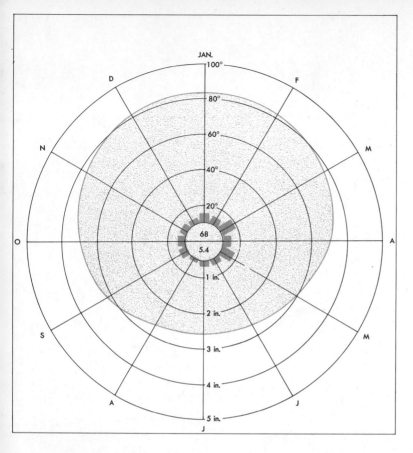

This type of climatic graph may be more representative of the actual conditions found in a region than is the conventional type, as there is no distinct break in the twelve-month cycle. What is the annual temperature range? 110° F. is often recorded in desert areas. Why does the graph not reflect these high temperatures?

Months	J	F	M	A	M	J	J	A	S	O	N	D	YEAR
Temp.	83	83	76	67	59	54	52	56	62	70	77	81	68
Precip.	0.5	0.4	0.8	0.4	0.4	0.7	0.3	0.3	0.4	0.3	0.4	0.3	5.4

CLIMATIC DATA FOR WILLIAM CREEK, AUSTRALIA

The tropical deserts are generally located outside the tropics of Cancer and Capricorn. A check of a world climatic map will reveal that the Sahara, Arabian, Thar, Mexican, Great Australian, Kalahari, and Atacama deserts are all closely related to these imaginary lines of latitude. The relationship between these is primarily one of air pressure.

Climate

The air which was forced to rise at the equator must eventually sink back to earth. Part of this air settles at the subtropical highs and part of it continues onward to settle elsewhere. When this settling occurs, the resultant effect is exactly opposite to that which is experienced at the equator. The air descends from a cold region to a warmer one and hence absorbs water instead of precipitating it.

This air, being relatively cool, is considerably more dense than the surrounding air; it, therefore, tends to spread out and push the lighter air before it. This outflow of air is known as the *trades* on the equatorial side of the high-pressure systems, and as the *westerlies* on the poleward side.

Because of the high rate of evaporation, there are very few clouds formed over desert areas. Occasionally the land heats to such a point that convection currents form clouds and may even cause precipitation. In many cases, evaporation occurs so quickly that the rain is reabsorbed by the air before it reaches the ground. When rains do occur, they are usually torrential and last only a short time.

The graph of this climate indicates that there are two fairly distinct seasons, one hot and dry, the other warm and dry. What the graph does not show is the *diurnal* range of temperature; that is, the difference between night and day. Because of the lack of clouds, insolation is extremely high during the day and radiation occurs rapidly at night. This may result in a daytime temperature of 110° F. and a nighttime temperature as low as 30° F. This gives an average of 70°, which is slightly misleading. This great diurnal range does not occur in all places, or at all times, as the amounts of insolation and radiation are influenced by ocean currents, humidity, etc. A temperature of 136.4° F. in the shade is one of the highest ever recorded. This occurred near Tripoli in North Africa.

Deserts are more commonly found along the west coasts of continents. Here the dryness is accentuated by the cold currents which flow along these shores. Along most west coasts, the ocean currents flow from the poles towards the equator. Onshore winds, crossing this cold current, pick up very little moisture. When they reach the land, they are heated by radiation and condensation very seldom occurs. This warming causes an increase in evaporation, and hence drier conditions.

Vegetation

Of necessity, the vegetation of desert regions is sparse and found only in particularly favoured places such as along stream beds or where there is a source of underground water. Desert plants have had to adapt themselves to their environment to a greater extent, perhaps, than any other type of vegetation. The adaptation is essentially one of attempting to obtain and conserve moisture. This is done in several ways.

The cactus family, of which the saguaro is the largest, sends out a fine mesh of shallow roots so that water can be absorbed and stored in the pulp of the plant.

The skin of these plants is very thick to prevent loss of moisture; its corrugated exterior allows for expansion and contraction so that it can take advantage of torrential but unreliable rains. Many of the other perennial plants store water in huge tubers which they develop on their root system. This necessitates a dying back of their foliage in dry periods to prevent moisture loss. Such a plant is the bi of the Kalahari and the night-blooming cereus of North America.

Those plants which develop leaves either lose them during prolonged periods of drought or have a very thick leathery exterior. Along the stream beds, larger bushes such as the mesquite, ocotillo, and the occasional acacia or palm tree send roots down as far as 30 feet to take advantage of all available moisture.

Another interesting adaptation of desert plants to their environment is the practice of the so-called annuals of growing, blooming, producing a new crop of seeds, and dying—all within the space of a few weeks. The procreation of the plant species is thus ensured, for the seeds develop a hard outer shell which prevents drying out and which can preserve the seed for several years. This is essential in an environment which may receive two or three heavy rains in one year and then be completely devoid of precipitation for three or four years. Among this latter group are the sand verbenas, desert daisies, and purple nama.

Soil

The soils of tropical deserts are very high in soluble salts, because, owing to the lack of moisture, they have undergone very little leaching. Their colour is closely related to that of the parent rock, but in general, they are light coloured. Reds, browns, yellows, and greys are all apparent, and their light texture is accentuated by the accumulation of lime and salt near the surface. In very arid regions, no vegetation grows, little rainfall occurs, and the soil profile does not develop to any extent. These are the regions of sand dunes and rock outcrops. In slightly moister areas, the soil is often cemented together by soluble salts; playas are in evidence and reg surfaces cover much of the area.

The dreaded d e s e r t sandstorm such as this one of the 1930's may carry dust for several hundred miles. What harmful effects can such a storm have?

U.S.D.A. Photo

Agriculture is possible, under irrigation, where the salinity of the soil is not too high. Most of the soluble salts are present in desert sands, but because of the lack of vegetation, nitrates often have to be added. Farmers in such areas may have to contend with encroaching dunes, prolonged drought, a high salt content in the soil, or an invasion of locusts. All in all, it is a very precarious type of existence.

Fauna

The parched stillness of a desert noonday may give the impression that no life exists in this forbidding sea of heated sand and rock. This is far from the truth, however, for many species of animals are to be found here. In most cases, they have adapted their habits to suit the desert cycle. The first and most notice-able adaptation of the animals is that they are almost all nocturnal. Secondly, they are nearly all burrowing animals, or have fashioned their lair to protect them against the sun's rays.

The animal life is almost completely dependent on vegetation for its livelihood. With the coming of a heavy rain, eggs of insects and animals alike hatch, and beetles, ants, wasps, moths, and locusts begin to feed on the desert vegetation. After a few short weeks, the vegetation shrivels up; the insects mature and lay their eggs, which may lie dormant for several more years. Shrimp eggs have been known to hatch in a playa which had been dry for 25 years. Frogs, toads, and salamanders feed on these insects, but with the onset of drought, they dig into the mud to begin a period of *estivation* until the next rain occurs.

The reptiles—lizards, tortoises, and snakes—are best suited to desert con-ditions, for they have developed tough scales or plated skin which resists drying. Their eggs are deposited in damp soil and the young emerge with a built-in coat of armour. The larger animals such as the deer and rabbit overcome the desert heat by migration. The carnivorous group are nearly all burrowing animals and include the fox, badger, and skunk.

The Bindibu

In the Great Sandy Desert of Western Australia lives a small tribe of aborigines, the Bindibu, who remained practically unknown to white men until the past few years. These people live in the most arid parts of Australia's huge *dead heart* under conditions where few animals or even plants survive and where there may occur a drought of several years and then a huge violent downpour of rain.

In 1957, using jeeps and Land Rovers, Donald Thomson led an expedition to locate and study the Bindibu; the men found, however, that in many ways camels would have been preferable. Their vehicles had to steer between dunes, for the jeeps and Rovers were unable to cross them; yet an earlier expedition using camels had crossed as many as 107 dunes in one day. Of course, the jeep does not require much water; but to offset this was the fact that fuel consumption of a loaded jeep was often as much as a gallon per 5 miles.

From May till August is the coolest part of the year in the Australian desert and these are, therefore, the best months for expeditions. On the way across the semidesert, the travellers encountered *mulga*, a type of coarse thicket vegetation. Mulga can be almost impenetrable, growing as it does to 15 feet in height and having thin, sharp-pointed leaves which reduce transpiration but which can tear clothing and damage equipment. The wood of these low trees is extremely hard; indeed, broken branches leave tough jagged points which can ruin tires. Stifling heat and dust make movement in the mulga even less pleasant.

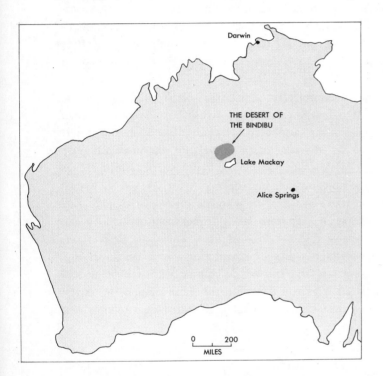

The map shows us the general location of the remote desert home of the Bindibu.

To the travellers, the bright sun and clear vistas of the true desert presented a sharp contrast to the mulga. However, the absence of animals and birds resulted in a silence which quickly became oppressive. Variety does exist in the desert. Over wide areas there is a covering of clumps of tough, grey spinifex grasses, each blade of which is needle sharp. These clumps make a jeep toss like a ship in heavy seas. Worse still are patches of loose sand and shifting dunes into which vehicles rapidly sink above the axles. An occasional desert oak or beefwood tree is a welcome sight, but the shade these give is negligible, for their long narrow leaves turn to present their thin edge to the sun at all times. Broken limbs and

246

branches of these trees are very hard and do not rot quickly owing to the aridity. However, this meant for the travellers that gathering timber for fires was not as difficult as might appear.

Water is the liquid gold of this region and is the principal determinant of life. On calm nights dew was so heavy that members of the expedition had to cover their blankets with heavy waterproof canvas. Washing was a luxury reserved for days spent at water holes. The water holes themselves are of various types and are usually carefully looked after by roving Bindibu. In one locality in an outcrop of granite there is a great fissure 17 yards long which contains a great mass of sand and silt. Underneath the sand is a hard impervious layer and water has, therefore, collected in the loose, porous sand. At a depth of about 11 feet in the fissure are three separate wells with toe holds carved in the rock to facilitate climbing. The water in these wells is often hard and mineralized.

Close to each water hole there was evidence of a Bindibu camp. This revealed that each family occupied a separate site and that all the sites were as close together as conditions permitted. As a windbreak, a low semicircular wall of bush about 2 feet high had been built. On low wispy mulga trees, rough platforms of bush and branches had been constructed to provide shade for women and children and to act as racks for their meagre belongings.

The Bindibu in their harsh environment lacking a cyclic rhythm of seasons, are essentially collectors. It was a surprise to find that these people do not lead a simple hand-to-mouth existence. Although the Bindibu are the most primitive tribe in Australia, and perhaps in the world, they have advanced to the point where they build up reserves of dried vegetables and prepared seeds and pastes. Even in drought years they are able to collect small seeds from which they make an edible and sufficiently nutritious food. It is interesting that the seeds of many of these plants are poisonous; yet these people have acquired the knowledge to be able to collect only those which are safe.

All Bindibu tools and utensils are of stone or wood. The men's spears and women's digging sticks are carefully shaped and hardened over fire. Their yandandakko is an important multipurpose utensil cut from the natural elbow of a gum or mulga tree and hollowed out before being finished with a stone axe. This shallow trough is used for digging, carrying food and water, cradling an infant, and also, when inverted, resting the head on. This, indeed, is their only real utensil. Without any of the rope or twine which many primitive peoples use, the Bindibu make out of two strands of acacia bark slings to carry their children. Sinews which have been chewed to bring pliancy are used to repair spears that have cracked; however these people take the utmost care of their spears and other wooden objects.

Being a nomadic people, the Bindibu have a number of camps located beside the dispersed water holes beyond Lake Mackay. Two or three families will use a camp at the same time and then move on together. Nearby there is always a special camp for the young men. In the lee of the brush windbreaks already described, can be seen a number of shallow, gravelike depressions—one for each member of the family. Fires are maintained at night between each two of these beds. Close to the water hole at each camp there is a large flat slab of sandstone, their millstone, together with a smaller topstone nearby.

The Bindibu, though perhaps smaller than the other aboriginal tribes of Australia, are a hardy, well-built people, long in the limbs and heavy of shoulder. They are a dark-skinned people whose hair may be straight or wavy but never curly. The men wear thick beards. For clothing they wear only a primitive belt in which the men carry their throwing sticks when hunting—throwing sticks which do not, like boomerangs of other tribes, return to the thrower. Shyness is no problem with these people, for they rapidly became friendly with the members of Thomson's expedition. A happy, talkative people they held several *corroborees* or parties at which they performed their music—singing to the accompaniment of rhythmic hand clapping.

This wiry, self-reliant Bindibu thrives in an area where few people could survive.

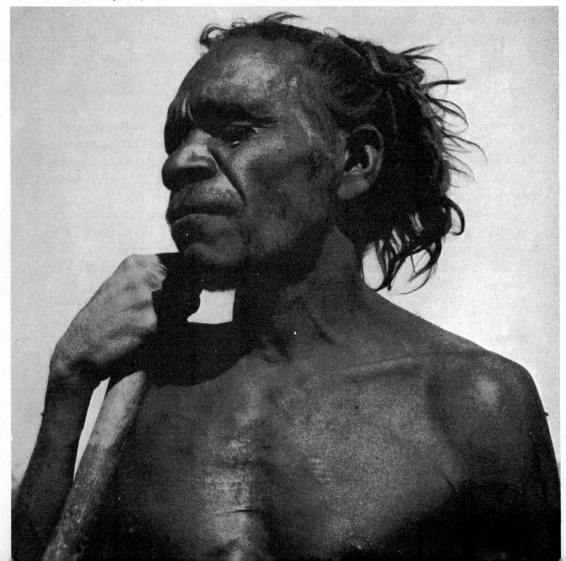

A Bindibu wannagudo or shade shelter is made of mulga branches. Why is it necessary? How would you describe the landmark in the background?

Something has already been said about the food that these people manage to find in their harsh environment. In addition to the vegetation and seeds, the Bindibu also eat pigeons, cockatoos, and budgerigars, all of which they kill with throwing sticks at the water holes. Deep in the sand they sometimes find frogs; and along the edge of the dunes, which often reach heights of over 40 feet, they catch various species of lizards, rodents, and similar small creatures. Feral cats— a type of wild domestic cat—are occasionally encountered in this remote area and are regarded as a delicacy by the Bindibu. After the sudden downpours of rain which are so welcome but so rare in this part of the world, clay pans in the stony desert fill up with water and attract kangaroos and emus. These creatures never enter the land of the dunes, but when they come into the desert zone, the Bindibu take the opportunity to build up a rich larder. Nothing is wasted of such a kill, even the bones being split to yield their precious marrow.

Life in the desert is simple. Early in the morning the young men set off to hunt while the women and small children move out to sit in the sun. During the day the women may set out to collect vegetables, lizards, or similar small animals. Another division of labour between the sexes among these simple people is the leaving of all woodworking and the use of stone implements entirely to the men, whereas the collecting and preparing of slings is woman's work.

The contented efficiency of these people impressed the members of the expedition, who at different times found the silence, the *furnace* heat, the loneliness, and the dark swirling sandstorms almost more than they could bear in spite of all their modern skills and equipment.

2 THE MEDITERRANEAN ENVIRONMENT

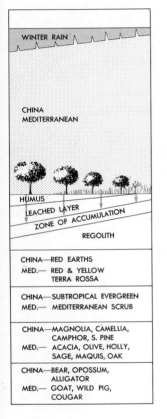

WINTER RAIN

CHINA
MEDITERRANEAN

HUMUS
LEACHED LAYER
ZONE OF ACCUMULATION
REGOLITH

CHINA—RED EARTHS
MED.— RED & YELLOW
TERRA ROSSA

CHINA—SUBTROPICAL EVERGREEN
MED.— MEDITERRANEAN SCRUB

CHINA—MAGNOLIA, CAMELLIA,
CAMPHOR, S. PINE
MED.— ACACIA, OLIVE, HOLLY,
SAGE, MAQUIS, OAK

CHINA—BEAR, OPOSSUM,
ALLIGATOR
MED.— GOAT, WILD PIG,
COUGAR

Italian Trade Commissioner, Toronto

Months	J	F	M	A	M	J	J	A	S	O	N	D
Temp.	45	50	54	59	67	75	82	80	73	64	54	46
Precip.	4.6	3.9	3.2	1.7	1.1	0.5	0.0	0.1	0.8	1.3	2.9	4.3

CLIMATIC DATA FOR RED BLUFF, CALIFORNIA

Construct a graph for this climatic type similar to that shown for the desert climate and answer the following questions:

1. When does this climatic type receive its maximum of rainfall? Which other type received rain during this season? What is the cause of this seasonal maximum for the second climatic type?

2. What is the annual average temperature and annual rainfall for this station?

250

3. Judging from the graph you have constructed, what are the main characteristics of Mediterranean climate?

4. Which climatic area that you have studied would you expect to have similar vegetation to that found in this region?

5. At which season will the greatest diurnal temperature range be experienced?

Mediterranean climate obtains on the west coasts of continents because of the prevailing systems of wind and pressure belts. California, South Africa, central Chile, southern Australia, and the countries bordering the Mediterranean sea—all these experience this type of climate. A glance at a world climatic map will show that most regions with this climate lie between 30 and 40 degrees of latitude in both hemispheres. This places the Mediterranean type of climate in a relationship similar to that of the high-pressure area of the horse latitudes with respect to the savanna climate.

Climate

The characteristics of this climate are summer drought and winter rain. Lying just poleward of the high-pressure systems, the regions of Mediterranean climate are influenced by these systems in summer. At this time of year, the gradual outflow of dry air brings drought conditions to these regions. In winter the subtropical high-pressure cells migrate equatorwards and the westerlies are allowed to penetrate the area. These bring rain and are the chief source of moisture for Mediterranean regions. Two other factors that are influential in locating this climatic type along the west coast are the cool offshore currents and the drying winds. The winds of summer are usually light, variable, and outflows from the high-pressure area, and being offshore, they have very little moisture content. Any onshore winds, crossing the cold current, will increase the dryness of the region.

Because these regions lie some distance from the equator, the amount of insolation varies considerably between winter and summer. This results in a marked difference in temperatures between these two seasons. Also, the lack of cloud coverage in summer is conducive to higher temperatures, whereas the cloudiness of winter shuts out much of the sun's heat. In all cases, the average winter temperature is above freezing, and usually approaches the 45° F. mark. Frosts are extremely rare but are very damaging to crops when they do occur. The summers are hot and dry with average temperatures approaching 80° F., and the conditions are remarkably similar to subtropical steppe, or even desert, climates.

Vegetation

Just as the climatic influences of the horse latitudes are felt in the savanna in summer and the Mediterranean in winter, so does the type of vegetation found along the poleward margins of this high-pressure belt bear a resemblance to the parkland of the savanna. The grass and chaparral growth of the subtropical steppe gives way to stunted, open forests of oak, olive, eucalyptus, and citrus trees. These plants, in contrast to the parkland trees, do not lose their leaves during any particular season. Instead they have adopted other means of combating the long drought of summer.

The olive tree has an extensive root system which allows it to collect moisture over a wide area. The leaves are thick and leathery and the bark rough and deep. These are adaptations which prevent drying out in summer. The cork oak has a similar appearance but has a bark which may be 3 or 4 inches thick. Other species of trees have very few leaves but have substituted thorns to perform the function of leaves. The ground is usually covered with a sparse growth of grass or dusty-coloured bush vegetation. In drier areas or regions of thin soil, the forest gives way to chaparral or *maqui* growth, which has been described under the chapter on steppe climates. One of the most important aspects of the vegetation of this area is the large number of plants which have been successfully cultivated. These include the oranges, lemons, etc., of the citrus family, the olive, the fig, and the grape.

Soil

The red and yellow soils of Mediterranean areas are a curious combination, for they are leached by the winter rains, dried by the heat of summer, and enriched by the slow but continuous dropping of leaves. The rains are not heavy enough to leach the soils to any great depth. The evaporation in summer brings some of the soluble salts to the surface again. The humus content, and hence the supply of acid for leaching, is low.

The result is a relatively fertile soil, most of the minerals necessary for plant growth being present in some quantity. The *terra rossa*, or red soils, are the result of a slight amount of oxidation of the iron in the soil. The yellow soils are more highly leached and owe their colouring to slightly different iron oxides plus some aluminum compounds.

These soils all require a certain amount of irrigation if they are to produce the crops which they are capable of growing. Too much cropping quickly uses up the organic matter and the soils become susceptible to rapid erosion during the winter rains. Mediterranean soils must be carefully husbanded and fertilized if they are to remain fertile and capable of growing crops. The summer drought, while aiding in the retention of soluble minerals, also prevents the accumulation of humus, which tends to hold the soil together. A comparison of the lush orchards of the California valley with the denuded and barren slopes of Sicily serves as a good illustration of what mismanagement of the soil can do.

Fauna

In many areas of this climatic type the wildlife has nearly all disappeared or become domesticated by man. Where animal life is found, it consists of medium-sized deer, prong-horned antelope, sheep, goats, rabbits, foxes, and many species of birds and insects. Generally speaking, the dry summers, the tough vegetation, and the open bushland are not conducive to a suitable habitat for wildlife.

It would appear, however, that we owe much to Mediterranean regions, for they have provided us with mules for beasts of burden, sheep to produce wool, goats for leather and milk, and hens to produce eggs and meat. All species of these animals did not originate here; but early civilizations along the Mediterranean Sea led the way in the domestication of these animals.

Vasilika

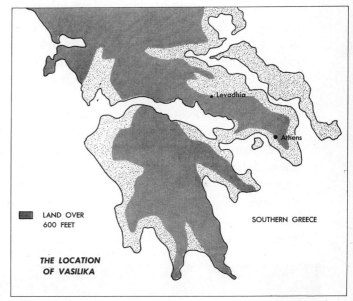

Greece is a land of promontories and peaks, mountain ranges and narrow inlets. Vasilika stands near Levadhia in the mountainous interior but is not remote from the influence of the Mediterranean.

LAND OVER
600 FEET

SOUTHERN GREECE

**THE LOCATION
OF VASILIKA**

About ninety miles northeast of Athens lies the little Greek village of Vasilika with a population of less than 300 people and a setting and a way of life that are repeated time after time in little settlements around the Mediterranean Sea. The visitor travelling by bus to Vasilika might at first be puzzled by the fact that the signpost at the corner of the dirt road points to Kravasaras, and many of the older women in the village also use this Turkish name, a reminder of the centuries of Turkish occupation. This continuance of a double nomenclature is common throughout these lands.

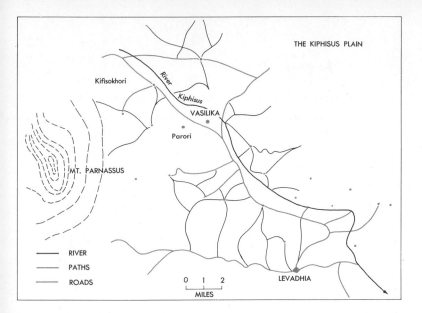

THE KIPHISUS PLAIN

Kifisokhori

River Kiphisus

VASILIKA

Parori

MT. PARNASSUS

RIVER
PATHS
ROADS

0   1   2
MILES

LEVADHIA

Most of the settlements shown here are many centuries old, as are the tracks between them. These mountain-girt valleys often blend the very old with the new quite successfully.

The plain in which Vasilika stands is drained by the Kiphisus river, but the fact that most of the plain is developed on limestone means that the river flow is often seriously affected by underground drainage. At times, silt blocks some of the subterranean channels and results in widespread flooding, especially during the period of the winter rains for which no special drainage channels have been prepared. Winter flooding is a subject of concern in Vasilika, but the alluvium carried by the flood-waters does benefit the farmlands. The village itself stands on a low ridge about half a mile from the main two-lane road, one of the few paved roads in the valley. Breaking the flat green and brown surface of the plain are occasional clumps of mulberry trees, numerous little grey- or orange-coloured villages and, framing the whole scene, the magnificent peaks of the surrounding mountain ranges. Mt. Parnassus towers over Vasilika to a height of over 8,060 feet.

Here you are looking over Vasilika's roof tops towards Pirori and Mt. Parnassus. In which direction is the camera pointing?

Ernestine Friedl

On entering Vasilika, one would find a little haphazard village stretching for about a quarter of a mile along the rough dirt road. The houses and buildings are not in line, but, instead, each one has been built either giving easy access to the street or else facing away from Mt. Parnassus. Outhouses are added on any side of a building, and often a low stone wall is built around the property. From every house, a tiny path leads directly to the road, to another house, or else winds away around various properties until at last it reaches the road. Buildings, too, are of different heights and designs. Most houses are of stucco on a brick frame or of local stone, and the majority of them are of two storeys. Every two-storey home has an outside staircase (there is none inside) leading to the second-storey verandah. Newer buildings have flat, terrazzo roofs, but the village is still dominated by the peaked, red-tile roofs of older buildings. Most people in this village own their homes, and around the larger homes one can see a small cluster composed of a stone-walled oven, a brick latrine, a few windowless store houses, perhaps the low parapet of a stone well, a yard with shady mulberry trees, and sometimes a small vineyard and garden.

The public buildings of the village are grouped close to the road near the west end of the village. Here, amidst a clump of newly planted pines and cypress trees, is the small, new, one-room schoolhouse. The village cemetery and the small church of St. Nicholas are nearby. A little nearer the village itself is the stone church of St. Athanasius, the largest building in Vasilika and the scene of regular Sunday services, weddings, and baptisms. The bell in the church campanile announces school, services, and public meetings. Before the church, lies the *agora* or market place, the scene of business transactions and village celebrations. The bus stop is here, and wandering peddlers and musicians make this the centre of their activities. The village hall stands on one side of the square, a one-room building used by government officials and possessing the village's only telephone. Probably the busiest buildings on the agora are the two tiny coffee houses-cum-stores that are also the homes of their owners. Villagers come here to buy cigarettes, sugar, salt, fish, canned vegetables, aspirins, thread, and other small household articles. The men of the village gather at the tables outside the two coffee houses on summer evenings and during the day in the winter; here they drink coffee or soft drinks, play cards, and discuss local affairs. It is interesting that women do not frequent the agora, but appear there only in passing through.

The pattern of life at Vasilika is one of extremely hard work, but people do not rush. We would find their pace rather slow and leisurely, but it is the pace to which they have long been accustomed. The largest farm here is about 20 acres; 10 acres is considered to be sufficient to support a family, and the running of the farm is the work of every physically able person in the family. As soon as the winter rains are over, the round of a year's work begins with the pruning of the grapes. Every family has between ¼ and ½ an acre of vines, and the pruning is the man's work, hard and back-breaking after the relative relaxation of the winter. When the pruning is finished, the women hoe the vineyard and pile the earth around the short vines. In February and March, the wheat fields have to be hoed and fertilized, and small pumps are used to spray weed killer around the growing cereal. During late March and April, the women work to keep the young tobacco plants free of snails and worms and then transplant them into the fields. Meanwhile, in March, the men plant cotton, using one of the village's two tractors and a mechanical planter. The hardest work of the year is done in May and June when the sun is high, the weather hot and humid, and the cotton fields need thorough hoeing and weeding. The weeds are chopped up and packed around the growing cotton as a mulch. Although no one has more than 5 acres of cotton, this work always requires extra help. Women come in by tractor from adjoining villages to assist in such work.

These women are laboriously hoeing in a Vasilikan field. Suggest reasons for their dressing in this manner.

Ernestine Friedl

Harvests begin in June. During this and the following month, tobacco leaves are picked; then, the women and children occupy spare moments cutting and stringing the tobacco while they sit in the shade of the houses. A combine appears in Vasilika in June and every farmer engages it to reap and thresh the golden harvest of wheat, paying for the service by giving the owner 12% of the crop. Loose chaff and straw is left in the field to be utilized for animal bedding. Every farmer, however, usually keeps about an acre of his wheat for fodder for the horses and donkeys. June and July are months of heat and drought, and during the latter month the men and boys irrigate the growing cotton. This work involves digging and clearing the ditches in which the workers must stand up to their knees in muddy water, often working by lamplight far into the night. Soon, the grape harvest is ready. Men pick and trample the fruit to prepare the must for the new wine. Most families get about two barrels of wine and, after the local chemist has made his analysis, sugar or white alcohol is added and also about 2% of resin bought from travelling dealers. The use of resin in wine dates back to the time. of the Romans when it was used to help preserve the wine, but now the Greeks like its strong taste and reject wines that lack it. As a result, the term *retsina* is used to describe Greek wines. No sooner is the winemaking over than two major tasks have to be undertaken, often simultaneously. Throughout October and November, the ripening cotton is picked by hand (largely women's work), and about the same time the wheat field is ploughed and the seed sown broadcast. This ploughing is usually done by horses unless late seasons delay the work, in which case the farmers will pay for one of the two tractors in the village. Opinion in Vasilika is that while the deeper ploughing of the tractor helps produce a better cotton crop, the shallower ploughing of the horses is adequate for wheat.

In addition to all this activity, every family also tends its own vegetable garden in which beans, onions, spinach, tomatoes, melons, cucumbers, and squash are grown. *Khorta* is a popular vegetable grown along the edge of fields and paths and gathered by women and small children throughout the year. Fig, peach, pear, pomegranate, and quince trees grow in and around the village but they receive little attention other than the picking of the ripe fruit. Every family owns one or two horses and a mule or donkey; these are used in ploughing, as pack animals, and also for riding sidesaddle through the fields. The average family owns 10 to 20 sheep, looked after by a shepherd, who takes them out of the village early every morning in winter but who in summer often moves up to the cooler hills for a few weeks at a time. The sheep are hardy and are raised for wool and also for their milk used in yoghurt and cheese. Sheep are slaughtered only for a special occasion (such as the lamb at Easter), but one dying of age or disease is normally eaten. Goats, one or two to every family, provide most of the meat and also the milk for the villagers. This milk is always boiled before serving and is usually drunk while still warm. The dozen or so chickens kept by most families roam all over the yard and often into the house or out onto the road. Eggs are a popular food, as is the chicken meat. Tied up in each yard is the family dog, but at night the farmer will release it to guard the property. An important point in regard to these animals is the attitude of the people to them. Switches are used to beat them, and the animal is compelled to obey and is seldom treated or spoken of as a friend in the manner common here. Cruelty, however, is very rare.

The women of Vasilika also have the usual chores to perform: washing and ironing, cleaning the home, cooking the meals. Once a week, they will rise at 2 or 3 o'clock in the morning to knead the dough and bake the week's supply of bread.

Ernestine Friedl

Roasting the Paschal lambs is the first step in Vasilika's largest annual celebration. The building in the background has few windows and even these are small. Why are such buildings common in Mediterranean and tropical areas?

Since the introduction of cotton in 1936, Vasilika's economy has become quite complex. Cotton and tobacco are grown as cash crops; wheat meets local needs and also provides a small surplus, and the other crops are for village use. Hired labour is occasionally used during the grape-pruning, when a man will be paid 40 to 60 drachmas a day ($1.50 to $2.00), and during the cotton picking when as many as thirty women may be brought into the village from some distance away. Farming has become quite mechanized, the farmers taking the view that they will use the machine if it will help produce a better crop. Two farmers own tractors, in each case bought with a loan from the Greek Agricultural Bank and then financed by hiring them out to other villagers. Other machinery used in the wheat and cotton industries is brought into the village by companies from adjacent towns and these people always accept payment in kind. The owner of the combine takes 12% of the wheat crop; the analyst, who examines the grapes, must receive payment on the basis of the number of barrels of wine; the cotton-gin operator receives 6% of the cotton crop. Wheat, cotton, and tobacco are also acceptable forms of exchange between villages and even travelling peddlers will accept these in lieu of money. Although cotton is a major source of income, the farmers of Vasilika find that tobacco is their best cash crop and a good yield from 1½ acres of tobacco can bring in as much as $720, a very good income by their standards. However, improved varieties of seed and other improvements can provide a drain on what is already a rather short money supply. In March of each year, the Agricultural Bank of Greece issues its loans so that they are in time for Easter with its celebrations and also for the fertilizing of fields.

The inhabitants of Vasilika resemble those of dozens of little mountain-girt villages throughout the eastern Mediterranean. Twice a day, at 6 a.m. and at noon, a bus passes through to Athens, 90 miles away. Levadhia, fifteen miles away, is the provincial capital and a prosperous town of 12,000 people where Vasilikans change buses on the way to Athens. Kifisokhori is a large village with which Vasilika has close links, and here there are flour mills, grocery stores, doctors, drug stores, a movie house, and even several taxis. The main road through Vasilika is narrow, rutted, and always either dusty or deep in mud. Trucks and buses can only negotiate it slowly and with some difficulty. A mile up the highway is the railway station of Helikon, and the rail fare to Athens is quite cheap even for the rather poor villagers. Of much greater importance in the lives of the villagers is the network of footpaths linking one village with several others and used by practically all the traffic of the district as well as by the postman on his rounds.

The greatest satisfaction for the people of Vasilika is in seeing their children become successful and in leaving them sufficient land and property to live on. Many young men, after completing their military service, take up residence in the cities, but at certain times most of these will return for a family reunion. About thirty children attend a small village school opened in 1959 where they learn Greek reading and writing, arithmetic, geography, history, and something about modern farming methods. A child's success in school is a source of great pride to his or her parents, and the village teacher commands a certain amount of authority in the community. On national holidays, the centre of village life is the village school in which dramatic performances take place after the religious service.

3 THE CHINA CLIMATE

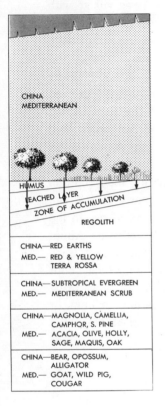

CHINA
MEDITERRANEAN

HUMUS
LEACHED LAYER
ZONE OF ACCUMULATION
REGOLITH

CHINA—RED EARTHS
MED.— RED & YELLOW
TERRA ROSSA

CHINA—SUBTROPICAL EVERGREEN
MED.— MEDITERRANEAN SCRUB

CHINA—MAGNOLIA, CAMELLIA,
CAMPHOR, S. PINE
MED.— ACACIA, OLIVE, HOLLY,
SAGE, MAQUIS, OAK

CHINA—BEAR, OPOSSUM,
ALLIGATOR
MED.— GOAT, WILD PIG,
COUGAR

U.S. Forest Ser

*This stand of longleaf pine in Mississippi grows
in the sandy coastal area.*

Months	J	F	M	A	M	J	J	A	S	O	N	D	YEAR
Temp.	50	52	58	65	73	79	82	81	77	68	58	51	
Precip.	3.0	3.1	3.3	2.4	3.3	5.1	6.2	6.5	5.2	3.7	2.5	3.2	

CLIMATIC DATA FOR CHARLESTON, S.C.

Determine the annual average temperature and total annual precipitation for this city. Also note the annual range of temperatures and the rainfall pattern. Compare your findings with the data for the Mediterranean climatic region. By consulting an atlas, attempt to account for the reversal of the rainfall pattern even though these regions are at approximately the same latitude. How will the difference in annual precipitation affect the vegetation and the soil?

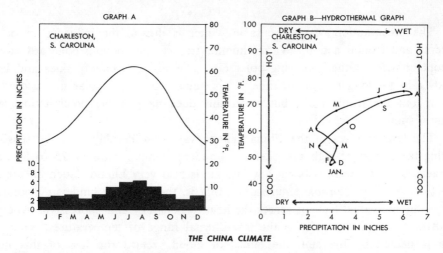

THE CHINA CLIMATE

The graphs shown here are made from the same climatic data. Graph A gives us a picture of the climate and shows the variations in temperature and pressure throughout the twelve months of the year. Graph B expresses a combined temperature and precipitation in terms of their variation throughout the year. This latter graph may be more representative of the climate of an area than the conventional chart presenting one feature over a limited period, for climatology is essentially the study of temperature and precipitation variations over a long period of time.

Climate

This type of climate is found in the southeastern part of the U.S.A. and China in the Northern Hemisphere; it is found in southern Brazil and Uruguay, southeastern Australia, and Africa in the Southern Hemisphere. It is influenced by warm ocean currents, by a monsoonal wind in summer, and by frontal action in winter.

The ocean currents which flow along the east coasts of continents are called warm currents because, in moving poleward, they penetrate relatively cooler waters. These currents, which are caused by the rotation of the earth, have a distinct effect on the climate of eastern shores. Onshore winds, crossing the current, pick up considerable moisture. Heavy rainfall occurs as these winds strike the landmass.

These rains are often carried far inland by the monsoonal winds of summer and so the oceanic effects of the warm currents are quite extensive. The monsoonal winds are actually a poleward extension of the tropical monsoons, though much reduced in strength and influence. These winds are most strongly developed in the U.S.A. and China, but Brazil has a considerable inflow of warm air in the summer. An offshoot of this invasion of air is the precipitation caused by the numerous thunderstorms that accompany it. The result is a summer maximum of rainfall.

The precipitation which occurs in winter is due to the influence of ocean currents and frontal action. Warm, humid, tropical air moving poleward comes in contact with southerly-flowing polar air. The result is cloudy skies and light steady rain for long periods of time. Very seldom does the polar air succeed in driving out the tropical air, but when this does happen the precipitation may occur as snow.

The temperatures of the China climate vary considerably with the seasons. During the period of high sun (i.e., in summer), temperatures of 75 to 80° are characteristic. As well as being hot, the air is also very humid. Such an area is said to have a high *sensible* temperature; that is, the humidity hinders evaporation and so the individual feels or senses the heat to be sticky and oppressive. Another result of this high humidity is the low diurnal range of temperatures. Once an area is heated by the sun, the banks of clouds retard the loss of this heat; accordingly, night temperatures differ very little from day temperatures during this season.

Late summer and fall is the season of the dreaded hurricane and the typhoon. These are the result of huge, very deep low-pressure areas that are spawned in the tropics and move poleward with the flow of warm air. Although relatively short in duration, the ferocity of their winds, together with the deluge of rain accompanying them makes them of considerable climatological importance. Hurricanes and typhoons are essentially the same weather phenomena; the word typhoon is used in Asia to describe the same type of storm which we call hurricane in North America. Storms are much more prevalent in the Atlantic than in the Pacific regions.

With the advance of the polar front in winter, temperatures drop to the forties or fifties. Here again, a monsoon effect may be experienced, and, generally speaking, the larger the landmass, the colder the winter. The outflow of cold air conflicts with the warm tropical air to form depressions and cause cyclonic storms. Occasionally the temperature drops below freezing and here, just as in the Mediterranean climatic region, the chill does great harm to fruit trees and winter crops.

Vegetation

Because of the long hot summers and the abundant rainfall, the forests of this region are luxuriant and rapid growing. The type of forest and the species of trees differ considerably according to local physical phenomena and maritime location. Along the coast where the marine influence is greatest and the temperature range is low, forests of *broad-leafed evergreen* trees can be found. These include the cypress swamps of Florida, the magnolia and camellia trees of China, the camphor of Formosa (Taiwan), the eucalyptus of Australia, the yerba mate of South America, and the wild banana of South Africa. This area has many shrubs and flowering plants; of the latter the orchid is perhaps the best known.

As we move poleward or inland from the coast, the broad-leafed evergreen forests give way to *deciduous* trees. Many of these are of the species similar to those which are found along the coast but which have adapted themselves to the cooler and drier environment. The leaves of these trees are thin and delicate; they require no protective leathery covering, for they are dropped when winter approaches. Among the species found here are the hickory, oak, quebracho, chestnut, walnut, and sycamore. Many valuable shrubs are native to this region. Among the species which have economic significance are the ramie, cinchona, mulberry, and tea.

The red gum hard-woods of Mississippi grow to giant size in the warm, wet climate. What are the chief uses for red gum lumber?

Coniferous trees, which we normally associate with cold subarctic climates, are also found in the China region. These trees usually owe their existence to local features such as poor, infertile soil. Large portions of the Gulf Coastal Plain and the Atlantic plain are composed of sandy soil that is not conducive to the production of deciduous trees. In the U.S.A. these areas are covered with ten different species of pine, of which the loblolly and the slash are best known as they are used for lumber and paper making. From southeastern Brazil comes the Parana pine, which supplies most of Brazil's lumber needs and is still in sufficient quantity to leave some for exporting.

Soil

The *red earths* that characterize large parts of the China region are similar to the laterites of the tropics, but as they have been formed under conditions of cooler temperatures and less moisture, they are not as deep or as highly leached. They retain more of their mineral compounds and, owing to the dense forests which cover this area, have a considerable quantity of organic material. It is thus possible to say that these soils are favourable for cultivation. However, where man has destroyed the natural protective covering of forests, or has intensively cultivated the soils without fertilizing them, serious erosion and soil impoverishment have occurred. Owing to continuous cultivation of commercial crops such as cotton and tobacco, many areas in the U.S.A., where yellowish soils are found, have experienced these conditions. This soil, to remain productive, must be husbanded more carefully, probably, than any other soil in the world. The Chinese have done particularly well in this respect, for their method of terracing is admirably suited to preventing run-off.

Fauna

Many of the native animals of southeastern China have been displaced or become extinct. It is only in such regions as Florida and Brazil, where the forests still remain, that animal life is found in any abundance. The deer is the dominant animal of the larger beasts in America, whereas the giant panda bear is widespread in parts of China. Among the smaller types are the opossum, skunk, raccoon, rabbit, and porcupine. The swamps of Florida are the habitat of wild turkeys, quail, and grouse; in addition, they provide a summer home for migrant geese and ducks from the Canadian north. The muskrat is trapped along the waterways for its fur, and the alligator provides leather for purses, belts, etc.

There are few domesticated animals because the heat and humidity are injurious to such animals as the sheep and the horse. In areas where highlands modify the climate and bring cooler temperatures, cattle are raised. The Brahman breed is being introduced into this climatic region as it is more resistant to disease. The donkey is the chief beast of burden. Hogs are raised in most areas.

4 THE TEMPERATE STEPPE AND TEMPERATE DESERT

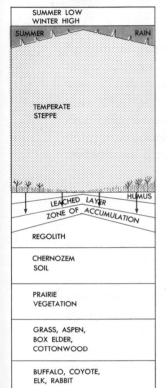

SUMMER LOW
WINTER HIGH

SUMMER   RAIN

TEMPERATE
STEPPE

LEACHED LAYER   HUMUS
ZONE OF ACCUMULATION

REGOLITH

CHERNOZEM
SOIL

PRAIRIE
VEGETATION

GRASS, ASPEN,
BOX ELDER,
COTTONWOOD

BUFFALO, COYOTE,
ELK, RABBIT

U.S. Forest Service

This tall-grass prairie in Colorado has been left in its natural state.

Months	J	F	M	A	M	J	J	A	S	O	N	D	YEAR
Temp.	0.7	2.0	17	38	51	60	65	62	51	39	21	8	34.6
Precip.	0.5	0.4	0.7	0.7	1.8	3.3	2.4	1.8	1.3	0.9	0.6	0.4	14.8

CLIMATIC DATA FOR REGINA, SASKATCHEWAN (STEPPE)

Months	J	F	M	A	M	J	J	A	S	O	N	D	YEAR
Temp.	31	36	41	50	56	65	74	72	61	51	40	32	50.6
Precip.	0.6	0.5	0.5	0.4	0.6	0.3	0.1	0.2	0.3	0.4	0.3	0.6	4.7

CLIMATIC DATA FOR FALLON, NEVADA (DESERT)

Construct climatic graphs for the above two stations. Determine the range of temperatures, and also the frost-free period and the growing period, for each station. What is the essential difference between the two types of climate? What type of vegetation would you expect to find at Regina and at Fallon, respectively? Will the soil be rich in mineral content? Why? How will the amount of humus in the soil at Regina compare with that in the soil of New York?

These two climatic types are discussed together as they are both caused by the same factors and influenced by similar conditions. The interior location of these areas is chiefly responsible for the climate, as the distance from the ocean shuts out the maritime influences. This circumstance results in a dryer, more extreme (or *continental*) climate. The term continental means a great difference in temperature between winter and summer. The above-mentioned conditions exist in the middle latitudes above 40° F. Patagonia (in Argentina), central U.S.A. and Canada, central Asia and China are the only places in the world where this climate is found.

Climate

Although mid-latitude arid and semi-arid climates duplicate the meagre and undependable rainfall of the tropical and subtropical steppes, the temperature conditions are different. The mid-latitude dry climates, like the west-coast marine and the east-coast continental, experience a period of severe cold. Because of their distance from the sea, or because mountains block out marine influences, the summers are hot and the winters cold. It is impossible to speak of typical temperature conditions as there is such a variety, and so wide an annual range, of temperatures. At Tehran, in Iran, the range is 51 degrees and the July temperature is 85° F.; at Urga, Mongolia, the July temperature is 63° F. but the range is 79 degrees. Diurnal ranges also being high, it is, therefore, possible to speak of this climate as one of extremes.

Account for the location of these grasslands in New Zealand.

High Commissioner for New Zealand

Precipitation is slight, and the 10 inch-rainfall line is usually the demarcation line between steppe and desert. Interior location, high mountains, and winter high-pressure cells combine to create the arid and semi-arid conditions. On the poleward side of this climatic type (Regina), the maximum rainfall occurs in summer and is caused by low-pressure areas and convectional rainstorms. On the side toward the equator (Fallon), the Mediterranean influence creates drier summers than winters. In Asia, some rain is brought in from Europe during the summer by the westerlies, while at the same time monsoonal winds may bring rain from the southeast. Winters often experience precipitation in the form of snow, and howling blizzards carrying both sand and snow are common on these treeless plains.

Vegetation

Since the precipitation is not sufficient for trees, grasses and shrubs represent the indigenous plant life. True desert vegetation is found in the drier areas of Sinkiang province (China), Russian Turkestan, and southwestern U.S.A. Cacti and thornbush predominate since they are able to live in this adverse environment. Surrounding these areas are the belts of sagebrush, mesquite, and grass tufts. As the rainfall increases outwards from the centre, a continuous coverage of short grass is achieved; this gives way to long grass, and eventually to light forest or parkland. In this respect, temperate steppe, or *prairie*, vegetation is very similar to that of the tropical steppe and the savanna parkland. Another similarity of vegetation is the galeria forests of cottonwood, willow, and box elder which extend along the watercourses. These are sometimes dense ribbons of *tunnel* forests under which the streams flow.

Soil

The *chernozem* and dark-brown soils of the tall- and short-grass prairie are among the most productive in the world. Humus is added yearly, for the grass dies during the winter season. Leaching is slight, and when rainfall occurs (mainly in summer), wheat, corn, oats, soybeans, sunflowers, and sugar beets are among the chief crops of the temperate steppe. In the drier areas irrigation is usually necessary in order that crops may be grown. Generally speaking, the soil is light-coloured in the desert areas and is high in soluble salts. This soil becomes darker brown in hue, and finally black, as one crosses from short- to tall-grass prairie. The dark colouring is due to the high humus content, but many minerals are still available for plants to use.

Fauna

Of necessity, most of the temperate-steppe animals are herbivorous. The once-numerous buffalo is perhaps the best-known animal of this region. Deer and elk also once roamed this area, but they, too, have had to seek refuge in more remote areas. Coyotes and wolves stalked these animals for food. Foxes, rabbits, and gophers are among the better-known small animals. Prairie chickens (a type of grouse), ducks, and wild turkeys provided food for the early settlers.

Today the wild game of the prairie has been almost entirely replaced by herds of cattle, sheep, and swine. The corn belt of the U.S.A. is one of the leading meat-producing areas in the world; in addition, the western short-grass region supports huge herds of beef cattle. The horse has been practically replaced by the tractor. Many varieties of fowl are raised on the grain grown in the area.

A Prairie Grain Farm

Our own prairies hold an important place among the great wheat-producing areas of the world. By virtue of the topography of the land together with the soil types and climatic conditions prevailing, the area comprising this vast plain has become noted for its production of bread wheats. Dispersed through the country are areas that, owing to their location, are better adapted to the raising of livestock and the production of hay for fodder than to wheat raising. In contrast to earlier years, there is now a tendency in prairie agriculture to specialize. Thus, land more suited to grazing and intermittent cropping is being devoted to larger cattle enterprises. By contrast, land adjacent to rivers and large towns or cities, possessing a high degree of fertility, and having excellent transportation facilities, is being utilized in market-garden production. Because grain production does utilize the largest portion of the cultivated land, several farms specialize in growing seeds of various types and strains.

Ralph Faurschou

The photograph shows an aerial view of the farm buildings. Notice the large number of grain storage bins. Draw a map of the farmyard as it is shown here.

1. Owner's residence; 2. Farm-labour dwelling; 3. Bunk house for seasonal help; 4. Building for machinery and cleaning; 5. Two-car garage; 6. Lubrication and fuel storage; 7-12. Main grain-storage bins; 13. Poultry house (unoccupied); 14. Hay stacks derived from moving of roadsides and headlands; 15 and 16. Summer-fallow fields; 17. Harvested field showing residue straw ready for ploughing; 18. Home-garden area; 19. Municipal roadway and access to main highway; Gravelled entrance lane.

This study will deal primarily with a specific grain farm that specializes in the production of seed grain of cereals. For the purpose of illustration we shall describe the farm of Mr. J. L. Faurschou, and its major operations. This farm is located on the flat fertile soils of the Portage Plains, approximately 5 miles west of the city of Portage la Prairie in central Manitoba. The farm comprises a total of 1,280 acres, or two sections of land.

The land in the Prairie Provinces is measured off into townships that are six miles square and that consist of 36 sections each. A section of land is one mile square and subdivided into quarter sections of 160 acres. Each section of land in a township is numbered, beginning from 1 to 36. Farms are recorded by their location on a particular section within a specific township in a specific range. This reference is calculated from the original survey that established east-west lines, or latitude lines, at 6-mile intervals beginning at the Canadian-U.S. border, or 49th parallel. These lines, or rather the areas between the lines, are numbered consecutively from south to north beginning with number one. Meridian, or range, lines are established every six miles east and west of the first principal meridian located in central Manitoba; they run in a north-south direction. Each range is numbered consecutively both east and west of the first principal meridian. This method of land·survey aids one to locate quickly for reference purpose within the prairie provinces any area or tract of land.

The Faurschou farm is located by description as being on the S.E.¼—12 (Section)—12 (Township) 8 W1 (Range). To pinpoint this farm on a map would require our counting northward from the 49th parallel beginning with number one area until we reached the twelfth township. This would take us beyond eleven 6-mile-wide townships or past a point 66 miles from the border of the U.S.A. This location establishes the third figure of the abbreviated description. We would then assess the fourth or last figure, stating that the farm is in the 8th range west of the first principal meridian. We would then take the second number (12) and locate this section of land in the established township in the given range. Finally, we would locate the farm on the southeast quarter of that section.

Ralph Faurschou

Mr. Faurschou is in a field of barley. Notice the height of the barley. The farmyard is in the background.

The outstanding characteristic of the whole area near the Faurschou farm is its flatness—an important asset in the use of large machinery. It has, however, a slight decline in elevation toward the north and east in the direction of Lake Manitoba. This natural condition assists normal run-off of excess moisture, particularly in the spring season when heavy winter snows melt and accumulate more water than can be absorbed by the still-frozen ground. With the addition of roadside ditches and natural shallow waterways, excess summer rainfall is fairly successfully drained from the surface soils. Owing to the generally rich and finely textured condition of the soils of the Portage plains, their water-retention capacity is quite good. A factor to be considered, however, is that soils of finer and heavier textures require a longer period of time to absorb surface moisture than coarser, sandy soils do. This is because the normal percolation downward in heavy soils is slower than in the coarse or sandy soils. The normal precipitation in this area ranges from 15 to 20 inches per annum and is ample for general cereal grain and grass production. Periods of excess rainfall will cause temporary saturation of the heavier soils and can create difficult conditions in the planting and harvesting of crops. Part of this condition can be offset by the use of such green forage crops as clover or grasses used in rotation, and also by the return to the soil of all plant residues such as straw and chaff after harvest. These residues add humus to the soil and allow for better downward passage of water with less compacting of the heavier textured soils.

The land operated by Mr. Faurschou and his two sons is used primarily for seed grains of registered class. A four-year rotation of crops, including fallow, is generally employed. This rotation consists of wheat or fallow, followed by flax, then barley or oats, a portion of this latter being undersown with clover. The clover will be incorporated into the soil in the fourth, or fallow, year. The cropping procedure followed is such that in each succeeding year on each field, the subsequent crop is one that will not conflict with the preceding or the following crop in the maintenance of varietal purity and freedom of other kinds of grain. In most seasons there is a small percentage of scattered, or unharvested, seed that will in the succeeding year sprout and grow. This *volunteer* grain will cause contamination of the seed crop being grown. To offset the reduction of a seed crop's value because it contains another kind of grain, a cropping procedure is used that reduces this harm to a minimum. To illustrate this procedure, we may note that a crop of barley or oats would not follow wheat in the rotation cycle. Instead, these kinds of grain are separated in the rotation by the production of flax and peas. In this manner, crops for seed are produced that can easily be separated from one another in the process of seed cleaning.

Another important factor in the Faurschou programme of seed production is the extensive use of herbicide sprays for the control of various species of weeds. In recent years the introduction of chemical sprays for the control of wild oats has contributed tremendously to the excellent results on this farm. Very important to the grain-growing industry has been the extensive use of fertilizers to promote increased yields, to shorten the seed's maturing period, and to balance a deficiency of certain elements in the soil necessary for the growth of high-quality seeds. The Faurschou farm has made good use of fertilizers in each year of the cropping programme. One of the chief aims of this enterprise is to produce the best and newest varieties of seed, in keeping with the ever-constant effort to create or maintain high-quality food products. The Federal Department of Agriculture in Canada maintains several laboratories and breeding stations in western Canada to develop and test new strains of cereals and grasses; by this means it assures among agricultural producers the maintenance of quality production.

The ever-present dangers resulting from new strains of rust, as well as from plant diseases, insects, and drought, present problems that have faced agriculture since its inception. Professional personnel are, therefore, essential to the development of strains of cereals that are resistant to rust and disease or otherwise adaptable to the many hazards that beset seed grains. Without such professional help the continuance of high-quality production would be jeopardized. It cannot be overemphasized that the Prairie grain farmer, like all others in competitive enterprises, must employ the best of his abilities to maintain production. He must compete against elements of nature that in their own way maintain a balance necessary to the country as a whole, but which in various places is to the detriment of his specialized production.

In keeping with the general trend towards larger, and hence more economical, units and also towards specializing in one or perhaps two fields of endeavour, the Faurschou farm can be classified as a medium-to-large production unit engaged in seed growing. To envision more clearly the operations of this unit, we must consult an account of its annual activities. Such an account will best illustrate the part in grain production that this farm serves. Quite evident from such an account will be the relationship that this operation maintains with associated and supply industries. As previously stated, the area under ownership embraces two sections of land comprising approximately 1,230 acres under cultivation and forage.

Mechanization on the farm increases the efficiency. Here you see the three combines at work and also the grain hoppers and truck which remove the grain from the field.

The remainder of the land provides space for buildings, a yard area, and a portion of dry creek permanently sown to grass. The fields are divided into 80-acre units (2 units per quarter section) with the exception of the field containing the creek, the latter serving as a boundary between two fields. Land activity begins after the spring thaw and a period of waiting in which the soils dry out sufficiently to be worked. This period is usually in late April or early May. Seeding of the various kinds of crops takes place during the month of May or, in late seasons, in the latter part of May and the first week of June. During this period, the land is tilled and seed is planted at the most appropriate time for the crop concerned. As a general rule, crops requiring a longer period of time to reach maturity are sown first. Cereals normally require from 90 to 100 days, whereas flax and peas usually take a week or two longer. It must be remembered that not all varieties of one kind require the same period of time to grow, and should a late planting season be in prospect, the producer is often obliged to choose a variety that will with reasonable assurance reach full maturity in time to harvest. Early fall frost is perhaps the predominant deterrent to late planting. Other factors, such as amount and timeliness of rainfall, together with warm or cool temperatures during the growing season, largely determine the harvest date and the yield and quality obtained. Growth of crops is most rapid in June and early July. During this period, sprays for the control of weeds are applied to the growing crop. Summer-fallow land is cultivated and tilled throughout the entire summer as often as necessary to control weed growth and promote fertility. This operation may require four to six cultivations; these vary on different farms and on different types of soil. The summer is also the season of mowing and maintaining grass headlands and keeping in a state of cleanliness the dividing strips between different kinds of crop. In average years the harvesting of the cereal crops begins in early August and continues throughout the period that the crop is maturing until late October. In favourable seasons the harvest is completed much earlier, but often fall rains prevent or delay operations until more favourable drying conditions prevail. The harvest machinery consists of two 16-foot swathers, three combines, and three grain trucks. The swathers cut the standing crop and lay the material in continuous windrows in each field. The cut material is supported by the stubble of the crop and is allowed to lie several days in order that the seed may become cured and dried. Mr. Faurschou and his sons use the three self-propelled combines to gather and thresh the crops. These machines are equipped with pick-ups to convey the swaths into the threshing mechanism. At the rear of the machines are straw cutters that chop and flail the straw, spreading it back on the land to be ploughed into the soil at a later date. Since Mr. Faurschou came to the present farm on Portage Plains in 1946, he has always returned to the soil the residues from the combine harvester. On his former farm located in the inter-lake country west of Lake Manitoba, the grain binder and a stationary thresher were used to harvest the grain. This method has now been almost completely replaced by the combine harvester on the Portage Plains since the combine eliminates stooking and hauling of sheaves, thus reducing the labour required on the farm. The method is, however, still used wherever the accumulated piles of straw from the thresher can be utilized for livestock forage. The Faurschou harvest operation also utilizes a hoppered grain tank of 300-bushel capacity with unloading auger attached. This unit is mounted on a heavy, four-wheel running gear and is both pulled and powered by one of the farm tractors. Its purpose is to collect the grain in the field from the moving combines and to discharge its load into the grain trucks at periodic intervals. The trucks haul the seed on to the yard site and by means of elevators store the seed in large bins. Under favourable conditions each harvester combine will remove from the field 1,000 bushels or more per day of grain. The most important consideration at harvest time is to secure the seed grain in a dry condition (under 14.5% of moisture content for cereals) and to retain its natural colour and soundness. Periods of prolonged wet, or unfavourable, harvest weather will reduce the quality of the seed and its appearance.

Following the harvest, there is the task of ploughing or tilling the land. Depending upon the succeeding crop, the land may be either ploughed, or disked at a shallower depth. Some farms do not turn under all the crop residues but use relatively light surface tillage in order to maintain a surface-trash condition that will prevent light-textured soils from drifting in high winds. In areas of lesser rainfall, this practice is preferred because the crop residues left near the top of the soil will catch and hold a better snow covering during the winter months.

Interspersed throughout the summer and fall seasons, are periods devoted to the care and maintenance of special plots of seed, a garden, shelter-belt trees, and farm buildings. A large part of the daily routine work consists in the maintenance and repair of five diesel tractors, three gas tractors, three trucks, and their allied equipment. The winter season, which in this area begins in mid-November and lasts until the end of March, is occupied with the cleaning and processing of the grain for seed. A large portion of the seed wheat is exported by truck or railway into the northern mid-West states of Minnesota and North

Dakota in the U.S.A. Other kinds and varieties of seed are processed for local and interprovincial areas depending upon their degree of adaptability. Additional farm labour is employed throughout the year as required to maintain the schedule of work planned out.

On this farm the buildings represent a major investment and include a modern home, a second home for farm labour, a large machinery and cleaning building, several smaller storage buildings, a garage, and six large grain-storage buildings. Under consideration at the present time is the possible construction of a permanent grain-drying system to assist in the earlier harvesting of grain in seasons when the normal drying of grain in the swath is hampered by unfavourable weather.

Here is a view of Mr. Faurschou's home from the southeast.

Ralph Faurschou

Mr. Faurschou has travelled abroad and has visited plant-breeding stations in Europe as well as in Canada. He has done this in an effort to acquire a better knowledge of new techniques that are being applied, and also to ascertain the desired requirements of Canadian seed and grain exported to other countries. The trend to seed production on the Faurschou farm can be attributed directly to the owner's personal desire to maintain high standards of purity of cereals and to apply strictly sound practices to soil management. This trend has been further enhanced by the necessity of marketing additional grain from farm production over and above what could normally be sold on the regular commercial market. As no livestock was being carried on the farm, it became difficult in years of good production to receive a sufficient quota to handle all the crop. The deliveries by quota system of cereal grains to the commercial grain trade is regulated equitably by the Canadian Wheat Board. This system of Prairie grain marketing has become a necessary part of western grain production and serves to regulate the flow of grains from farms to market channels in a more uniform manner than formerly; it also tends to spread deliveries over a longer period of the year, thus alleviating congestion of transportation and terminal-storage facilities during the harvest season. Moreover, this method is quite acceptable to the producer in that it permits an equitable delivery per acre of a specified number of bushels. The producer is thus enabled to sell or deliver according to the number of acres that he has cultivated, rather than according to the number of bushels per acre produced.

Part of the Selkirk seed is bagged and ready for local markets. Railway cars are used to carry the seed destined for the U.S. market.

Farms such as the one described are a necessary part of the Canadian way of life and its economy. The substantial purchases of machinery represent a wholesome stimulus to production of manufactures in other parts of Canada. When combined with the requirements for fuel, electricity, lumber, trucks, cement, grain bags, chemicals, and fertilizers, the Prairie grain or livestock farm becomes a tremendous potential market for the output of Canadian industry from coast to coast.

This study has tried to furnish a brief insight into the geographical position of a specific Manitoba farm, some of the activity in progress on the farm, and its relative position in the Canadian economy. In contrast to early Prairie expansion in grain production, there is now a very marked and ever-changing pattern of agriculture, one, indeed, which is much more closely associated with the needs and demands, as well as requirements, of the nation as a whole. The Prairie farm is required to produce products that are needed at home and for export abroad. To serve this purpose, the farm operators and owners will be required to become increasingly efficient and capable in specialized activities; they must, in particular, become capable of evaluating scientific advances made available to them. There will remain one variable factor that is subject to very little control throughout the Prairie area: the changing seasonal weather conditions and the vagaries of nature. The farmer must make the best use of facilities available to him, but for him the key to the door of prosperity will probably for many years remain in the hands of a fickle weatherman.

Unit Three

Mid-Latitude
and Polar Climates

1 WEST-COAST MARINE CLIMATE

U.S. Forest Service

CYCLONIC STORM BELT

LOW

EAST-COAST CONTINENTAL
WEST-COAST MARINE

HUMUS

LEACHED LAYER

ZONE OF ACCUMULATION

E.C.CONTINENTAL—BROWN PODZOL
W.C.MARINE—BROWN FOREST

E.C.C.— BROAD LEAFED DECIDUOUS & MIXED
W.C.M.—BROAD-LEAFED DECIDUOUS & CONIFEROUS

E.C.C.— BEECH, OAK, ASH, ELM, MAPLE, BIRCH,
　　　　PINE, CEDAR
W.C.M.—OAK, ASH, BEECH, ELM, FIR, SPRUCE, PINE

E.C.C.— FOX, BEAVER, BEAR, DEER, RABBIT,
　　　　WOLF
W.C.M.—FOX, DEER, COUGAR, BEAR

Virgin stands of ponderosa pine can st
be found in Oregon.

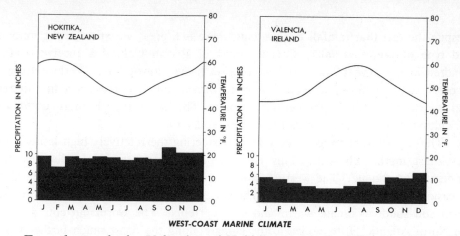

WEST-COAST MARINE CLIMATE

From the graphs for Valencia and Hokitika secure the following information: the monthly average temperature and precipitation; the average annual temperature and precipitation; the annual range of temperatures. Consult an atlas to determine the latitude of these stations, the winds that affect them, and the ocean currents that influence their climates. From the information you have gained determine why the temperature range is so similar even though Valencia lies at a higher latitude. What physiographic feature is responsible for the increased precipitation in Hokitika? Why is the annual range of temperatures so narrow? Retain the statistical information for use later.

Climate

The west-coast marine climate is found on the western shores of continents at mid-latitudes where the westerly winds strike the landmasses. Depending upon the physiographic features which are encountered, the oceanic effect may be carried far inland over a plains area, or blocked at the coast by north-south trending mountains. The former situation is found in western Europe, whereas mountains are encountered in North America, Chile, New Zealand, and Tasmania.

The precipitation' which occurs in these areas is principally relief rain caused by the westerlies striking the land and being forced to rise. Another cause of rain is the low-pressure cyclones which accompany the winds in their trek across the continents. In most of these regions there is an abundance of rain throughout the 12 months of the year, but a slight winter maximum is experienced in some parts. Along the southern boundaries the summer drought of the Mediterranean climate may influence the precipitation and decrease the amount of summer rainfall. This condition is experienced along the west coast of North America. In Europe, much of the precipitation is carried inland in summer as the winds are attracted by the low-pressure area over the land. In winter, most of the precipitation occurs along the coast as the high-pressure cell on land prevents the penetration of the westerlies. On the other hand, New Zealand has a very even rainfall distribution on South Island as the landmass is not large enough to create pressure cells.

Despite the fact that rainfall is abundant, there is a great variation in the amount and type of rain that falls. Certain areas of British Columbia receive over a hundred inches a year, most of it coming in heavy downpours. Western Europe receives less than fifty-five inches on the average, but it comes as a fine drizzle and is extended over longer periods of time. This latter type is more useful for agriculture and has been termed *the million-dollar rain*.

The temperature range is very low considering the relatively high latitudes of west-coast marine climates. This is principally due to oceanic influences that moderate the climate. The west-coast marine areas lie almost directly in the path of easterly flowing ocean currents. When these strike the land, they tend to veer north and south to create warm and cool currents. The warm currents such as the North Atlantic Drift moderate the climate along the coast much farther north than is normally the case. Most of the southern areas, however, are not greatly influenced by the flow of water as the southerly currents are not well developed at this latitude. The general effect, therefore, is to maintain a fairly constant temperature throughout the year without excesses of heat or cold.

Several climatic phenomena are experienced in west-coast marine climates. The artists' sketches of European scenes usually show huge banks of cloud or overcast skies. This is particularly true of winter, when the rainfall maximum occurs. London is noted for its fog, which is partly a result of the warm air over the Gulf Stream striking the cooler air over the North Sea. Vancouver and Victoria occasionally experience prolonged periods of drought in summer as they lie on the leeward side of Vancouver Island. Many of the ports along the coast of North and South America undergo a rapid reversal of weather conditions as the cold, heavy air on the mountains pushes the inflow of warm air aloft and rushes down the valleys to bring colder temperatures and grey skies. In winter a sudden outburst of cold, high-pressure air from the interior may bring freezing weather and snow for periods of a week or more.

Why has this section of forest in Washington not been logged over?

U.S. Forest Service

British Columbia Forest Service

How must the techniques used in the Douglas fir forest of British Columbia differ from those used in eastern Canada?

Vegetation

The forests of the west-coast marine climate do not fit into any simple classification, for they vary with the physiography and the rainfall. Generally speaking, broad-leafed deciduous trees are found in Europe, whereas coniferous forests cover the cooler mountain slopes of western North America, southern Chile, New Zealand, and Tasmania. This statement is not entirely true, for deciduous trees are often found at the lower elevations in the mountainous areas, whereas most of the highlands of Europe are covered with coniferous trees.

In western Europe, most of the original vegetation has been removed for agricultural purposes, but broad-leafed deciduous forests once covered southern Scandinavia, the Netherlands, France, northern Spain, Germany, Poland, western Russia, and most of the British Isles. In monsoon areas, we saw how the trees lost their leaves during the drought season. In more temperate areas, the winters are sufficiently cool to prevent continuous growth. The trees protect themselves from loss of moisture during this period by losing their leaves in the fall, and growing new ones each spring. The commonest varieties found in Europe are the oak, beech, elm, ash, birch, and walnut.

The coniferous trees, which are evergreen but have needle leaves, protect themselves by transpiring very slowly during the cool winter period when their roots are absorbing very little moisture.

Western North America has some of the world's most magnificent stands of coniferous forests. The trees increase in size as one journeys northward from the drier Mediterranean region and reach their maximum height in Washington and Oregon. The true forest begins just north of San Francisco and extends northward to central Alaska. Characteristic of this area are the dense stands of a single species. The California redwood, the Douglas fir, the Sitka spruce, and the western red cedar abound on the Cascades, the Coast Range, and the offshore

279

islands, and often a single species will provide 90 per cent of the forest coverage. So dense are these forests in some places that the sun's rays do not reach the earth's surface, and as with the rainforest, little undergrowth is found. In the Southern Hemisphere, the forests contain more deciduous trees, but Chile produces the Chilean pine, and New Zealand provides us with magnificent stands of kauri pine.

Reforestation, as practised in New Zealand, prevents soil erosion and provides valuable lumber.

High Commissioner for New Zealand

Soil

Just as the forest and the precipitation vary with the physiography, so does the soil type change with the location. In Europe, the heavy forest coverage deposits annually a thick layer of fallen leaves to provide humus for the soil. Because these leaves are not as acidic as coniferous needles and because the precipitation is less in Europe than in the mountainous west-coast, marine-climatic areas (of America, New Zealand, etc.), the *brown-forest* soil which develops is very fertile. The leached layer is not as thick, and, therefore, the soluble minerals remain available for the roots of the crops.

In the cooler, more humid west-coast areas, the coniferous needles and the heavier precipitation combine to produce a more strongly leached soil, often called brown podzol. These areas are, generally speaking, not good for agriculture. There are exceptions, however, for the material eroded from the mountains is often deposited in the valleys or as deltas to provide very good agricultural soil.

Fauna

The wildlife of Europe, like the forests, has been greatly depleted. The hounds still chase the fox, but only on private estates or in hunting preserves. The noble stag is still seen, but it has been preserved from extinction only by hunting restrictions. Smaller, more adaptable game, such as the hare, the pheasant, and the partridge are still found over most of the area. Gone are the wolves, bears, and wild boars which once roamed freely over this area.

The mountainous areas have retained much more of their animal life. Here are to be found several varieties of deer and mountain caribou. Black, brown, and grizzly bears are among the larger animals. Here, too, are to be found the mountain goat and the mountain sheep. Vancouver Island has one of Canada's most ferocious beasts, the cougar, or mountain lion. When game is scarce, these animals have been known to attack human beings in their search for food. South America has contributed the llama and the alpaca for wool, meat, and beasts of burden. New Zealand has practically no native four-footed animals and no snakes but the deer, a European import, has been making a nuisance of itself, as, having no natural enemies, it has multiplied rapidly and has eaten much of the fodder intended for sheep and cattle and contributed to soil erosion.

Richmond Downs Farm

Compare this map closely with atlas maps showing the relief, temperature, and rainfall patterns of South Island.

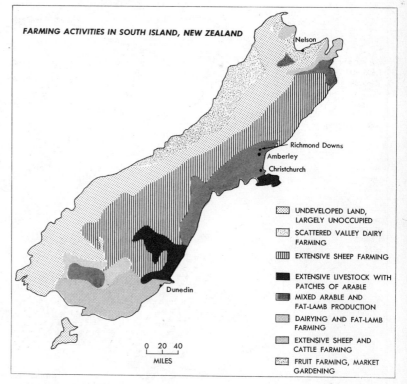

FARMING ACTIVITIES IN SOUTH ISLAND, NEW ZEALAND

Nelson

Richmond Downs
Amberley
Christchurch

Dunedin

0 20 40
MILES

UNDEVELOPED LAND, LARGELY UNOCCUPIED

SCATTERED VALLEY DAIRY FARMING

EXTENSIVE SHEEP FARMING

EXTENSIVE LIVESTOCK WITH PATCHES OF ARABLE

MIXED ARABLE AND FAT-LAMB PRODUCTION

DAIRYING AND FAT-LAMB FARMING

EXTENSIVE SHEEP AND CATTLE FARMING

FRUIT FARMING, MARKET GARDENING

Less than 40 miles north of Christchurch, Mr. Ronald Croft and his wife own and operate a small sheep farm. The farm, called *Richmond Downs,* is on the downland at the edge of the Canterbury Plain; the word downs in New Zealand describes low-lying, gently-sloping hills. This 790-acre farm now grazes 1,600 sheep; but, as the map shows, the farm is carved by numerous steep-sided gullies that are often of little value as pasture. The farm is divided into 21 fields, in this part of the world called *paddocks.* Its soils are largely silty loams which are essentially forms of wind-blown loess. The topsoils are grey to black and the sub-soil is generally a yellowish clay, except in the northernmost paddock, which is very sandy and quick draining, and in the southernmost paddock in which there is a very strong subsoil. Leaching results in a deficiency of lime and phosphate throughout the farm.

The number in the centre of each paddock indicates the number of acres in the particular paddock. The inset shows in detail the paddock of 5 acres to the northeast.

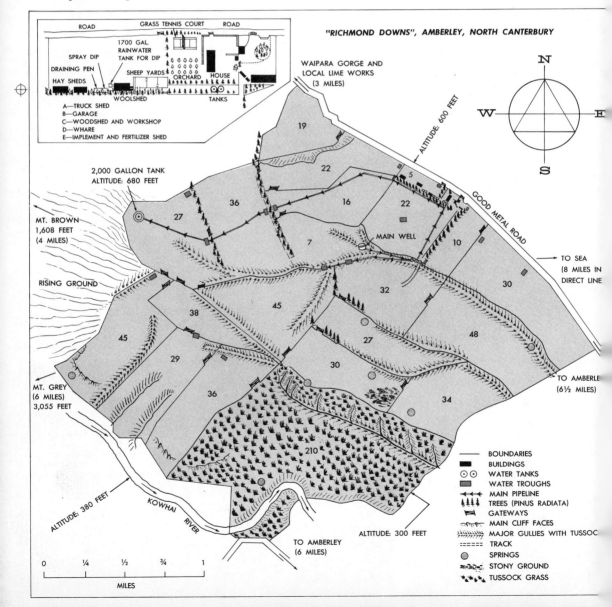

Lying in the rain shadow of the Southern Alps, Richmond Downs receives only about 24 inches of rain, but this is well distributed throughout the year. Winds can be strong here, especially the northwest wind (called the *nor'wester*), which is usually very dry and causes rapid evaporation. Snow is rather a rarity, but severe frosts are common in winter. Mild droughts are sometimes experienced in the summer months of February and March.

Mr. Croft and his wife and their one farm hand are kept very busy operating a farm of this size; indeed, without their collies, Top, Ben, and Jill, the work just could not be finished. With so many sheep on such a small area, maintaining the quality of pasture is of prime importance. At every re-seeding, 1 ton of lime and 1½ cwt. of superphosphate per acre are added to the soil and clover is sown with the grass seed to add nitrogen to the soil. The tussock grass, which grows in clumps 2 to 4 feet high in this area, is coarse and wiry and of no value as feed; it is important, however, in preventing soil erosion until a scientific pasture management programme can be instituted. Rabbits, too, can add to soil erosion problems, but until recent years the biggest threat in this regard on many farms was over-stocking—the farmer simply keeping too many sheep for the area of his land.

Since taking over the farm in 1939, Mr. Croft has given the greatest attention to improving the quality of his pasture. Using a mixture of English and New Zealand seeds and clovers, he follows a *long-rotation* system in which the field is under grass for 8 to 10 years, then rape for a year or two, and then back to grass. In four of his paddocks, cocksfoot is grown because this grass provides rich growth late in the year (*late bite*) and so the other pastures are not over-grazed at that time. One paddock is usually given over to lucerne hay for the winter feed for the flocks. In addition to improving his pastures for the feeding of his flocks, Mr. Croft at times sets a paddock or two aside and allows the grass to mature to seed, which he then sells. New Zealand seed is sold in many countries of the world.

The photographer of this picture looks west from Native Paddock towards Mount Grey. Note the tussock in the foreground and the typical cliff faces in the background. What problems does such a terrain p r e s e n t to a farmer? Why is live-stock farming definitely m o r e practical than arable farming?

Association of Agriculture, Great Britain

In 1949 Mr. Croft began one of the most expensive, but also most rewarding, of his farm-management schemes, namely, top-dressing from the air. He was among the first in New Zealand to have his annual dressing of superphosphates applied from the air. The advantage of this aerial farming is that the hilly country made any other method very slow and in some pastures quite impossible. However, at nearly $10 an acre, it is an expensive process. A quarter of New Zealand's fertilizers are dropped by air now, and there are 46 private aircraft companies involved in this work.

This sample of New Zealand's wool wealth shows classed wool laid out for buyers' inspection. How might the grades of wool differ in their characteristics?

Richmond Downs is a fat-lamb farm. The flock consists of 1,300 Corriedale ewes, 300 ewe hoggets (young female lambs kept as replacements), and 42 rams. Most of the rams are Southdowns; the cross of Southdown with Corriedale produces *Down-cross* lambs. These animals provide excellent meat and are graded as prime Canterbury lamb. The breeding pattern on the farm begins with the mating of Corriedale ewes and Southdown rams in March and the birth of the lambs in August. About a quarter of the lambs are sent from the farm to freezing plants about Christmas time; the rest are fattened on rape and turnip for another six weeks. When Mr. Croft has a batch of lambs ready for market, he informs a buyer at Amberley, who then comes out to inspect the animals. The lambs are transported by truck to a freezing plant, where they are killed. After the carcasses have been graded and weighed, Mr. Croft receives his payment. Each year about 300 of the best lambs are kept for breeding.

A major source of income for Mr. Croft is the high-quality wool of his sheep. This is marketed locally at Amberley and eventually sold to the large market in England, where the fine wool is used in quality knitting yarn and fine dress materials. Shearing time is a period of intensive activity in late spring and early summer (October-November) and at this time Mr. Croft employs a number of additional shearers. The woolshed is the centre of operations. Here a number of sheep are kept overnight in case there should be rain—shearers cannot work with wet fleeces. Outside are four *collecting pens* where a further 200 sheep are kept ready for an early morning start; beyond these pens are the large *sheep yards*, enclosures each large enough for more than 100 sheep. Activity within the woolshed follows a definite sequence. Sheep are moved into one of the two small catching pens, from which they are taken to the *shearing board*. Here electrical equipment is used in the shearing, and the fleece is immediately put in the wool room, where it is *skirted* (that is, the neck, belly, tail, and leg pieces cut off) and folded before being placed in the wool bin. Eventually about 40 fleeces are packed into a tight bale which will weigh about 320 lbs.

Although the lambing and shearing seasons are times of great activity, Mr. Croft is also quite busy throughout the whole year. Adjoining the woolshed there is the spray dip; this is a set of showers where between January and April all his sheep must be sprayed as protection against insects. Preparing his hay is an annual chore. Many miles of fencing require regular attention. Although the sheep gain by the dry-foot run of the upper slopes on the hilly farm, they also need water to drink; accordingly, Mr. Croft has added wells, pumps, and storage facilities. Strong winds can be dangerous to the flocks, especially during the lambing season; so shelter belts of pine trees have been planted—over 2000 yards of them in the last sixteen years. All of this work is handled by Mr. and Mrs. Croft and one hired worker who lives in the *whare* (house) adjoining the main farm building.

The Crofts are active members of several Amberley organizations such as the lawn-bowling club. They and their three daughters all enjoy and play musical instruments. The two eldest daughters attend high school at Rangiora twenty miles away; this means that during the school year they leave home by 7.30 a.m. and do not get back until 5.30 p.m. Vacation attractions include a beach about 8 miles away and their own tennis court.

2 EAST-COAST CONTINENTAL CLIMATE

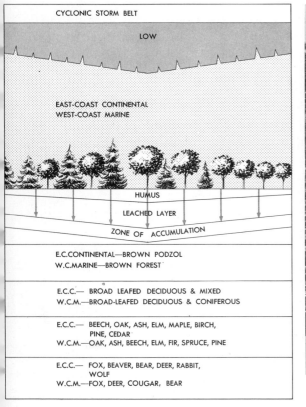

Stands of a single species, white pine, are characteristic of Wisconsin.

From the graphs for New York and Peking secure the following information: the monthly average temperature and precipitation; the average annual temperature and precipitation; the annual range of temperatures. Compare the latitudes of these stations with those for Valencia and Hokitika in the west-coast marine climate. Determine the winds and ocean currents which will affect this east-coast climate. Why do you suppose that the annual range of temperature is so much greater, and why is there less rainfall, than in the west-coast, marine-climatic regions?

Compare the graphs for New York and Valencia. Attempt to account for the difference in the rainfall pattern. Even though these two stations are at approximately the same latitude, Peking has a considerably greater range of temperature than New York. Consult a world map to see whether you can explain the reasons for this. Next, determine in weeks the lengths of the frost-free period and the growing period for each area. Which region appears to have the most suitable climate for agriculture?

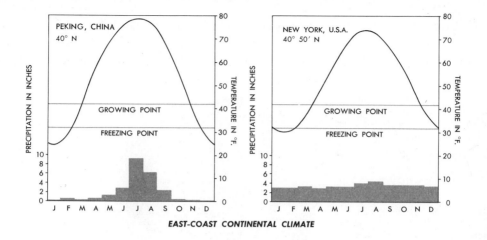

EAST-COAST CONTINENTAL CLIMATE

Climate

Poleward from the China type of climate lies the region of east-coast continental climate. It is found only in North America and northeastern Asia. As there is no landmass in the Southern Hemisphere large enough to create the necessary conditions, no east-coast continental climate is found there.

Summers are characteristically long and hot, the temperatures often averaging in the 80's for several weeks. On the other hand, winters are cold, with several months averaging below or near freezing. It is from these extremes of temperature that the term *continental* is derived. Continental, as opposed to maritime, implies an area where the temperatures are not modified by oceanic influences. Even though these regions of east-coast continental climate border the ocean, the offshore westerly winds tend to bring influences from the interior rather than from the ocean. As the land cools off rapidly in winter, a high-pressure cell of cold, heavy air builds up. This moves eastwards and creates similar conditions along the east coast. In summer, the land heats up rapidly and a low-pressure area is created. These lows usually move from the interior towards the east and so cause climatic conditions which are characteristic of the interior of the continent. Where the landmass is large and the heating is great, a monsoonal effect may occur, e.g., Peking.

Precipitation in this climate ranges from light to medium, with certain areas along the coast receiving 50 to 55 inches a year. Summer rains predominate, with convection currents causing thunderstorms and low-pressure rains. A slight monsoonal effect is felt in North America; but in Asia this effect is marked, thus adding to the summer maximum of rain.

Frontal action accounts for much of the rainfall of spring and autumn since the warm tropical air vies with the colder Arctic air for dominance of the area. In winter, precipitation is less because the cold, dry air of the Arctic air mass is

287

usually dominant. Invasions of warm air from the south may bring rain, freezing rain, or the so-called *January thaw* during this season. The summer weather, dominated by tropical air masses, is occasionally interrupted by hurricanes that work their way north from the tropics and expend their fury in the mid-latitudes.

The cold of winter has robbed these elms in Ontario of their foliage.

Canada Department of Agriculture

Vegetation

Poleward from the broad-leafed evergreen trees of the China climate, the forests change to broad-leafed deciduous. A definite seasonal rhythm becomes pronounced as spring brings in the processes of budding, flowering, and leafing; summer develops the foliage to the zenith of its greenery and abundance; autumn ushers in a season of brilliant colour; and winter exposes the bare branches so characteristic of deciduous forests. Many of the species of trees are the same as those found more towards the equator, but these have adapted themselves to their environment by losing their leaves in winter.

Undergrowth and forest litter are usually heavy, because, owing to the cold winters, the rate of decay is slow. The annual shedding of leaves, coupled with this slow decay, allows a considerable quantity of humus to build up and enrich the soil. Low bushes, such as alder, prickly ash, hazelnut, and dogwood, hinder man's passage through this forest. Pure stands of maple, oak, hickory, and ash, attract the forester, for these hardwoods provide some of the world's finest lumber. Other species to be found here are birch, elm, poplar, beech, basswood, walnut, willow, and pagoda.

On the colder margins of these forests, the deciduous trees are mixed with conifers. Cedars and junipers can be found in most marshy areas, while the poorer or drier soils are often covered with pine, spruce, hemlock, or balsam. This mixed forest may cover quite an extensive area before giving way to the true coniferous forest of the subarctic region.

This stand of white pine and oak is found in West Virginia. Account for such a type of forest growing so far south.

U.S. Forest Service

Soil

The soils of this climatic zone vary from *brown-forest* in the south to *brown podzol* in the north. Underneath the true deciduous forests, the soil is rich in humus, but the amount of leaching depends on the precipitation. In areas which receive from 20 to 40 inches of precipitation, the soil is not too strongly leached and is, therefore, quite fertile. The brown colouration, derived from the humus content, is quite apparent. The plant roots can usually reach the mineralized area to obtain the necessary nutritive elements. Much of this area has been cleared for agriculture, and the use of the plough has succeeded in mixing the humus and the soluble salts of the subsoil to produce a very fertile topsoil.

In areas where conifers are intermixed with the deciduous trees, the climate is usually colder, precipitation may be heavier, and the conifers' needles create a more acidic soil. These conditions combine to create a poorer, more highly leached soil, which is generally classed as brown podzol. Although not all crops will grow well in this soil, certain roots and trees flourish under these conditions. Potatoes, turnips, carrots, etc., provide the essential food for many people, while apples, plums, cherries, and small fruits are sold as commercial crops.

289

Fauna

Most of the animals of this region have, like the deciduous trees, adapted themselves to the colder environment. Many of the animals found here have a warm covering of fur or hair to protect them against the cold. Others actually change their colour with the seasons to provide camouflage as a protection against predators. Undoubtedly the large mammal which characterizes this region is the white-tailed deer. This animal provided the North American Indian with one of the main staples of his diet. Considerable numbers of these still inhabit the area, browsing on cedars, maples, and balsams.

Some animals avoid the long winters by hibernation. Among these are the bear, raccoon, skunk, and groundhog or woodchuck. Other animals do not hibernate but avoid the cold by burrowing underground, e.g., the fox, badger, squirrel. The streams of these areas are inhabited by several semiaquatic animals. Beavers dam the streams for protection and fell poplar trees for their food. They survive the winter by imbedding tree branches in the mud of the stream; then they emerge in winter to eat the bark of these branches. The muskrat is still trapped throughout this climatic area; in addition, mink and marten are taken for their fur. The rabbit and weasel usually turn white in winter to match the snow cover.

This region is also inhabited by a number of game birds. The ruffed grouse, or partridge, is native to the area, but the pheasant and the Hungarian partridge have been introduced successfully. The turkey has been domesticated with marked success. Many ducks and migrating geese are bagged by hunters each fall.

One of the more notable features of this area is the great variety of domesticated animals and fowls. Some of these are native to the area but a great number of them have been introduced. Horses, cattle, sheep, goats, swine, rabbits, chickens, turkeys, geese, and ducks are all raised for domestic purposes.

Canada Department of Agriculture

Why are the fields so long and narrow in this cleared area of Quebec Province?

3 THE SUBARCTIC

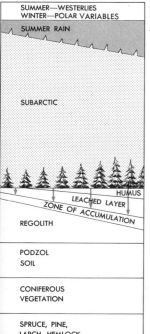

Embassy of Finland

Taiga covers most of Finland.

Months	J	F	M	A	M	J	J	A	S	O	N	D	YEAR
Temp.	1.7	2.4	14	31	46	57	62	60	51	39	22	6.3	32.4
Precip.	2.0	1.1	1.6	1.8	2.1	2.3	3.4	2.9	3.5	2.5	2.4	1.9	27.5

CLIMATIC DATA FOR KAPUSKASING, ONTARIO

Months	J	F	M	A	M	J	J	A	S	O	N	D	YEAR
Temp.	−46	−35	−10	16	41	59	66	60	42	16	−21	−41	12
Precip.	0.9	0.2	0.4	0.6	1.1	2.1	1.7	2.6	1.2	1.4	0.6	0.9	13.7

CLIMATIC DATA FOR YAKUTSK, U.S.S.R.

Using the above data, construct graphs to depict this type of climate. Be careful in arranging the temperature scale as allowance must be made for 46° F.

below zero. Determine the annual range of temperature, and the lengths of the frost-free period and the growing period. By using an atlas determine the latitude of these two stations. What other factors besides latitude are responsible for the severe winters of Yakutsk?

On the poleward side of west-coast marine, east-coast continental, and temperate-steppe climatic zones lies a broad belt known as the subarctic. Northern Canada, Alaska, northern U.S.S.R., and the interior of Scandinavia are the only areas where this type of climate is experienced. Certain highland areas have a similar climate that could be classed as subarctic. Generally speaking, this area lies on the poleward side of the 50° isotherm and extends to the Arctic Circle. However, owing to the rotation of the earth and the wind circulation around the world's pressure cells, this climatic region is found much farther polewards on the west coast than on the east; it also extends much south of 50° latitude on the east coast.

Climate

This climate is characterized by a long, bitterly cold winter and a relatively shorter, but warm, summer. Spring and autumn are transitional seasons that are often cool and damp, due to frontal action. The range of temperatures is very great and varies with distance from the sea. Yakutsk is an example of the wide range which is common in interior locations. Along the coasts this range is somewhat modified.

The winters experience some of the coldest weather on earth, but during the summers the July temperatures may reach 80° or 90° F. This is a daytime temperature and not the average for the month. Such warm summer weather is partly due to the longer days of these high latitudes. Whereas at the equator days and nights are of almost equal length, at latitude 60° there is a possibility of 18.8 hours of sunshine. The amount of insolation received at 60° latitude during the summer solstice is equal to that received at the equator. Conversely, however, during winter the nights are 18.8 hours long and sunshine is received for only a short period during the day. The seasonal shift of the sun's rays is mainly responsible for the subarctic climate. Outside of the true Arctic, the coldest temperature ever recorded was at Oimekon, in the Verkhoyansk area of the U.S.S.R. —108° F!

Precipitation in the subarctic is not great and varies with the location. Most of the Siberian subarctic receives less than 15 inches, while in Canada it averages less than 20 inches. Interior locations will receive even less, though more favourably situated areas may get as high as 30 inches or more. As much of this precipitation comes in the form of snow, it may remain on the earth's surface for periods of 6 or 7 months. This accumulation of moisture is available for the plants when spring comes. In effect, the net result is the same as if all moisture fell in the warmer season.

As it is, most of the precipitation does occur in summer. During this time the land is heated and convectional rain falls. Few thunderstorms occur, and whenever they do happen they are usually associated with the hottest spells when convection is at a maximum. The warm, low-pressure system of summer gives way to a cold high-pressure system in winter. This pressure area tends to divert the moisture-bearing winds so that little precipitation occurs. Spring and fall are often cloudy and damp as the cold Arctic air battles the warmer air masses from the south. The frontal action that ensues delays the melting of snow and the arrival of spring and, therefore, often is instrumental in hindering the ripening of crops in fall. Along the southern boundaries of this climatic zone, precipitation may be more evenly spread or there may be a slight autumn maximum, e.g., Kapuskasing.

Vegetation

Subarctic North America and Eurasia are covered by *taiga,* or coniferous forest. So great is the extent and immensity of this forest that travellers become bored with the monotony, emptiness, and silence of the region. So much does one section of this forest resemble another, that hunters have become hopelessly lost within a mile of their camp site.

The conifers, of which spruce, cedar, pine, balsam, fir, and larch or tamarack are the dominant species, occupy over 75 per cent of the forested areas. Hardier species of birch, poplar, and willow comprise most of the remainder. The forest floor is often devoid of underbrush, which is replaced with a thick coating of coniferous needles. The tamarack, or larch, is unique among conifers as it loses its needles in winter. The other trees continuously add to the humus layer as they shed only a part of their needles at any one time.

The cold weather hinders the decay of this fallen material, so great quantities of partly decomposed humus accumulate. This organic matter is carried into depressions, ponds, and lakes to create the *muskeg* swamps so typical of the subarctic.

This Alaskan muskeg swamp supports little vegetation. How is muskeg formed?

These peat-filled bogs support a few stunted trees, low bushes, and mosses. They are the favourite haunt of wild animals; but they create a serious obstacle to transportation routes. Partly because of this water-logged humus layer, and partly because of the severe climate, much of the forest growth is small and more suited to the manufacture of paper than of lumber.

Soil

The *podzol* soils are as characteristic of the subarctic as is the taiga forest itself. The slow rate of decay, coupled with the acidic nature of coniferous needles, tends to create a highly leached layer in the subarctic soil. Although not as thick or as well developed as the laterites of the tropics, podzols bear a remarkable resemblance to them. A thick layer of humus lies on top of a sandy, light-grey, leached layer. Beneath this is the zone of accumulation, which is identified by its brown colouration. The whole profile is shallow, usually less than two feet in depth, and its natural fertility is low. Often these layers are water-logged owing to the excess of moisture in spring and the poor drainage system.

As these climatic regions were the most recently freed from glacial ice, morainic deposits have tended to dam up streams and interrupt drainage. This has created many swamps, lakes, and bogs. On the other hand, where morainic deposits are thick, or where lake beds have been exposed by drainage, areas of relatively fertile soil may occur in the midst of the podzols. The clay belts of northern Ontario and Quebec are examples of the latter. Agriculture, even here, is limited by the severity of the winter and the short growing season.

Fauna

The coniferous forests are the home of most of the world's important fur-bearing animals. The severity of the climate has made it necessary for them to develop a thick, protective covering; yet (though much to the disadvantage of the animals) their fur has proved valuable in also keeping man warm. The most important of these animals are the beaver, fox, weasel or ermine, sable, muskrat, otter, mink, and marten. In Canada, the Athapaskin Indians lived off the woodland caribou, using its flesh for food, its hide for clothing, and its bones for tools. A similar type of economy is practised among the Samoyed, Tungus, and Chukchi tribes of the U.S.S.R. who live off their herds of domesticated reindeer. The largest game animal is the moose, which feeds on the marsh and muskeg vegetation. Several varieties of deer are found throughout these areas; these provide much of the food for the huge timber wolves. Most of the bird life is migratory, but the snowy owl roams the Arctic and subarctic in search of rabbits or rodents. The cat family is represented here by the ferocious bobcat or wildcat, and the lynx. These are no longer numerous, but the brown and black bears have managed to survive in considerable numbers.

4 THE TUNDRA

High Commissioner for New Zealand

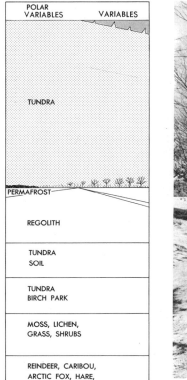

POLAR VARIABLES   VARIABLES

TUNDRA

PERMAFROST

REGOLITH

TUNDRA
SOIL

TUNDRA
BIRCH PARK

MOSS, LICHEN,
GRASS, SHRUBS

REINDEER, CARIBOU,
ARCTIC FOX, HARE,
SEAL, MUSK-OX, WALRUS

Stunted growth is found on Mount Cook, New Zealand.

Months	J	F	M	A	M	J	J	A	S	O	N	D	YEAR
Temp.	−19	−27	−17	−4	19	36	43	41	30	14	−6	−15	8
Precip.	0.4	0.2	0.4	0.3	0.6	0.6	0.7	1.5	0.7	0.7	0.2	0.4	6.7

CLIMATIC DATA FOR ARCTIC BAY, CANADA

Months	J	F	M	A	M	J	J	A	S	O	N	D	YEAR
Temp.	−34	−36	−30	−7	15	32	41	38	33	6	−16	−28	1
Precip.	0.1	0.1	0.0	0.0	0.2	0.4	0.3	1.4	0.4	0.1	0.1	0.2	3.3

CLIMATIC DATA FOR SAGASTYR, U.S.S.R.

Tundra climate is transitional in character, being between that of the taiga forest and the icecap. It is found mainly in the Northern Hemisphere north of the

295

tree line. It includes the Arctic Archipelago, a belt along the coast stretching from Alaska to Labrador, and a similar area in the U.S.S.R. The coastal fringes of Greenland and Antarctica might also be classed as tundra.

Climate

All places within the tundra area have periods of high and low sun. Within the Arctic Circle, the sun may disappear entirely for periods of from one day at the Circle to five months on the islands near the pole. The opposite of this is true in summer when the sun may shine continuously for the six months' period. The climate of this region is distinguished from that of the subarctic by the annual average temperature and the July average temperature. Generally speaking, the yearly average is below 10° F. and the July average does not exceed 50° F. The range of temperatures is again great, but owing to coastal location the tundra may not receive the extremes of cold that the subarctic does.

Precipitation is scant because low temperatures lessen the evaporation and reduce the amount of moisture in the air. The high-pressure cells which build up here tend to increase the dryness. Much of the tundra receives less than 10 inches of precipitation; indeed, were the evaporation higher, desert conditions would prevail. As it is, many areas in eastern Siberia do not receive enough snow in winter for sledding. The precipitation which does fall is mainly cyclonic in origin and comes mainly in the warmer months. In winter the anticyclones of the polar regions create strong, outblowing blizzards which may remove the snow from wide expanses of terrain and build huge drifts in the lee of projecting rocks or hills.

Typical tundra vegetation grows high in the mountains of Colorado.   U.S. Forest Service

Vegetation

The coniferous trees of the taiga give way, on their poleward side, to a stunted growth of birch, elders, and Arctic willow. These seldom exceed 5 feet in height and gradually thin out and are replaced by hummocks of tough grass or beds of soggy sphagnum moss. Mosses have become adapted to this environment, for they can be frozen to a stage where they are so brittle that they will crumble at a touch yet spring to life at the first sign of warm weather. Lichens and algae are the simplest and hardiest of the plant life here. In the Antarctic over 150 species of algae have been found growing on the drab slopes. The lichen is the chief plant of the tundra, for it grows over a wider area and supports more animal life than any other plant. It is a combination of an algae and a fungus. The fungus fibres anchor the algae cells to the rock and supply them with moisture. In return the fungus receives chlorophyll, which is necessary for its livelihood, from the algae. The lichen is an incredible plant, for it can survive on one day of active growth per year and some species have been revived by watering after a period of fifteen years. This type of vegetation extends in some instances to the very foot of the icecaps of Greenland and Antarctica.

Soil

Despite the fact that the tundra area usually receives less than 10 inches of precipitation a year, the soils of the tundra are waterlogged. Throughout the year, the subsoil remains frozen. This *permafrost*, as it is called, never thaws, and varies in thickness from a few inches along the southern limits to 50 feet near the icecap. The soil and vegetable waste act as a protective insulation during the period of warm weather. The grey decomposed rock mixes with the decaying vegetation and lichens to produce a dark-brown soil. This soil occurs only in the more favourable areas, for much of the Arctic does not support vegetation and, therefore, the surface is one of barren rock or of *regolith*.

Among the peculiarities of the Arctic are the patterns and landforms which the frost creates in the soil. The *pingo*, a giant frost heave, may tower 300 feet or more above the tundra. These pingos are thought to have been formed by the expansion of permafrost localities during periods of intense cold. As a result, water may have been forced to the surface and frozen to create a landform similar to a volcanic cone. *Stone rings*, 2 to 6 feet in diameter, cover wide areas. They are thought to have been caused by the frost's moving the stones upwards and outwards during freezing. *Polygons,* peculiar many-sided formations, are created in low, wet areas by the freeze-thaw action of the surface water.

Fauna

As the greater part of the tundra is unsuited to agriculture, its chief wealth lies in its animal life. In spring the caribou and reindeer emerge from the forests and migrate across the tundra, feeding on the reindeer moss, which grows quickly at this time of year. The calves are born in the north on the open tundra. This calving in the open ensures a certain amount of protection from predators, as the Arctic wolf is unable to stalk the herd without being sighted. The musk ox, however, was lord of the tundra until rifles depleted his ranks. Their thick coats protect these oxen from cold and their massive horns discourage wolves.

The smaller animals, the lemming, the Arctic hare, and the rodents, form the staple diet of owls, foxes, and wolves. Here, too, these smaller animals protect themselves by changing colours with the seasons. It is during the winter period that the common weasel produces the valuable white fur known as ermine.

During the summer, the tundra abounds in wild fowl. Here the wild geese, tern, jaeger, plover, and many varieties of ducks and swans migrate to spend the summer and raise their young. It is thought that these birds first came north in search of the numerous insects which hatch each spring. Their migratory habits were induced perhaps by the cold of winter and their taste for Arctic insects. Shortly after the young are born, the birds moult and are easy prey for the wolves and foxes and the barren-ground grizzly. Among the birds which winter in the Arctic are the ptarmigan and the snowy owl.

Semiaquatic animals are prominent in the Arctic. This is so because water cannot fall much below 32° F. without freezing and, therefore, is much warmer than —50° F. which prevails on land. These animals live on the fish and plankton of the ocean. Many varieties of penguins, walruses, and seals are to be found in Arctic waters, but the monarch of this domain is the polar bear. Usually born on an ice pack, the polar bear spends his life roaming from ice pack to ice pack to prey on seals, walrus, or fish. The most carnivorous of all bears, it will attack almost any living animal or human being when it becomes hungry enough.

Icecaps

Icecaps today cover Greenland, Ellesmere and Baffin islands, and Antarctica. In a sense, the North Pole may be said to have a floating icecap as it is never free from pack ice. Until recently data for this climatic type of terrain has been meagre. However, the expeditions of the International Geophysical Year of 1957-58 have provided us with much new information. Defense installations and polar observatories have been set up by both the Soviet Union and the U.S.A.

Despite the fact that the annual average temperatures are much below freezing and that the periods of night extend up to six months, man has been able to survive in these areas. He has survived the lowest temperature ever recorded on earth —121° F. in Antarctica and blizzards of up to 70 mph at temperatures in the minus forties.

The purposes of present-day Arctic explorations are basically scientific and strategic. Man's ever-increasing numbers have made it necessary for him to search for new supplies of food and sources of energy. The ideological battles which are being waged under the guise of a cold war have made it necessary that he build bases for defense and research in both the Arctic and Antarctic regions.

Scientists have determined that considerable quantities of minerals are locked up in the Arctic and Antarctic regions. Oil, coal, iron, lead, and zinc are known to exist. Research is being done on methods of harvesting the fish and plankton of the icy waters. Efforts to determine the cause of the earth's glacial periods have led to careful measurings and recordings of snowfall, ice growth, and snow losses by iceberg calving. The suggestion has been made that huge icecaps be towed from the Arctic to supply fresh water for the cities of San Francisco and Los Angeles, which suffer from summer drought. Another use for the icecap could be the storing of America's vast food surpluses for future use.

In the space age, the poles provide ideal sites for tracking and guiding of satellites, as stations there can encompass the observation of nearly the entire globe. The poles may also provide the best sites for launching men into outer space, since it is at these points that the deadly Van Allen radiation belt is thinnest. Finally, the icecap provides an ideal laboratory for the study of man under conditions of duress. Most of the physical discomforts, such as frostbite, snow blindness, and exposure, can be overcome. As of now, the *white-out* has not been overcome. This is a condition wherein daylight filtering through an overcast sky is reflected back and forth between the snow and sky until the horizon disappears. Under these conditions a man loses all sense of distance and direction and may wander off to certain death from within a few feet of his camp. Aeroplane and helicopter pilots have trouble judging elevation and several have lost their lives in crashes under such circumstances.

Another, and more insidious, danger is the psychological effect of isolation on man. Confinement of up to a year in close quarters can cause boredom, frustration, and even mental illness. Some lose their appetites and weight; others compensate for the monotony by eating much more than usual; still others spend sleepless days or weeks waiting for *morning*. The *Long Eye* is a condition which some develop; its peculiar name is derived from the fact that anyone afflicted with it will stare silently at a person, yet never see him. The victim of Long Eye appears to be looking through a person.

Future prospects for the Arctic look bright. A nuclear reactor has already been installed at McMurdo Sound in the Antarctic and brings light and heat to the community there. Scientists envision many more of these reactors and have been experimenting with under-ice communities to be served by them. As it is much easier to heat the dwellings of this type of community, man will in all probability some day inhabit these areas in the guise of cave dwellers.

Survival in the Far North

In contrast to the cold, mysterious, but uninhabited, Antarctic lands of snow and ice, the lands around the *roof of the world* have long supported many different peoples, each having its own distinctive civilization and culture. The Yukaghirs and Chukchi of Siberia have probably lived in these Arctic regions centuries longer than any other people. Reindeer herding by the Lapps is a highly developed way of life, the people deriving food, clothing, transport, and even fuel, from these animals, and migrating seasonally with their herds. Of greatest interest to us, however, are the Eskimos of our own Arctic lands. These people entered our continent about a thousand years ago, probably from Siberia. In all there are now about 55,000 of them eking out an existence along the harsh northern fringes of Canada and other countries: in fact, they are spread out in little isolated colonies stretching from the islands of the Bering Sea to the southern coastlands of Greenland. When one considers the enormous distances involved in these regions, the similarity of the language, customs, and way of life of these scattered groups is remarkable.

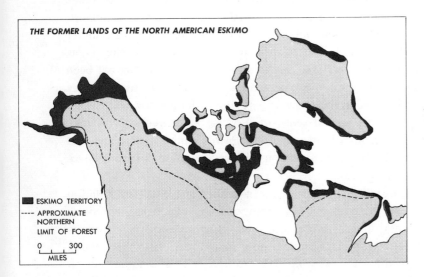

THE FORMER LANDS OF THE NORTH AMERICAN ESKIMO

■ ESKIMO TERRITORY
---- APPROXIMATE
NORTHERN
LIMIT OF FOREST

0   300
MILES

Using Canadian government publications, map the present Eskimo settlement. What areas do Eskimos now favour for their homes?

The Eskimos are a short, rather thick-set people with black hair, dark brown eyes, and sallow skin. Their narrow slanting eyes suggest their kinship with the peoples of Asia, although this relationship must certainly go a very long way back. Among the peoples of the world who have come under western influence only in recent centuries, few have shown such skill and ingenuity as these dwellers of the north. Considering their harshly limited environment, their achievements have been really remarkable. They live in a land where the intense cold and the length of the winter drastically restrict activity, where animal and plant species are less varied and less numerous than in any regions except the hottest deserts; where metals are few and difficult of access, and where even wood is a rare and valuable substance. Within these limitations, the Eskimos have constructed boats, built homes, fashioned clothing ideally adapted to their climate, and designed bows, arrows, knives, and other utensils, many of them artistically and skilfully adorned.

300

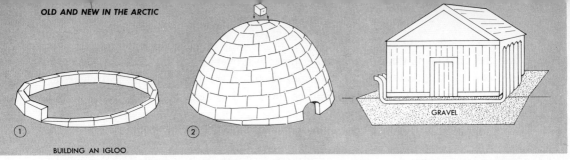

GRAVEL

① ②

BUILDING AN IGLOO

Formerly, the Eskimo surrounded himself with ice to keep warm. The new building technique relies on a bed of gravel and then a series of metal pipes that allow cold air to blow under the building. The aim is to counter the thawing of the permafrost. What effect would such a thaw have?

They have used wood in the making of dog sleds, harpoons, pots, and, of course, boats. Nuggets of pure copper found along the Coppermine River have been beaten to fashion chopping knives. Animal bone and tusk have provided harpoon barbs and arrowheads, snow goggles, small utensils, needles, and a multitude of small but important objects. Stone, too, has been utilized for pots, lamps, and weapons.

Eskimo homes are of different types depending on location, materials, and the season. In summer the inland Eskimo may live in a skin tent that can be easily folded and moved. Along the coast there are certain locations where more or less permanent stone and earth dwellings are found in little communities; however, many Eskimos have never used such buildings, but have passed instead directly from summer tent to winter igloo. The igloo, or snow house, is one of the finest examples in history of man's taking the most unpromising materials around him and using them to his best advantage. Having cut blocks of compacted snow with a bone or ivory knife, the Eskimo lays them in a circle sloping inwards and spiralling to a dome. Crevices are packed with ice, and the whole structure becomes stronger throughout the winter as the inner walls melt and freeze again. To enter the igloo, one follows an ice corridor and then crawls on hands and knees through a low door. Within, one finds a crude wooden table on which stands a fat or blubber lamp and a soapstone pot; on the floor are a number of sealskin or caribou-hide bags. Against one wall there is a high ledge of snow that is covered with hides and constitutes the family bed. Wrapped in parkas and

These two Eskimo grandmothers are in an igloo at Chesterfield Inlet. Although the kettle is of modern manufacture, the means of heating it is traditional. Describe the clothing of the two old ladies.

National Film Board

hides, the Eskimo is quite comfortable here; however, since the feet can become quite cold on the snow floor, it is warmer to sit on the bed with the feet clear of the snow. Occasionally the walls may be lined with hides. Standing in the centre of a typical igloo, one can normally touch the ceiling and all four walls; yet here a whole family can live in safety while deadly blizzards rage all around.

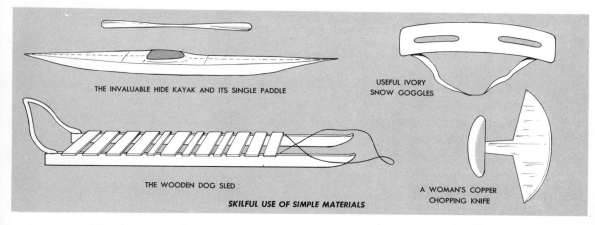

THE INVALUABLE HIDE KAYAK AND ITS SINGLE PADDLE

USEFUL IVORY SNOW GOGGLES

THE WOODEN DOG SLED

SKILFUL USE OF SIMPLE MATERIALS

A WOMAN'S COPPER CHOPPING KNIFE

The pattern of life of these people varies but little from one area of the Arctic to another. In the central Arctic region and in Baffin Island, the seasonal sequence is most interesting. From early winter until March or April, using the igloo as a base, the Eskimo engages in maupok hunting, but starvation always threatens. *Maupok* means *he waits* and is a well-chosen term to describe this type of sealing, for in practising it the hunter places a small bone pointer in a seal breathing-hole and then waits for its movement to indicate that a seal has come up for air. A strong, swift stroke with the harpoon is followed by the seal's dashing off with the detachable harpoon head, to which a cord made of sinew is attached. After enlarging the hole, the Eskimo pulls out the seal—to become his chief source of food and fuel for the dark, long winter months ahead. When the day lengthens and the water begins to open up, the hunters scatter to *utoq* (stalk) seals, which will then be either swimming at the surface or basking on the broken ice floes.

Mr. Dick and his family live in their one-room house at Inuvik. Now drawing a regular salary from the Department of Public Works, Mr. Dick still fishes, hunts, and traps. What is the principle upon which snowshoes are constructed?

National Film Board

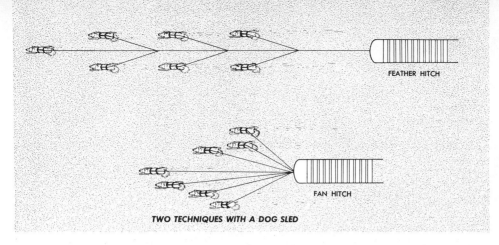

FEATHER HITCH

FAN HITCH

TWO TECHNIQUES WITH A DOG SLED

Explain briefly why the feather hitch is used in timbered country and why fast driving in open country is usually done with the fan hitch.

Harpoons are even more important in April and May when game becomes more varied as, in addition to the seals and their new-born young, the whales and walrus move into these waters. The manoeuvrable one-man kayak is used in this water-hunting, except when a large whale is sighted; when this happens, the umiak, with several hunters aboard, is used. At one time man and fierce huskies co-operated in the killing of grazing musk ox, but in recent years few musk ox remain and the occasional polar bear now supplies their place. This early summer period is a season of comparative plenty when meat and blubber are stored in hide bags under rock cairns as a protection against preying animals.

As the land thaws out and the growing mosses and lichens attract herds of caribou to their northern feeding grounds, the Eskimos set out inland on extensive group hunts. Caribou are usually killed in rivers by means of arrows and spears plied from kayaks. Wolves, hares, and birds are trapped. Char and other fish are netted or, more commonly, speared. Meanwhile, the women and children collect the scanty edible berries and plants that the barren land grudgingly yields. During this time the people travel in small groups of a few families, all living in tents. It is curious that this is the season in which the Eskimo has the greatest difficulty in moving overland, since his sleds are now of no use and he has never developed any other form of overland transport.

The close of the caribou season marks the trek back to the coast and ushers in a brief period of relative inactivity. This is the season for festivals and merriment; indeed, one fact that even the earliest travellers have generally commented on, is the cheerful attitude and simple happiness of these people. As they journey back, they count distance by sleepings and chart a course by the sun, stars, or wind.

Social organization among these people has been severely limited. To them, the world was populated by evil and brooding spirits of ancestors, but they had no concept of a god and no true religion. No marriage or funeral rites existed. Family relationships were close and equality among the members of a group was acknowledged, but one hunter was often accepted as a leader. Though children were often spoiled, their training was done conscientiously. The curses that bedevilled these remarkable people were starvation and family blood feuds, both of which were common.

Recent decades have witnessed dramatic changes in this way of life. The rifle has drastically altered hunting techniques—and has depleted the herds of caribou, thus increasing the danger of starvation. New diseases, social customs, and economic conditions have undermined much that was admirable in these people. Small groups have gradually acquired new skills or new outlets for old ones; yet in general it is true to say that these once proud, independent, self-reliant people would now have great difficulty in surviving without assistance from Ottawa.

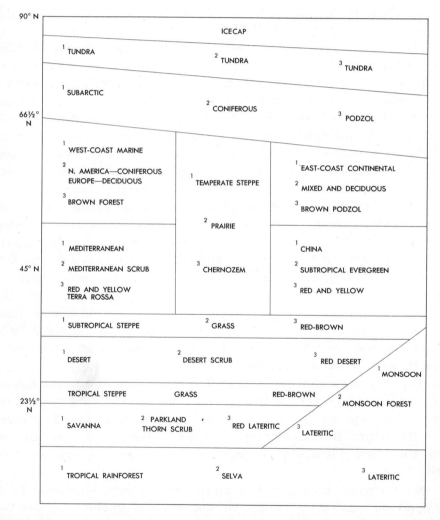

This diagram of a model continent in the Northern Hemisphere shows typical (1) climatic regions, (2) vegetation type, and (3) soil classification. In the diagram no consideration is given to actual continental shape or landforms and, therefore, the effects of these on climatic regions cannot be seen.

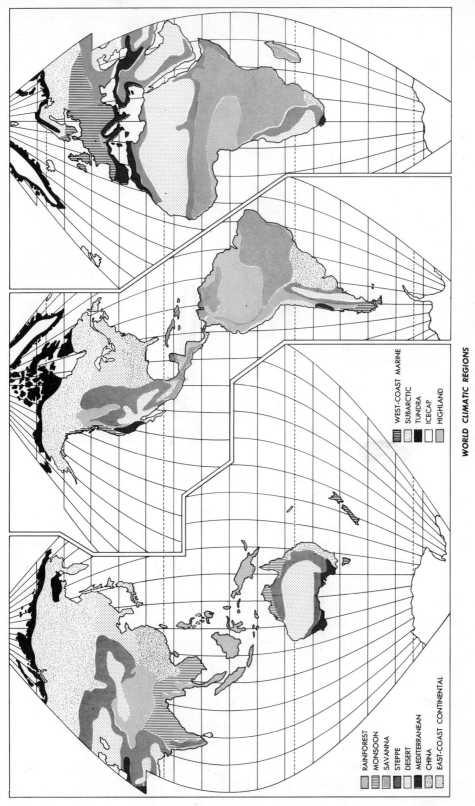

WORLD CLIMATIC REGIONS

The climatic regions shown here are used as the basis for the discussion of climate in this text. One must remember that exceptions occur within each region.

RAINFOREST
MONSOON
SAVANNA
STEPPE
DESERT
MEDITERRANEAN
CHINA
EAST-COAST CONTINENTAL

WEST-COAST MARINE
SUBARCTIC
TUNDRA
ICECAP
HIGHLAND

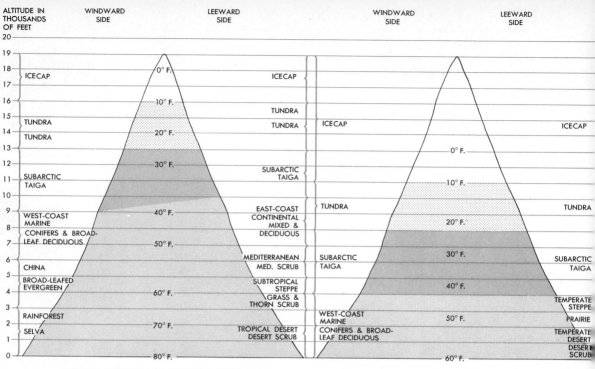

VERTICAL ZONATION OF CLIMATE & VEGETATION ON A TROPICAL MOUNTAIN

VERTICAL ZONATION OF CLIMATE & VEGETATION ON A MID-LATITUDE MOUNTAIN

Vegetation on a mountain varies with the altitude; in a similar manner, vegetation on level terrain varies with the latitude. Thus, a climb up a tropical mountain gives the geographer an experience similar to a trip from the equator to the North Pole. Refer to a geography text of Switzerland or South America and prepare a report on human occupancy in mountainous areas. Be certain to include a discussion on the advantages and the problems of living in such an area.

UNIT REVIEW

1. On a world map show the prevailing winds, dominant pressure cells, and ocean currents experienced during summer in the Northern Hemisphere.

2. On a second map show the prevailing winds, dominant pressure cells, and ocean currents experienced during winter in the Northern Hemisphere.

3. With reference to the above maps and the climatic regions that you have studied, illustrate the effect or effects which each of the following has on world climate: latitudinal location, ocean currents, mountains, prevailing winds, air masses, interior location, pressure cells, altitude, the shift of the sun's rays, and the differential heating of land and water.

4. State and explain at least three of the factors which combine to create,

   (a) the Atacama Desert,

   (b) the heavy summer rains of the Ganges Delta,

   (c) summer drought in the Mediterranean area,

   (d) the aridity of central Asia, and

   (e) the humidity of the St. Lawrence Lowlands.

306

PART FOUR

CULTURAL AND ECONOMIC STUDIES

1. The World's Natural Wealth
2. Man's Industrial Activity
3. Transportation
4. Social Geography

The World's Natural Wealth

1 WORLD AGRICULTURE

Among the most valuable of the natural resources is the soil. Many types of economy can usually be observed in a particular area, but some form of agriculture or soil utilization, is generally the dominant activity. From the steaming tropics to the vast reaches of the subarctic, man can be found carefully tending his crops to protect them against cold, heat, or aridity. Agricultural practices and crop species vary greatly from place to place, but the soil is the basis of our foodstuffs and, therefore, of our economy.

Within the rainforest area, two distinct types of agricultural activity are carried on: migrant agriculture and plantation cropping. In certain favoured parts of the area, intensive subsistence cultivation may be carried on and migration may become unnecessary owing to an increase in soil fertility.

Migrant Agriculture

Migrant agriculture, perhaps the most primitive form of agriculture, is carried on in the hot, equatorial forests of South America, central Africa, southeast Asia, and the East Indian Archipelago. These regions were originally, all covered with selva and hence have developed lateritic soils. As the fertility of these is quickly exhausted, the farmers are forced to migrate to new lands every 3 or 4 years. In some cases the entire village is moved, whereas, in others, only the fields under cultivation are changed.

The photograph shows a typical native settlement in Gabon. In what ways have these people utilized the resources of the area for their livelihood?

The farmers usually clear the land by burning off the forest. This may destroy some of the humus layer which contains much of the organic compounds and mineral elements upon which the tropical vegetation flourished. By means of a hoe or a planting stick, the crops are then planted among the charred roots of the trees. This method, while primitive, is actually most suitable for the tropics as it does not disturb large areas of ground to expose them to the erosive force of the torrential rains.

The chief crop of the Indians in the Amazon Basin, is manioc, a shrub that develops tubers on its roots. These plants, grown from cuttings off older shrubs, develop their bulbous root expansions after about a year of growth. These are then dug, squeezed to extract the poisonous prussic acid, and powdered by hand into flour. The flour, called cassava, produces hard, leathery bread when mixed with water and baked. This bread, the staple food, is supplemented by yams, sweet potatoes, pumpkins, peppers, beans, pineapples, and bananas. Tobacco and coca, two stimulants, are second and third in importance after manioc. The leaves of the coca plant, not to be confused with cocoa, produce cocaine, a narcotic, which is consumed in considerable quantities by the Amazon Indians. In Africa the yam is the chief food; peanuts, kola nut, palm oil, and palm wine have also been added to the diet. In southeast Asia and the East Indies, taro (another bulb-producing shrub), breadfruit, and coconuts are cultivated extensively.

After the soil is exhausted by continuous cropping, the fields are abandoned and new ones must be created. Each group migrates within a certain, well-defined area. Most groups work together as a tribe in land clearing, but each family has its own garden plot which it must plant, weed, and harvest. Hunting and fishing are engaged in by most of the migrant agriculturalists in order to supplement their highly vegetarian diet.

Commercial Plantation Farming

Plantation farming or commercial agriculture is carried on in some rainforest regions such as Java, Sumatra, Malaya, Ceylon, Nigeria, Brazil, and Ecuador. Its purpose is the production of a single crop which can be sold throughout the world.

Unlike the migrant agriculturalist, this type of farming is executed on a large-scale basis. A plantation house is usually erected to accommodate the owner (or manager) and his family. On larger plantations some of the supervisory staff may also live in the plantation house. The workers live in a house, or houses, supplied by the company and usually located in the same general area. If the product of the plantation has to undergo some processing before shipment, a factory or mill is also erected on the property.

The capital to finance such an undertaking is usually forthcoming from some large corporation of an industrial nation. Many plantations are owned outright by foreign companies. Skilled personnel for management, machinery for cultivating, harvesting, and processing, and food for the workers are imported from outside the locality.

The crops most susceptible to plantation methods of production are those that are required in large quantities throughout the world. Bananas, tea, rubber, cacao, hemp, coconuts, quinine, and chicle are the chief products of rainforest plantations. Owing to the 365-day growing season, the cheap labour of the tropics, and the demand for the products, plantation agriculture is usually a very profitable activity. Unfortunately, any economy based on a single crop is subject to severe fluctuations in its fortunes. Overproduction can create a depression in the industry; synthetic products can undercut markets; a poor or diseased crop can result in the loss of millions of dollars; poor management or lack of fertilization can exhaust the soil. All of these factors contribute to making plantation agriculture a risky and expensive proposition.

A heavy crop of bananas in Mali must be propped up. How long will these trees continue to bear fruit?

Cacao pods cling to the trunk of a tree in the Ivory Coast Republic. How are the pods processed before shipment?

Embassy of France

Account for the small cultivators used in this Japanese rice field.

Monsoon Agriculture

This type of agriculture, often termed intensive subsistence farming, or oriental rice culture, is carried on principally in southern China, southeast Asia, parts of India, Japan, and the Philippines. The type of agriculture and the kinds of crops grown, are closely related to the seasons. Characteristic of rice culture is the intensive use of all available land and labour. All of the readily cultivable land is used; indeed, many of the hills have been terraced to provide extra growing space. In addition, most of the villages have been built on land unsuited for agriculture. The steeper slopes often are used for orchards or tea growing, while the least productive areas provide pasture for cattle, water buffalo, or goats.

Because of the large yield per acre and the suitability of this crop to a monsoonal climate, rice is the dominant plant grown. This is planted on the flood plains of rivers, the deltas, and the terraced hillsides just prior to the period of heaviest rains. The rains and the subsequent flooding of the rivers cover the fields with water, and it is in this environment that the rice grows best. By the time the rains have stopped and the fields have dried out, harvesting can begin. The planting, weeding, and harvesting of the rice is nearly all done by hand and requires a vast amount of labour. As a result of this, the average plot yields usually just enough to sustain a large family for a year.

During the dry winter season, a second, or even a third, crop can be grown on the land. Sufficient moisture may be left in the soil or obtained through irrigation to grow wheat, beans, peanuts, sweet potatoes, etc. This crop rotation aids to some extent in preserving the fertility of the soil. Annual deposits of silt laid down during the flood season also enrich the fields.

In areas where it is impossible to flood the fields, a variety of upland rice can be grown, but it is customary to devote these areas to the cultivation of tea bushes, orchards, or even pasture for the few animals that are kept. Livestock raising is not well developed, for the major part of the land must be used for the production of cereals and vegetables for human consumption. Swine and poultry, which can subsist on household waste and on foraging, are raised in most areas.

Wealthier families may own a water buffalo, which is used to pull the plough. Farm ponds and irrigation ditches are used for raising fish and waterfowl to supplement the diet.

Little plantation cropping is done in the monsoon area, but a notable exception is the jute-growing region of the Ganges delta. Here, in marshy areas too wet for most plants, jute is the principal crop. The plant grows from 12 to 20 feet high and its stalk produces the hemp fibres. The stagnant waters of the marshes provide excellent ponds for retting, or soaking, the stalks in order to soften them so that the fibres can be separated from the pulp. The Ganges area enjoys virtually a world monopoly in the production of this fibre.

South Africa Information Service
In which part of South Africa would people grow sugar cane?

Embassy of France
What areas, besides the Ivory Coast, produce coffee?

Savanna Agriculture

Several types of agriculture are carried on in these regions of relatively fertile soil but of insufficient rainfall. Migrant agriculture, plantation farming, intensive subsistence agriculture, and ranching are all practised in the savanna. The wetter areas on the borders of the rainforest are the chief crop-producing regions, while the drier sections are devoted to animal raising.

Migrant agriculture is carried on chiefly in the savanna regions of Africa. The same method of cultivation, namely, by hoe or planting stick, is used here, but the crops are very different from those of the rainforest. Peas, beans, lentils, and peanuts are the staple foods in many an East African's diet. Among the cereals, millet, maize, wheat, and sorghum are grown. Sugar cane and pineapples can be produced in the wetter areas. Despite the wide variety of crops, the migrant leads a precarious existence. During the summer rains his crops do well but, with the coming of the arid winter season, they wither away. It is, usually, because of the lack of water for irrigation during this season that the agriculturalists persist in their migratory ways. Where some water is available all the year round, as in India, the migrant peoples have taken up permanent residence and settled down to raise the same kind of crops. This is termed intensive subsistence agriculture and is usually carried on with the aid of irrigation. Certain crops, such as sisal, cotton, pineapples, sugar cane, and peanuts are grown on plantations for exporting.

Ranching, or the raising of livestock, is done separately, or sometimes in conjunction with crop raising. The chief animal is the cow. The commonest kind raised in India and Africa, and recently introduced into South America, is the humped or Brahman cow. The layer of fatty tissue which forms between the shoulder blades is actually a food reservoir to be used during drought periods. These humped cattle are preferred in the savanna regions because of their reserve food supply, and their ability to resist disease and withstand the great heat. Sheep, goats, and donkeys are kept, but in much smaller numbers.

The majority of the savanna ranchers are nonmigratory, for their flocks can obtain sufficient food from the grasses of the area. Seldom is the forest cover dense enough to prevent light from reaching the ground and producing a good carpet of grass. In the dry winter months, the herds must range widely in search of edible grass.

The people live off the herds and seldom engage in agricultural activities. They milk the cattle, sheep, and goats and use the milk to make butter or cheese. The cattle are seldom slaughtered, but their flesh is eaten when they die. The Hindu of India, of course, is forbidden by his religion to eat beef. The hides are used for clothing and tents. A peculiar custom of many of the African herders is that of drawing blood from young bullocks and adding it to their diet.

Nomadic Herding of the Steppe Regions

Herding in the steppe regions is the chief activity of those areas where there is insufficient rainfall for agriculture. This type of nomadic life is best developed in the semi-arid lands of North Africa, Arabia, central Asia, and Mongolia, where seasonal rainfall makes it necessary that the herders migrate with their herds in search of pasture.

The tribes usually have a permanent headquarters near some oasis or protected valley; here they spend the dry or cold season, whichever the case may be. With the coming of the rains, the entire camp, save for a few caretakers or gardeners, packs up and begins a rapid migration. As the grass has not yet fully developed, considerable ground must be covered in order to find sufficient food for the animals. During the period of maximum rainfall, the herds move slowly and grow fat in preparation for the difficult drought season ahead. As the rains cease, the pastures dry up, and it is once again necessary to move quickly to obtain forage. During the period of greatest drought, the tribes migrate to the oasis, where a reliable supply of water can be obtained. In some cases, the people who have remained behind will have cut and stored some fodder for the animals. Despite the proximity of an oasis, forage is often poor and many animals are consequently forced to survive on the stored fat in their bodies during this dry period. A severe winter may cause the death of over half the herd.

The kind and number of animals that are herded vary with the tribes and the climatic conditions. In the Arabian peninsula many camels and horses are kept; in central Africa cattle are the main animals; North Africa produces camels and sheep; central Asia and Mongolia raise mixed herds of cattle, sheep, goats, and horses. In this latter area of severe winters the animal species are quite different as they must be able to adapt themselves to both drought and cold. The hump-backed cow and the fat-rumped sheep are not as common in the severer winter areas as in the tropical and subtropical steppes. Animals that produce a thick protective coat or fleece are preferred.

The people, e.g., the Bedouins, the Masai, the Kazaks, and the Mongolians, live off their herds almost exclusively. Some agriculture may be carried on near their permanent quarters but, generally speaking, their food is the milk and flesh of their herds, while their clothing is obtained from the fleece and hides. In order to make migration easier, most of the people have portable tents or *yurts* which can be quickly assembled and easily carried. The precarious existence that these people appear to live belies the fact that it has provided them a livelihood for thousands of years, and indeed, it seems destined to do so for many thousands of years more.

Why do these cattle, seen here near Lake Chad, differ from those raised in Canada?

Embassy of France

Why are cattle not used as beasts of burden in Canada? How do people in the Chad Republic guide their animals?

Dates, in Senegal, ripen on the tree. What areas produce most of the world's dates?

This Berber in the Sahara keeps his lonely watch over his flocks. Why do the Berbers wear the peculiar clothing shown here and what animals do they herd?

Oasis Agriculture

Oasis agriculture is carried on in both the steppe and desert areas wherever a sufficient supply of moisture is available to grow crops. The term oasis does not necessarily mean a water hole in a desert region, but is used rather to describe such areas as the fertile Nile valley where water is obtained for crops by irrigation; in fact, Egypt is a great oasis supporting some 22 million people.

In the desert belt of Africa and southwest Asia, the oases are nearly all watered from wells, springs, or small streams. They vary in size, but because of a lack of water, are usually quite small. These oases usually have a similar pattern in respect to agriculture. The fields which produce grain and vegetables surround the water hole so that water can be applied to the crops. Beyond the area that has access to irrigation water are planted the groves of dates or citrus fruit trees. The homes are often built in this area, as the trees supply some protection against the intense heat of the sun. The area surrounding the orchards often supports a thin growth of coarse grass. This is used to pasture goats, camels, or sheep. In these areas, man is often engaged in a struggle against encroaching sand dunes.

Large-scale irrigation projects for oasis agriculture are in operation, or in course of construction, in both tropical and temperate arid regions. The particular crops which can be grown depend on the climate and, therefore, fall into two main categories: those which require a great amount of heat, such as dates, cotton, sugar cane, and rice, and those which will grow in cooler areas, e.g., maize, millet, vegetables, grapes, and citrus fruit.

The most important tropical and subtropical oases are the Tigris-Euphrates, the Indus, and the Nile valleys. Many primitive methods of irrigation are still

315

used in these areas, but dams and reservoirs are being constructed which will provide irrigation all the year round. In some areas these measures will double or triple the agricultural output, as two or three crops can then be grown. The canal system from which water is drawn or siphoned on to the fields is still the commonest irrigation method, although the sprinkler system has been introduced in some areas.

In the temperate deserts, large-scale oasis agriculture is carried on. This is especially true of the Imperial and Gila valleys of the U.S.A., the Volga and Aral Sea areas of the U.S.S.R., and the Murray and Murrumbidgee river valleys of Australia. Most of these regions produce grains, vegetables, and fruit, but much fodder is grown in the U.S.A., cotton in central Asia, and grapes for raisin production in Australia.

A serious problem of most irrigated areas, in general, and of tropical ones in particular, is that of adequate drainage to ensure that the soil will not accumulate salt. Where the evaporation is high, deposits of alkali are left on the fields by the evaporating water. More water must, therefore, be added to dissolve and remove these salts; otherwise the soil will become unfit for cultivation. Mexico is experiencing great difficulty with salt pollution of soil, because she must often use the run-off from U.S. fields to irrigate the crops.

Agriculture of the Mediterranean Regions

Mediterranean agriculture is carried on in all areas having a Mediterranean climate, the products being very similar in all such regions. Because of drought during the summer, warmth-loving fruits are usually grown under irrigation in this season. In the cooler, wet winter, grains are the chief crops. Olives, grapes, figs, and citrus fruits (oranges, lemons, grapefruit, and limes) have long been associated with Mediterranean climates or climatic zones. These crops are often grown for export, whereas the winter crops, wheat, barley, maize, and vegetables, are consumed locally.

Why is most of South Africa's grape harvest marketed abroad as wine or raisins?

What use is made of bulrush millet seen here growing in the Bechuanaland Protectorate?

South Africa Information Service

United Kingdom Information Service

In areas around the Mediterranean Sea, irrigation water is obtained from the mountain streams and, while the coastal plains are not extensive, terracing has been employed to extend the agricultural area. A unique custom, still carried on in certain places, is the annual water auction whereby the owner of the dam on the local stream auctions off his supply of water to the highest bidders. Much of the work in this area is done with the hoe, few draught animals and little machinery being used. This is the chief area for the production of olives and olive oil. The olives themselves are a staple in the diet of the people, and the oil is used for cooking and to replace butter. Sheep and goats provide meat and milk for the populace. The milkman may stop outside the village houses and deliver the milk to the customer direct from the herd that accompanies him.

In contrast to the small, hand-labour farms of Mediterranean Europe, southern California farms are large, mechanized, commercial enterprises which use the most up-to-date and efficient methods yet evolved. This is possible owing to the lack of population pressure on the land and to the reliable supply of water that comes from mountain snows. Dams have been constructed on the Colorado, the San Joaquin, and the Sacramento rivers. From these a series of canals radiates throughout the Central Valley and southern California.

The low, level flood plains of these rivers produce most of the early vegetables which appear on market stands of Canada and the U.S.A. as early as March. Lettuce, tomatoes, celery, and cauliflower rank high in the list of products. In order to get these products to the markets of the more heavily populated areas, much machinery must be used in the planting, cultivating, and harvesting operations. Refrigeration, packing, and canning plants are located throughout the area. Branch railway lines connect these plants with transcontinental lines and, hence, with the manufacturing districts of the east.

Farmers have learned to plant the citrus groves on gently sloping land to avoid frosts during the winter. Oranges, lemons, and grapefruit are grown here under irrigation. Olives and avocados have recently made their appearance, while grapes have long been a staple crop. Almonds and walnuts are now being produced in considerable quantities. On bench lands too difficult and high to irrigate, some barley and beans are grown, but generally, these areas are left for pasture. Considerable quantities of alfalfa are grown for the dairy herds that supply Los Angeles and San Francisco.

Agriculture of the China Climatic Region

Agriculture in this region has reached its greatest development in southern China and southeastern U.S.A. Although the crops grown are similar, the method of production is different. In China much hand labour and intensive cultivation are used, whereas machinery and commercial plantations characterize the agriculture of the U.S.A.

Terracing is, once again, used in China to supplement the rich agricultural lands of the river flood plains and deltas. As there is a distinct monsoonal effect felt here, the rivers are subject to flooding in summer. Coupling this monsoonal flooding with the warmth of the climate, we are not astonished to find that rice is a staple crop of the coastal region. Indeed, where irrigation is used, two crops per year can be grown. Another product of this almost subtropical region is sugar cane. On the hills, corn and sweet potatoes are cultivated, while mulberry trees and tea bushes dot the steeper slopes. Farther inland the Szechwan or Red Basin produces cotton, hemp, tea, citrus fruit, tobacco, and wheat. The hillsides here are covered with tung trees, the seeds of which produce a valuable oil for paints and varnishes.

Once again, animals are conspicuous by their absence. Apart from their meat, Szechwan pigs supply the top-quality bristles that constitute one of China's important export items. The hills in the west provide pasture land for cattle, sheep, horses, and yaks. The hides and skins are important products of the area.

In North America, the agriculture of the China climatic region is very similar to that found in the Mediterranean areas with the exception that irrigation is not necessary. Truck farming supplies most of the vegetables grown during the winter months. Because the soils of this area are quite highly leached, the best truck crops are produced in marshy areas where the organic content is higher. Beans, cabbages, onions, tomatoes, watermelons, and strawberries constitute the chief cash crop. Orchards of citrus fruit are grown without irrigation, but great expense and labour are at times required to protect the groves from frost.

Among the grains, rice, maize, kaffir corn, and wheat are prominent. Inland lies the world-famous cotton belt. Here, in moderately leached pedalfer soils, enjoying a warm climate and a long growing season (over 200 days), is one of the world's largest commercial plantation-farming areas. Most of the cotton is grown on large mechanized farms, but the small, hand-labour farms still contribute a considerable quantity of the total output. To prevent soil erosion, corn, wheat, soybeans, or peanuts, are often grown on a rotation basis.

What is the purpose of breaking off the top of the tobacco plant as this Uganda farmer is doing?

What areas, besides the Mediterranean climatic regions, produce citrus fruit?

United Kingdom Information Service

Specialized crops grown in the area are sugar cane and flax. The Everglades area is the chief producer of sugar cane, while flax is grown as a winter crop in the Gulf region. Through the introduction of new cattle breeds, particularly the Brahman, the beef-production industry has rapidly expanded in recent years. Small dairy herds and huge poultry farms are also characteristic of the region.

In southeastern Australia, dairying is more predominant owing to the cooler temperatures experienced in the Great Dividing Range. Eastern South Africa has an economy similar to that of the U.S. area described above, while the China climatic region of South America specializes in raising livestock.

East-Coast Continental Agriculture

East-coast continental agriculture is carried on in only two major regions of the world—northeastern North America and northeastern Asia. Previously, northeast China had been an area of small land holdings, intensive cultivation, and hand labour—methods similar in most respects to the agricultural practices of southeast Asia. Today several scores of mechanized state farms have been set up by the Communist government of the People's Republic of China. These communes, as they are called, are fashioned after the collective farms of the U.S.S.R. Under this system the Chinese peasant is being encouraged to abandon the intensive subsistence method of agriculture that he formerly practised and instead to participate in a large-scale, state-organized agricultural plan. This method is being used in order that small holdings and inefficient methods of production may be done away with.

The main crops are soya beans, wheat, sugar beet, maize, flax, and tobacco. In the Shantung peninsula, peanuts are cultivated, and silkworms are raised on the mulberry trees grown in the area. Along the lower reaches of the Hwang Ho River, cotton is produced in Hopei province, China's chief cotton producer. Such temperate-zone fruits as apples and cherries are also produced in considerable quantities. The hills of the north are used as pasture land for sheep and cattle, but again, the people rely mainly on poultry and swine for their meagre supply of meat.

In northeastern North America, the agriculture is marked by a considerable degree of specialization. There are many mixed farms in the area, but generally speaking, each local region specializes in a particular product. In the St. Lawrence Lowlands alone, a great variety of specialized crops is grown. From the Niagara Peninsula come such temperate-climate fruits as peaches, pears, grapes, and apples. The Delhi-Tillsonburg area is Canada's chief tobacco-producing region. The Leamington district specializes in vegetable and root crops, while dairy farms extend from Lake Huron to Quebec City.

Most of the farmers of these areas gain their income from one principal source, such as the sale of milk, meat, or vegetables. Because of this aspect of the economy, the term commercial farming can be applied to most of the farming operations in the area. A problem that this type of economy experiences is similar to that occurring on plantation farms, namely, a loss of revenue when a particular specialty is not in demand.

The principal crops grown here are the cereals and vegetables. As winters are quite severe in this area, oats, barley, rye, and wheat, i.e., the hardier cereals, are grown quite extensively. Corn is a major product of north central U.S.A. A wide variety of vegetables is grown and marketed either fresh or canned.

Potatoes blossom forth in New Brunswick. What areas of N.B. produce the potato as a commercial crop? *What advantages do the plastic covers afford this Japanese farmer?*

Agriculture in the West-Coast Marine Climate

The west-coast marine climate produces crops similar to those grown on the east coast. The main area of production, western Europe, is characterized by intensive cultivation, little mechanization, small holdings, and varying degrees of commercialization. Along the wetter Atlantic regions, much of the land is devoted to pasture, fodder-raising fields, and temperate-zone fruit orchards. The main agricultural area, the north-European plain, contains one of the most productive areas in the world. Vegetables, cereals, and fodder crops can be grown throughout most of the area.

Much mixed farming is done, but there are certain areas of specialization. Denmark is noted for its dairy herds, Brittany for its apple orchards, Holland for its root and bulb crops, Germany for its hops and potatoes, and the highlands of England and Scotland for their sheep. So great is the variety of crops which can be grown here, that the European is usually faced with the happy situation of having to choose between what will grow best and what is in greatest demand on the market.

Owing to a high percentage of arable land, a knowledge of the use of fertilizers, and the desire to produce good crops, European farmers generally enjoy a standard of living above that provided by most agricultural regions. Peasant villages are commoner in Europe than among the isolated farming communities of North America. This is partly due to the system of landholdings, in which fields may be scattered, and also partly to past practices whereby workers grouped together to clear land. A unique feature of the Alps region is *transhumance*. This is the practice of the farmer's or shepherd's moving with his flocks of sheep, goats, or cattle to summer pastures in the mountains and then returning to spend the winter in a low, protected valley.

Other areas of the world where this marine climate is experienced are mostly mountainous, and hence the rainfall is considerably heavier. New Zealand specializes in raising sheep and cattle on a commercial basis. Much of the produce is exported in the form of butter, cheese, wool, or meat. Tasmania is an area of mixed grain and livestock farming but also produces many apples. Southwestern Chile has a narrow coastal plain where some grain and vegetables are grown, but the mountainous nature of the country dictates that most of the area be left in forest or used for pasture land. A similar situation exists in Canada and the U.S.A. The river deltas are cultivated to provide vegetables, fruit, and dairy products for the large cities. The uplands are used for pasture or forestry.

Temperate-Steppe Agriculture

Agriculture of the temperate-steppe type is practised on the plains of North America, the steppes of the U.S.S.R., the pampas of Argentina, and the higher plains of the Great Australian Basin. Here, the long hot days of summer, the fertile chernozem soils, and the wide expanse of level land combine to create an ideal set of conditions for the production of wheat. Even though the yield per acre may not be as high as in more humid climates, the level land allows the entire operation to be mechanized; hence, commercial farming is dominant.

What area of France is noted for its sugar beet industry? Why is the industry centred there?

Corn is irrigated by siphoning in Nebraska. What are the uses of this crop?

Embassy of France

U.S.D.A. Photo

The best wheat is grown in the tall-grass prairie. Bordering this on the cooler side is a zone of mixed grain and livestock farming. The short-grass prairie and the semi-arid regions are used almost exclusively for grazing beef cattle or sheep. Irrigation is now being extended to this area; e.g., the South Saskatchewan project is aimed at making fertile farmland out of a semidesert. Although many cereals and vegetables can be grown under irrigation, the sugar beet seems best suited to these conditions. It is now being cultivated in most temperate steppe areas and used for animal feed or the industrial production of sugar.

Agriculture in the Subarctic

The subarctic with its cool summers, short growing season, podzolic soils, and summer frosts is suited only to the hardiest of crops. What farming there is, is largely of the subsistence type and is supplementary to some other industry such as forestry, fishing, or mining. The subarctic type of agriculture is generally termed the fodder-root system, but some of the hardier cereals can be grown as well. The principal crops are hay, oats, barley, potatoes, and vegetables. In a few more favoured areas, such as the Clay Belt and the Lake St. John region of northern Ontario and Quebec, respectively, wheat and dairy cattle have been added to the agricultural economy. The annual harvest of such small fruits as currants, raspberries, strawberries, and blueberries is regarded as providing a delicacy that is welcomed as a supplement to an otherwise rather stolid diet.

Arctic or Tundra Agriculture

Agriculture is almost nonexistent in the tundra, but some crops started in greenhouses can be raised in the long days of an Arctic summer. As far north as the Arctic Circle cabbages, lettuce, turnips, radishes, and potatoes have been successfully grown under glass, or at least started in greenhouses. Granting that crop growing is not a normal practice, there may, nonetheless, be more agricultural possibilities in the Arctic than are generally supposed to exist. At present, experimental agricultural stations in Canada and the U.S.S.R. are exploring these possibilities with a view to making Arctic communities self-sufficient in garden produce.

Most of the native inhabitants of tundra regions live off the animal life, wild or domesticated, that exists in this region. The Eskimo, whom you have already studied, is chiefly a hunter and fisher, whereas the nomadic Lapps and Samoyeds of northern Russia live off their herds of domesticated reindeer.

2 FOREST WEALTH

The term forestry has been variously defined as the science of cultivating forests, the promotion of forest growth, systematic forest management, and the art of planting and managing forests. All of these imply that man, in some way, utilizes the forest or its products for his own ends; all of them imply, too, that forestry includes both the activities of the primitive food gatherers of the tropics and the highly scientific forest management of the Scandinavian countries. With this in mind, then, it is probable that the reader will better understand this particular field if he examines the way of life of forest dwellers in selected areas.

Food Gatherers of Equatorial Forests

The Semang, who are forest dwellers of the Malayan peninsula, represent man's early use and exploitation of forest regions. Here, in the hill country of Malaya, live small groups of dwarfed Negroes, or Negritos. Since these people are entirely dependent for their livelihood on the wild products of the forests, and since few plants of the same kind grow in close proximity, the Semang migrate continually.

Pan American Union

Besides breadfruit and yams, what does the Brazilian Indian collect for food?

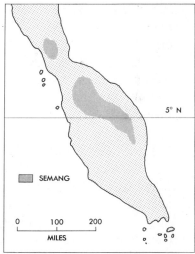

5° N

SEMANG

0   100   200

MILES

Why do the Semangs prefer the rugged hills of the interior instead of the more fertile coastal plain?

As the purpose of these migrations is food gathering, movement is slow, and each group usually covers only 4 or 5 miles a day. They collect a wide assortment of berries, leaves, nuts, roots, tubers, and the soft pith of certain trees. The most important food is the wild yam, which is dug with long, fire-hardened sticks.

323

Embassy of France

What is the purpose of the head-gear worn by this pygmy?

A native of Dahomey climbs a palm to harvest its fruit. What products are obtained from the various types of palms?

The daily produce is carried in baskets woven from rattan or bamboo. Much of the food is cooked in long tubes of green bamboo; the tubes burn slowly, thus allowing the vegetables in the interior to cook. During certain seasons of the year the group returns to its own territory to collect the fruit of the durian, mangosteen, and perak trees. The Semang regard these trees as private property, but the produce from them, as indeed the produce from all sources, is divided among the group.

The utensils or weapons of these dwarf peoples are also obtained from the forests. A heavy hardwood stake with a fire-hardened tip is the chief hunting weapon. Bows are made from pliant langset tree branches and strung with animal sinew or bark fibre. The arrows are made from bamboo and tipped with the deadly poison, ipoh, which is obtained by boiling down the sap of the upas tree. Fish traps and baskets are made from the fibres of rattan or bamboo.

The clothing of the Semang is scant and consists of a girdle or loincloth of woven bark. This cloth is made from the inner fibres of bark from the breadfruit tree, the fibres having been pounded with wooden bats until pliable. Necklaces of shiny black leaves and bamboo combs are often worn as good-luck or disease-prevention charms.

The habitation, or camp, of the migrants is of simple construction. It consists of a sloping roof held aloft at one end by forked sticks. The frame of the roof is made of bamboo poles tied together with fibres. Huge rattan leaves are folded and used to thatch the roof. This thatch is held in place by piling brush or tying poles over the leaves. A small platform or couch made from split bamboo is constructed underneath this shelter to provide a dry place to sleep.

Lumbering in the Rainforest and Monsoon Regions

This industry has not been as fully developed in the tropics as it has been in more temperate regions. The reasons for this are many. Solid stands of a single species do not grow in this climate. The heavy rainfall and heat produce a wealth of bushes that must be hacked through if one is to reach the more valuable species. Felling the tree is often a difficult process, for vines and creepers may cause it to lodge in another tree, thus necessitating the felling of the second tree. Then, too, transportation of the logs may be difficult, because the ground is frequently soft and swampy and machinery cannot be used to move the logs to water. Even when the logs arrive at the river bank, many of them are too dense in texture to float and rafts must be made in order to move them to a sawmill.

Mahogany is the most valuable hardwood exported from the tropics. Some of the natives engage sporadically in cutting these trees and floating them out of the swamps during the flood season. Some lumber companies employ the natives to locate the trees and cut trails to them. Where possible, small caterpillar tractors are sent in to bring the logs out. Once a mahogany tree is found, its location is noted and the tree is then climbed. Such a tall vantage point, emergent from, and towering above, the general forest level, is ideal for spotting other mahogany trees. The West Indies produce the best mahoganies, though Brazil and Africa ship larger quantities of this wood.

The second most valued tropical tree is the teak, which is found in relatively pure stands in the monsoon forests of southeast Asia. As teak contains an oil that acts as a preservative, it is prized for shipbuilding. In contrast to the mahogany of the rainforest, teak is not buoyant. The trees are prepared for cutting by girdling them and allowing them to stand for a few years before cutting. During this period the tree dries out, becomes lighter, and can, therefore, be floated to the mills. In areas where the teak is cut green, elephants are used to handle the logs, and rafts are built for floating the timber down the river. Mahogany and teakwood are so valuable that they are used mainly for expensive furniture or for veneer, the latter being a thin coating of wood glued over inexpensive woods.

What African countries are major exporters of mahogany?

What uses are there for these rosewood (okoumé) logs being floated to the mill in Gabon?

Among other trees felled as timber are cabinet woods valued for their grain and colouration. Rosewood, brazilwood, lignum, greenheart, ebony, and logwood are all used in the furniture and plywood industries. Spanish cedar is used in making cigar boxes and as wood for pencils. Balsa has found a market in the toy factories of the world. Furthermore, there is a wide variety of softwoods that can be used for paper making or shredded to produce the excelsior used as packing in crates.

Other Forest Activities of the Tropics

The collection of rubber from trees scattered through the rainforest has been carried on in Brazil and the Congo since the invention of the automobile created a demand for this product. The rise of rubber plantations in southeast Asia caused this industry to decline in Brazil, but it has never died out. Before chicle is shipped to the chewing gum factories of North America, it is gathered and coagulated in a manner similar to that used in the handling of native rubber. The oil palm, the babassu palm, and the brazilwood tree all produce edible nuts and vegetable oils suitable for cooking or making margarine. The tagua, or ivory, nut from a certain variety of palm tree, has a shell so hard it can actually be used as a substitute for ivory. The bark of the cinchona tree is boiled to produce quinine; tannic acid for the leather industry is obtained from oak bark. Among the many trees which are cultivated on plantations are the cacao, banana, coconut, and breadfruit, as well as the above-mentioned rubber and oil-yielding palm trees.

The Mixed Forests of the China Climate

The type of vegetation found in these regions has been termed broadleaf evergreen and mixed coniferous-broadleaf. On the sandy soils of the American southeast coastal regions are excellent stands of longleaf, loblolly, and slash pine. These forests produce lumber for pulpwood and resins and gums for naval stores.

The lumber derived from these pines is of a lower value per board foot than that which comes from subarctic forests. Owing to the quantity produced, however, (20% of U.S. softwood production) these forests are of marked economic significance. The yellow pine is used extensively in house construction; longleaf-pine lumber is used for flooring and house trim; both the loblolly and the shortleaf pines are used for making newsprint; and the sawdust waste of most varieties is used for making wallboard. As the markets for these products are mainly in the north and northeast, transportation by rail or ship must be provided. Much of this relatively infertile area has been opened up for forestry by the construction of transportation routes.

Because of their use in the days of wooden ships, turpentine, tar, and resin are called naval stores. The pines, especially longleaf and slash, are tapped by cutting long gashes in the bark and collecting the gum which exudes from the incision. This material is collected and distilled to produce the naval stores.

Many cypress swamps, such as the world-famous Okefenokee and the Everglades, produce weather-resistant shingles and exterior house siding. Inland from these swamps and the piney forests, one can find stands of oak, tupelo, and black gum. From these areas valuable hardwood lumber is obtained for furniture and cabinet making.

In the Asiatic regions of China climate, much of the original forest has been cleared for agricultural purposes. However, Japan and Formosa still have valuable timber reserves. Three products, distinctly oriental, come from this area. Formosa supplies three-quarters of the world's supply of camphor. Bamboo is planted and cultivated like a field crop to provide fuel and building materials, which have become scarce in southeast Asia. Lacquer, a glossy paintlike material, is produced from the sap of the lacquer tree.

Other forests of a similar nature but of local importance are the lumbering regions of the Great Dividing Range in Australia, which produce kauri pine and eucalyptus trees. Forests of yerba maté, the tree which produces Paraguayan tea, cover much of southern Brazil, Paraguay, and northern Argentina.

The Temperate Hardwoods

These forests, once regarded as obstacles to settlement and growth in the U.S.A., now provide a wood-hungry world with much of its hardwood products. Once extending throughout the east-coast continental climate of both North America and Asia, these forests have been reduced to less accessible areas of the U.S.A. Relatively pure stands of hickory, oak, walnut, chestnut, ash, maple, elm, and cherry can still be found in the Appalachians and southern Canada.

Logging of hardwoods is often done by small operators who own portable sawmills. When a lease is obtained for an area, the mill is moved in piece by piece and set up in a suitable location. Crews are sent out to fell the timber and several trucks are employed to bring the logs to the mill. The waste from the logs is often used to fuel the mill. When the area has been cut over, the trucks are used to move the mill to a new location.

The produce of temperate forests is usually sold in the form of lumber or veneer. The uses of the hardwood are many and varied. Furniture of all kinds is made from a variety of woods. Oak flooring and ornamental panelling are bought by the house-construction industry. Axe handles, hockey sticks, and salad bowls are just a few examples of articles which can be fashioned from wood.

A similar type of forest is found in western Europe. Here, too, much of the forested area has been converted to crop land. Although western Europe has to import a considerable amount of her lumber, the practice of forest management has reached its greatest development in this area. Owing to the scarcity of wood, the governments of many countries have become engaged in the lumber business and the regulation of forest industries is, therefore, relatively easy. Here forests are planted and tended as carefully as the Canadian tends his vegetable crops. The seedlings are planted very close together so that later thinning can provide bean and hop poles. A second thinning at a later date produces laths for cratings or for frameworks of plaster homes. At maturity, the remaining trees can be sawn into lumber or construction beams. Many of the German municipalities own forests which they use to supply local needs.

Forestry of the West-Coast Marine Climate

The forests of western North America contain the finest stands of coniferous trees in the world. The equable temperatures, the heavy rainfall, and the long growing season combine to create the best possible conditions suitable for the growth of California redwood, Douglas fir, Engleman and Sitka spruce, and western red cedar.

Because of the steepness of the mountain slopes, where possible, logging is done along the coasts of rivers. Here the huge forest giants are felled and transported with the aid of machinery. Giant diesel-powered trucks are used to pull the logs to the railhead or the seacoast. From here they are transported by rail, barge, or boom to the various mills.

The forest industries of the west coast of North America are highly mechanized and recent years have seen a trend towards modernizing and streamlining the various operations. In order to appreciate this more fully, let us examine the integrated forestry operations of Crown Zellerbach Canada Limited. This company operates a wide variety of installations and facilities: several logging camps on Vancouver Island and the mainland; the Ocean Falls and Elk Falls pulp and paper

What is the function of the portable steel spar shown here on Vancouver Island?

Crown Zellerbach Canada Limited

plants; paper products converting plants at Richmond and Kelowna; the sawmills at Elk Falls and Richmond; a combined sawmill and plywood plant at Fraser Mills; sales offices in ten Canadian cities; and many retail lumber yards in the Prairie Provinces.

Trees which are felled on company-managed timber lands are sorted and selected to be sent to the sawmill, the pulp plant, or the plywood plant. This initial selection insures the best possible use of the logs and a minimum of waste, for the larger trees supply lumber and plywood and the smaller ones pulpwood for the paper industry.

Fraser Mills serves as an example of the scientific processing of forest products. When the logs arrive at Vancouver, they are stored in the 10-mile-long booming grounds that extend along the Fraser River. Then they are hauled into the barker plant, where the bark is removed and stored for fuel. Depending on the size and quality of the logs, they are next sorted and sent either to the plywood lathes or the whirring saw blades. Previously, a shingle mill was operated at the same location, but as a result of the competition from asphalt shingles and for other reasons, it has closed down.

Some of the slabs and trimmings from the plywood plant and the sawmill are sent through a chipper that reduces them to a size such that they can be transported by conveyor belt and compressed air to the stockpile or a transport barge. These chips are an important by-product of the mill, because they can be conveyed by large, open barges to the plants at Ocean Falls or Elk Falls where they are used in making paper. This material, which had previously been burned as a waste product, now represents an annual saving of 43 million board feet, or one quarter of the output of the Fraser Mills lumber operation. Bark and sawdust, called hog fuel, are automatically fed into the burners at the sawmill and produce enough steam to operate two turbine generators which provide power for the plant. The electricity produced could provide lights for a city of 10,000 people. Drying, planing, and storage facilities complete the operation at this mill. Truck-loading facilities are available for deliveries arising from local sales; railways connect the mill with the Canadian and U.S. markets; and dock facilities provide an outlet for products going to overseas buyers.

wn Zellerbach Canada Limited

How is the sharp list acquired on this self-dumping barge?

At Elk Falls, Vancouver Island, newsprint rolls off a paper machine. How are the various grades of paper obtained?

Crown Zellerbach Canada Limited

This brief summary of integrated forest industries should serve to impress on the reader the big-business and long-range planning that marks much of the forest activities on the west coast of North America. However, many small logging firms operate in B.C., either independently or as contractors for larger firms. This integrated use of forest resources is in sharp contrast to that of forestry in the tropics, or even in most of the temperate hardwood areas. Similar operations are now being started, or have been under way for some time, in the Scandinavian countries, which lead the world in forest management and reforestation. Argentina, Chile, and New Zealand, now equipped with modern machinery, are also lumber and paper producers of note.

The Taiga

The taiga, or coniferous forest region, is the most extensive forest region in the world. It extends through the subarctic regions of Alaska, Canada, and the U.S.S.R., and, perhaps because of the climate, is the least exploited of the forest regions. Until recent years, lumbering was carried on only along the southern edges of this great forest. The introduction of paper-making processes has provided a market for the smaller trees of the cool northern areas. The result has been an expansion of the industry into the muskeg country of the north.

What furs are obtained from the Kamchatka peninsula? *Embassy of the U.S.S.R.*   *Embassy of France* Why are softwoods preferred for match production?

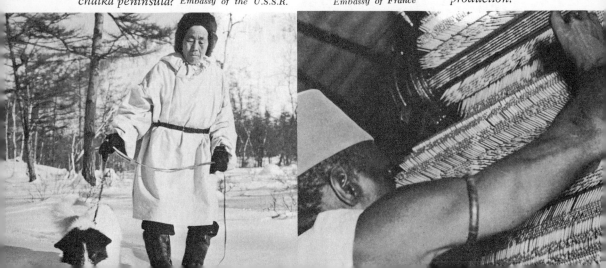

The Spruce Falls pulp and paper mill and the company town of Kapuskasing are situated on the Kapuskasing River. What are the advantages of this site?

Company towns are a feature of this recent expansion. Under this system, a large pulp company obtains the rights to a timber reserve. Choosing a site which is close to a river for its transportation and electric-power production, the company erects its mill. A town site for its employees is planned and built by the company. Schools, recreation facilities, public utilities, etc., are also provided. The employee enjoys a reduced rental rate, plus free use of the other facilities which have been made available. Kapuskasing, Smooth Rock Falls, and Terrace Bay were all built by private companies, although individuals other than the employees have subsequently bought land and taken up residence in some of the towns.

Canada is the world's leading producer of pulp and the second largest producer of paper. Many of the pulp plants are owned by foreign companies, but Canada does benefit from the wages paid to the workers, from the taxes collected on the exported paper products, and from dividends paid to stockholders.

Recently, Sweden, Finland, and Russia have been making gains in the pulp industry; indeed, much of Europe's paper products come from these countries. Because of her vast reserves of timber, the U.S.S.R. may become a strong competitor for markets that are now enjoyed by Canada.

Besides the pulp industry, lumbering and plywood manufacturing are also carried on in the coniferous forest. Spruce, balsam, and poplar are the chief species used for making pulp, whereas pine is the most valued for lumber and plywood.

Another activity associated with these forests is the fur industry. Many varieties of fur-bearing animals inhabit the taiga regions and provide a valuable raw material for the clothing industry. Muskrat, mink, beaver, and fox are the most important species; but others, such as otter, ermine, and sable are more valuable because of their rarity.

331

3 WORLD FISHERIES

Fish, one of the world's greatest resources, are found in quantity sufficient for commercial exploitation in only a few areas. The chief of these are the seas off northwestern Europe, the Canadian Maritimes, northeastern Asia, and northwestern North America. Several other fishing grounds of considerable local importance are located adjacent to California, the West Indies, the Mediterranean area, New Zealand, and Tasmania.

Because of the vast extent of ocean, it is astonishing that such a relatively small area of it is productive. This is due, mostly, to the particular set of circumstances which must combine to create a rich fishing ground. *Cool water temperatures* seem to be essential to ensure a catch which comprises only one or two varieties capable of being processed on a large scale. Accordingly, most of the food fish are caught in the cool waters of the mid-latitudes. The warmer tropical waters are not as productive and contain thousands of species. As each variety must be processed differently, it is almost impossible to carry on a commercial operation in equatorial regions.

Plankton, or marine plant and animal life, also is a requisite for the fishing industry. These microscopic, one-celled plants grow in abundance and form the principal food for relatively minute floating animals. Small fish feed on both the plant and animal life; they, in turn, are eaten by larger fish. Certain sea mammals, such as whales, feed on the fish. In this manner a plant-animal relationship is maintained.

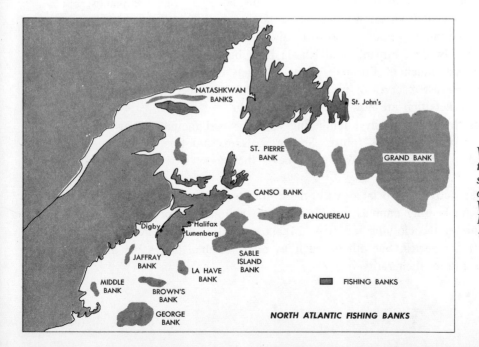

NATASHKWAN BANKS

St. John's

ST. PIERRE BANK

GRAND BANK

CANSO BANK

BANQUEREAU

Digby • Halifax
• Lunenberg

JAFFRAY BANK

SABLE ISLAND BANK

LA HAVE BANK

MIDDLE BANK

BROWN'S BANK

GEORGE BANK

■ FISHING BANKS

NORTH ATLANTIC FISHING BANKS

Why is it difficult to implement conservation practices on these banks? What problems do Nova Scotia fishermen have in marketing their catch?

Embassy of France

Mauritanians use gill nets to harvest the resources of the sea. Besides fish, what other resources does the sea contain?

What is the relationship between this method of marketing fish at Dakar, Senegal, and the light rainfall of the area?

All of the major fishing areas are characterized by the meeting of cold arctic **currents** and warm tropical ones. The mixing of these warm and cold waters promotes fish life for tropical waters abound in marine plants, whereas arctic waters have an abundance of animal life. Numerous **rivers** emptying into the ocean provide fresh-water plankton and spawning grounds for the fish. **Shallow water** is the most basic of fish-ecology requirements, for sunlight cannot promote sufficient growth of plankton below 600 feet. All of the major fishing grounds contain areas of shallow water called *banks*.

Many different varieties of fish and marine animals are used by man and many different methods are used to catch them. Salmon are trapped in the rivers; whales are harpooned at sea; sponges are obtained by diving; clams are dug out of the mud; and seals are shot or clubbed on the ice floes. All of these operations are included in the term fishery.

More conventional methods of catching the fish are the use of hand lines, gill nets, purse seines, and trawl nets. Seines are large nets that can be closed around a school of fish, whereas trawls or drags are conical-shaped nets that are pulled behind a ship. On the beach at low tide, dry-land fishermen often erect poles with gill nets suspended between them. After the daily tide has come and gone, the fishermen make their way along the beach by horse and wagon picking the fish from the nets as they proceed.

Recently, airplanes or helicopters have been employed to locate the schools of fish and radio the information to the fishing ships. An electronic depth recorder has been converted into a fish-finder, and indeed several other devices ranging from electronic to radar inventions have been used to locate fish with some degree of success.

What advantages do the Norwegian fishermen (right) enjoy over the Senegalese (left)?

The Pacific Salmon

As an example of the various activities that are connected with the fishing industry, let us consider the salmon-fishing industry of British Columbia. Here, in the almost perfect conditions of water temperature, ocean currents, and food supply, five distinct types of salmon thrive. These are the sockeye, pink, coho, chum, and spring—all species of the same race.

Salmon fishing is a seasonal industry as most fish are taken during the migrating period in summer. The fish return in cycles to their spawning grounds in the rivers; some come back every two years, others every four years, and a few species every five or six years. Because of the differences in the cycles, there will be some salmon returning each year.

The earliest fishing on the west coast was done in the streams and rivers by the Indians, who used dip nets, spears, hooks, baskets, and several kinds of sunken or suspended nets. They dried or smoked the fish and stored it for the winter. Today gill nets are the most important gear in taking salmon. Off the coast, these nets are suspended in the water and extend a quarter of a mile in length. Boats operating on the lower reaches of the rivers cannot use nets more than 900 feet long.

Power boats have increased the use of purse seines, dragnets, and trolling. This latter method consists of simply pulling through the water a line with a number of baited hooks or lures attached to it. By the use of these methods the fisheries annually catch several million of each species.

Once the catch arrives in port it must be quickly processed. Millions of pounds of salmon are frozen for shipment, but the canneries still handle the bulk of the pack. In earlier days it was necessary to have many small canneries scattered along the coast, but with the use of refrigeration the catch can now be transported over longer distances. As a result, the industry has tended to become centralized in a few major areas. Some factory ships process and can the fish on board, thus eliminating one stage in processing, and getting their catch promptly to market.

Recently many problems have arisen in the industry because certain manufacturing plants have added waste pollution to the waters. Moreover, hydro dams have hindered the progress of fish upstream and flooding by the these same dams has ruined many good spawning beds. Fortunately, far-sighted individuals have forced through legislation which has overcome these problems to some extent. As an aid to conservation of our fish resources, commercial catches are being limited, the lengths of nets are now determined by law, and fishways or ladders have been constructed to help the salmon reach the spawning grounds. Still further conservation measures are necessary if we are to continue to reap the wealth of the Pacific salmon.

UNIT REVIEW

Questions

1. What is meant by geographical adaptation in plants?

2. What problems peculiar to the tropics confront the operators of plantations in these regions?

3. Why are so many arid and semidesert lands devoted to pastoralism?

4. List and locate the world's main cotton-growing regions.

5. Name some products of the China climatic regions which are grown in the Orient but not in the U.S.A. Account for the difference in the crops grown.

6. Why is the goat the principal animal raised in the Mediterranean region of Europe?

7. Explain why dairying has developed to a greater extent in New Zealand than in Australia.

8. Explain the differences in ranching, transhumance, and nomadic herding.

9. Why do the Eskimos prefer the northern extremities of Canada as their habitat rather than inland regions of the Northwest Territories?

10. In what forest region are each of the following found: loblolly pine, cypress, oak, mahogany, yerba maté, hickory, teak, Parana pine, cottonwoods, larch?

11. Why have the dense tropical forests not been more fully exploited?

12. Locate the four major fishing areas of the world and name the warm and cold currents which affect them.

Research Assignments

1. In the areas of continental or temperate-steppe climates wheat is grown mainly between 40° and 50° latitude. Most of the important producing regions have between 15 and 30 inches of precipitation with the maximum falling in summer. Ninety days, at least, are required for the growing period, and summer temperatures must average above 60° F. Chernozem soils, developed under a prairie-grass vegetative cover, produce the best wheat.

   Consult an economic atlas or an economic geography text and prepare a map of world wheat distribution. Examine each of the major wheat-producing regions to determine how closely climatic and soil conditions correspond to the above requirements. Note any outstanding exceptions and attempt to explain why they exist. Note the critical summer average temperature above which wheat cannot be grown. Attempt to find out the winter average temperature which will determine whether the wheat will be planted in the spring or the fall.

2. Find the optimum conditions conducive to the best yield from the following crops: rice, citrus fruit, cotton, and flax.

3. List the climatic regions; opposite each one listed fill in the type of vegetation and soil and state the chief agricultural crops of the region.

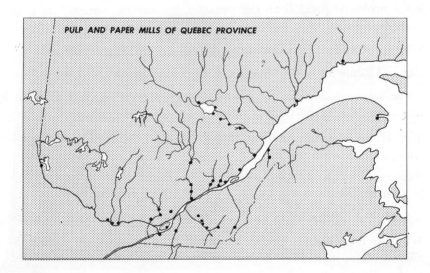

PULP AND PAPER MILLS OF QUEBEC PROVINCE

4. Identify as many as possible of the cities and towns marked on the map. Account for the peculiar distribution of the pulp-and-paper towns. What other associated industries are carried on in this region? If possible, visit a pulp company and prepare a report on its operation.

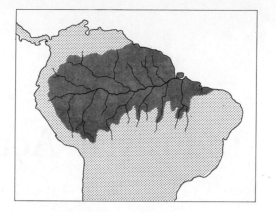

5. The distribution of rainforest in Brazil is confined almost entirely to the Amazon Basin. What does the drainage pattern tell you of the nature of the terrain? Why does only the southern part of the area have a pronounced galeria forest? Why is such a vast forested area not exploited more fully? Describe the way of life of a primitive tribe in this environment.

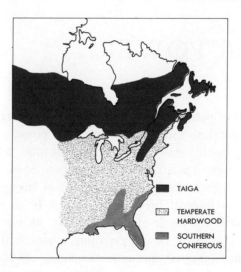

TAIGA
TEMPERATE HARDWOOD
SOUTHERN CONIFEROUS

6. What forest industries are common to all three of these areas? Which industries are confined to a particular forested area? What type of soil has probably developed in each forest region? Account for the temperate hardwoods in Nova Scotia. Prepare a report on the production of turpentine, maple syrup, or kraft paper.

7. With the aid of suitable reference books, prepare reports on the following industries: sealing, whaling, lobster fishing, and oyster farming.

8. Review the factors which contribute to the creation of an important fishing area. Which of these contributing factors are absent in these areas: the Mediterranean, the Baltic, the Caribbean, and the Arabian seas?

Man's Industrial Activity

1 WATER POWER

Long before coal or petroleum was used to turn the wheels of industry, water had provided an economical and reliable source of power. It was used by the ancient Egyptian to operate water wheels for irrigation purposes. In colonial America it was used to grind grain and to saw timber. More recently, it has been used to provide us with that most remarkable form of energy, electricity.

In contrast to the mineral fuels, water power is an almost inexhaustible resource. Man can strip the earth of its vegetation; he can cause rapid erosion of the soil or the silting of dams; he can even turn a once fertile area into a desert; but he cannot stop the falling of rain upon the earth. As long as this continues, man, if he uses water wisely, will have a reliable, if not abundant, source of power. Wise indeed is the country which makes full use of this gift of nature and does not plan its economy upon a limited resource base.

Obviously other factors must enter into the development of this resource or all potential water power would have been harnessed long ago. The essential conditions necessary for power production are **water** and **fall**. Within limits one can substitute for the other. A large volume of water falling a short distance may generate the same amount of electricity as a small volume falling a long distance. The ideal conditions, therefore, would appear to be a large volume and a long fall.

Another important factor affecting the production of hydroelectric power is the **seasonal distribution of rainfall**. In an area such as monsoon India, where flood conditions are followed by severe drought, water-power plants may be idle for several months of the year.

The **gradient** of the land influences the rate of run-off and, therefore, affects the production of power. A steep gradient may produce many fast-flowing streams that carry the water away quickly. Unless storage facilities are available the turbines will run only after rain showers.

Storage is, then, of vital importance, for electricity cannot be stored as most fuels are. This means, therefore, that its source, water, must be stored instead. Porous soil and rock, swamps, lakes, marshes, and spongy leaf mosses on forest floors, all store water, and, by holding it back, even out the stream flow. An almost ideal situation is encountered at Niagara, where a tremendous volume of water cascades over a steep escarpment and the Great Lakes provide storage. Many mountain streams are fed by glaciers that store the water in the form of ice and feed it to the streams during periods of summer drought. Lacking these facilities, man must create storage basins by building dams and creating artificial lakes.

Winter temperatures that remain below freezing for several weeks will reduce stream flow by changing the water to ice. The effect is the same as a summer drought, because the streams shrink to mere rivulets and power generation is impossible.

Perhaps more important than some of the foregoing factors is that of **site**. To generate power, a dam must be built. This requires certain conditions in the bedrock that are not present in all localities. Solid, impervious rock creates the best footing upon which to build a dam. Lacking such a site, a section of sedimentary-rock wall recently gave way in the Niagara Gorge and carried parts of a U.S. generating station into the Niagara river.

The **location** of good sites is also very important. As electricity cannot be stored or shipped like coal, it is necessary to have a market relatively close to the generating site. Owing to lack of markets, many excellent power sites in northern Canada have not been utilized. Under present technological conditions, alternating current can be transported economically for only about 300 miles. Beyond this distance, line losses become too great. Recent advances in electrical technology have allowed power to be transmitted some 600 miles, but to utilize this advance would entail the building of new lines. Direct current can be transmitted up to 1,000 miles; but this method is not in use in Canada as the cost of conversion is considered too great.

The **economic** factor is also important in power development. Hydro-electricity, though cleaner, more adaptable, and seemingly cheaper to produce, actually costs more per kilowatt than thermally produced power. This is due to the tremendous cost of dam construction and transmission of current. The copper wires which carry the current and the steel towers which hold the line are, in themselves, a tremendous expense.

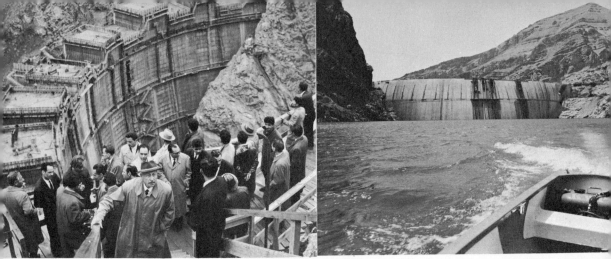

Besides producing electricity, what other advantages does a hydro dam provide?

Why are there few hydroelectric dams, like this one, in Iran, in southwest Asia?

The World Picture

In an energy-hungry world, it is amazing to realize that less than a quarter of the world's potential hydroelectric reserves have been developed, largely due in most cases to such unfavourable factors as remoteness or lack of markets.

The tropics have tremendous potential but lack the market for the power. In Africa, the doldrum rains fall continually in the basin of the Congo and thus create an even flow in the rivers. The Congo tumbles down from the African Plateau a distance of 3,000 feet and thus creates the world's most important hydroelectric site. In South America similar conditions prevail, for streams cascade down some 6,000 to 10,000 feet from the Andean Plateau to the Amazon Basin. Northern Canada and northeastern Asia possess many fine sites suitable for the generation of electricity but these await either markets or technical developments.

The areas that have developed their hydroelectric power are either the industrialized or the mineral-fuel-poor countries of Europe and North America. The countries bordering the Alps and the Scandinavian nations are coal poor but electricity rich. Without this latter resource, these countries would not be able to engage in any large-scale manufacturing enterprises. The U.S.S.R. is now transmitting power over long distances and plans to build a network of transmission lines that will span their continent. The advantage of such a network is that the power can be quickly transferred from any area of normal rainfall to one that may be experiencing drought.

Since the invention of electricity man has sought to find cheap ways of generating it. Some recent experiments with tides have been operated successfully in France and England. Proposals have been advanced for the harnessing of the tides in the Bay of Fundy. As tides ebb and flow, they could be used to generate power as they flow into a bay and again as they flow out. Doubtless this energy will be used some day when mineral fuels run short or when new markets create a demand for more power.

2 MINING AND MINERAL PRODUCTION

In comparison with settlements based on agriculture or forestry, mining towns are temporary in nature. Minerals are a nonrenewable resource and mining is a robber economy. The resultant ghost towns which survive after the mines have been exhausted are mute reminders of the limited supply of minerals that are available to man. Occasionally, mining towns will develop a second industry, such as lumbering, which will enable them to survive when the ore runs out. Occasionally, too, a mining town is reborn as new technological advances may make mining profitable once again. Such a rebirth occurred to some extent in the northern Ontario town of Cobalt.

Factors Governing the Extraction of Minerals

In 1911, Cobalt was mining 30 million ounces of silver a year. By 1936, only 1 million ounces could be obtained from the impoverished mines. A second mineral, cobalt, was used only to a very limited extent in those early days; as a result, huge quantities of the metal were dumped on the tailings pile. **Technological advances** of the atomic age, however, have created a new demand for cobalt, particularly cobalt bombs for medical purposes; consequently, this town has been partly revived; the previously discarded cobalt is now being recovered from the tailings pile.

Other factors affect the mining industry and the extraction of minerals. Recently the boom town of Elliot Lake was turned into a ghost town almost overnight. Most of the uranium produced here was exported to the U.S.A. under contract. However, owing to the discovery of the mineral in the United States, the Canadian contracts were not renewed. As a result the mines were shut down and the inhabitants of the town were without work. New markets have recently been obtained in Britain and the industry is slowly recovering. Thus we see that **world demand** for a mineral can greatly affect the rate of its extraction from the earth.

The **richness of a deposit** is one of the main factors governing its extraction. It can be readily seen that the greater the concentration of a mineral in an ore, the more profitable will be its extraction. The mineral content necessary to make extraction profitable varies greatly from one mineral to another. The more valuable a mineral is, the leaner its ores may be and still be profitably exploited. Iron ores below 35% iron content are seldom mined, whereas gold ores above .01% gold content are seldom found.

The **size of the deposit** as well as its richness must be considered. In order to justify the expenditure of the capital required to sink a shaft and build a refinery, the ore body must be sufficiently large to ensure recovery of the money invested before the mine becomes exhausted. Because of this economic fact many small rich pockets of ore remain untouched as it is not yet profitable to mine them.

The **nature of the deposit** is another governing factor. Gold nuggets can easily be extracted from river deposits by panning or hydraulicking, but it is another problem to recover gold flecks from solid quartz veins. In the latter case, much useless rock must be removed and crushed before the precious metal can be obtained. This operation necessitates the expenditure of large sums of money for machinery and equipment. A slight rise in the cost of recovery would militate against the mining of the ore body.

Some ore deposits may be of the necessary concentration and size to warrant exploitation. Nevertheless, **impurities** and certain chemical combinations in the material may render certain deposits difficult and costly to mine. Sulphur retards the mining and use of coal; aluminum is everywhere present but is recovered chiefly from bauxite; phosphates have hampered the use of the Lorraine iron for many years; and Canada has a vast reserve of oil locked up in the tar sands of the Athabaska country.

The stage to which a country's **industrial development** has proceeded, is also relevant; for certain countries with little industry have hardly even begun to use their mineral resources. Brazil, India, China, and many other countries have vast reserves of minerals, but it is only recently that they have begun to extract them on a large scale. These mining activities correspond with the rate of industrial growth of a nation; for coal, iron, etc., are the basic materials necessary for industrialization.

Whether or not a mineral will be mined often depends on its **accessibility**. The added cost of transportation from remote areas, such as Canada's northland, may make it economically impossible to mine even very rich deposits. Accessibility must also be measured in terms of depth below the surface and of the nature of the geological formation in which it occurs. Potash in western Canada was almost inaccessible because of a porous rock layer saturated with water that had to be penetrated before the potash deposit could be reached. Today, after engineers froze and broke through a quicksand-and-water level, a potash mine is producing at Esterhazy, Saskatchewan, following an initial expenditure of $40,000,000.

Other factors which influence mining are the **tariff policies** of a country's government, the amount of **subsidy** which may or may not be granted, **competition** from substitutes and synthetics, a country's **economic policy**, and its state of war or peace.

Methods of Mining

Placer deposits of gold, discovered in North America, have long been associated with sourdoughs and gold panning. This method of recovering gold from sand was simple and effective. The alluvial deposits were placed in a pan and saturated with water. Continuous agitation of the pan caused the heavier gold particles to sink to the bottom and the sand was then removed. **Rockering**, a refinement of this method, was later introduced and the gold and sand particles were separated in a box that could be agitated by means of a handle. **Sluicing**, not as thorough but much faster, was a method whereby the alluvial deposits were flushed down a long wooden sluice. Wooden cleats placed at right angles to the direction of water flow trapped the heavier gold particles.

Gold is sluiced from sand in Gabon. Why would this area be worked mainly in the drier seasons?

Embassy of France

Hydraulicking was next utilized, and is still in use today. A stream of water under great pressure is directed against the deposits and the material is washed down and flushed through a refined sluice. To mine the sands in the river beds, a dredge is used. This machine digs or sucks up gravel from the river bed, sorts out the gold, and dumps the gravel back into the water. Malayan tin is mined by this latter method.

Open-pit mining is done wherever the deposit is close enough to the surface to allow such mining. This is the most economical method if the depth of material, or overburden, is not too great to be stripped off the ore body. When this is accomplished the ore body can be drilled from the surface and trucks can be brought right into the mine to remove the blasted rock. The Marmora iron mine in southern Ontario uses this method, as does the Mesabi (Minnesota) iron-mining operation and the Estevan (Saskatchewan) coal-producing area.

Gold and uranium are obtained from this mine in South Africa. Why is underground mining more expensive than any other kind of mining?

Potash is mined by machinery in Alsace. Why has the pit not been deepened so that the machine operator could stand erect?

Drift mining is the next least expensive operation and is carried on in areas of relatively undisturbed sedimentary beds. Where coal seams outcrop along river banks or fault scarps, tunnels are dug horizontally into the strata to follow the seams. The coal does not have to be elevated to the surface and, in some cases, can be lowered into trucks or barges at the pit mouth.

Shaft mining is the most expensive of all mining operations as it involves extensive blasting, tunneling, and maintenance work. Pit props or back fill must be inserted to prevent cave-ins and elaborate safety programmes must be maintained for the welfare of the miners. Shafts are usually sunk vertically and tunnels run off horizontally from the main shaft at different levels. Added expense is incurred owing to the necessity of raising the ore to the surface.

Oil, gas, and salt are sometimes mined by **drilling**. Generally the oil and gas will flow naturally at first but when the pressure decreases the oil must be pumped out. Sometimes two holes are drilled and one is used to force air into the ground and create enough pressure to maintain a flowing well. Where salt is mined in this manner, water is pumped into the salt deposit, the resultant brine brought to the surface, and the salt removed by dehydration.

Metals

Metals are elements that possess a typical lustre, hardness, and ductility, as well as a sensitiveness to heat and electricity. Not all the metals have these qualities, and we must, therefore, observe their reaction to chemical compounds in order to determine whether they are metals.

Iron is probably the most universally used metal today. Only the richest of deposits are being mined, though much low-grade ore is still available, awaiting technological advances or increased demand before it can be extracted economically. The chief ores of iron are hematite, magnetite, limonite, and siderite, which are compounds of iron, oxygen, carbon, and various other elements classed as impurities. In the past, the U.S.A., the U.S.S.R., France, Sweden, and the U.K.

344

have been the chief producers of iron ore, but this order is likely to change as huge reserves are brought into production in Brazil, Canada, and India.

Some of the iron that is mined is smelted with coke and used in this state. Pig iron, as it is called, is used for castings where great strength is not required. By far the greater amount of iron is alloyed with another metal to make steel. Nickel steel is very rust resistant. Manganese, which is used as a purifier in the smelting process, adds durability to the steel. Chrome steel is used for high-speed tools because of its heat-resistant qualities. Tungsten steels remain hard at high temperatures and so are used for cutting tools, saw blades, and engine valves. Vanadium gives steel flexibility; hence vanadium-steel alloy is commonly known as spring steel.

The factors that govern the extraction of ores apply to iron as to other minerals, but in the case of iron several other factors must be considered as well. Huge quantities of coke, which is derived from coal, must be available for the smelting of the ore. It is, therefore, necessary to transport either the iron or the coal. Most of the world's steel-producing centres, such as the Ruhr, Donets, Sheffield, Pittsburgh, and Birmingham have been built on the coalfields and the iron is transported. The movement of such bulky material necessitates a cheap method of transportation. We find, then, that these centres are either located at tidewater or connected to their supply by canals. Sydney, Nova Scotia, obtains its ore by ship from Bell Island. Hamilton, Ontario, must transport both the iron and coal via the Great Lakes. Labrador iron is shipped by rail and water all the way to Sparrow's Point, Maryland.

Among the many problems associated with the iron-ore industry are the obtaining of sufficient quantities of high-grade ore, the removal of impurities, the cost of transportation, the obtaining of coal, limestone, and iron in close proximity, and the added cost of national tariffs that tend to keep the price of finished steel high. One of the advantages that this metal has over most others is that it can be re-smelted and recovered from scrap material.

Copper, because of its softness and ability to conduct electricity, is much sought after by hydroelectric companies. Lead and zinc are used in the manufacture of paints and storage batteries. Silver is found in many areas and is now chiefly used as a compound on films by the motion picture and photography industries. Aluminum is a valuable metal in the aircraft industry, for it can be alloyed with steel to form a light but strong construction material. Magnesium, a relative newcomer to the metallurgical world, is offering competition to aluminum in the light-metals field. Magnesium must be alloyed with another metal to be useable; nevertheless, so alloyed it is finding markets in the aircraft, automobile, and electrical industries. Tin is used for plating and rust-proofing steel; and nickel is a chief alloy in the production of stainless steel. Other minerals that are commercially exploited are tungsten, chrome, manganese, vanadium, mercury, uranium, and titanium.

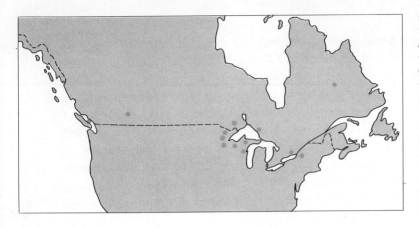

The iron-ore-producing regions of Canada and the northern U.S.A. are closely associated with the rocks of the Canadian Shield. How is the isolated Labrador deposit able to compete with the more accessible Lake Superior ores? What is the raw material being used in the Kimberley, B.C. operation? Duplicate this sketch and label the names of the various deposits.

Nonmetals

The nonmetals are elements, e.g. sulphur, or chemical compounds, e.g. potash, which lack the physical and chemical properties of the metals. The materials of this group are, however, very important to both the agricultural and the industrialized nation. These materials range in usefulness from an essential of life, salt, the only edible mineral, to a very complex and powerful explosive, dynamite.

The fertility of the soil depends on the presence and amount of soluble salts. In areas where rainfall is heavy, these salts are leached out and must be replaced in order to ensure further yield from the soil. Nitrogen, potassium, and phosphorus are the chief elements which are required to replenish the soil; these are, therefore, sought after as commercial fertilizers.

Nitrate occurs in beds of former lakes in the Great Valley of the Atacama Desert. Here, evaporation has succeeded in concentrating the leaching of centuries into beds of sodium nitrate. The few feet of alluvial deposits which overlie the mineral are stripped off by steam shovel and the crude nitrate is scooped up. The material is sent to a refinery, where it is purified by dissolving it in warm water and then allowing it to be redeposited. Evaporation of the water is left to nature and is done quickly in the dry climate. The purified material is then ready for sacking and export. Chile enjoyed a virtual world monopoly on nitrates until recent years, when technological advances have allowed nitrates to be concentrated and collected from the air. Besides being used as a fertilizer, nitrogen is used in the making of nitric acid and it combines with silver for use in photography.

Phosphate rock, from which phosphorus is obtained, is composed largely of the remains of animal life. The U.S.A. has the largest known deposits of phosphates in the world. The mineral ore is treated with sulphuric acid for purification and is then sold as a fertilizer. As phosphorus is the most soluble soil mineral, vast quantities of this substance are required. A third mineral fertilizer is potassium salts, which are derived from potash beds in Germany, the United States, France, Spain, and the U.S.S.R. Other uses of this mineral are for soap, explosives, glass, bleaching, matches, and medicines.

Sulphur is another important nonmetal which is mined in considerable quantities. Mica, asbestos, graphite, talc, gypsum, and precious stones are extracted in quantities that vary according to the fluctuations of the market. Among the materials which fit into the nonmetallic category, but which are not generally considered as minerals, are building stone, sand, gravel, and clay.

Mineral Fuels

The mineral fuels include coal, petroleum, natural gas, and recently, uranium. These substances, together with electricity, provide the energy for our modern industries. It would be almost impossible to imagine the human energy which would have to be expended to excavate even one of our modern mines.

Coal is formed by physical and chemical action on masses of vegetable material that usually collect in marshes and swamps. It is found in varying amounts in most of the sedimentary areas of the world. The type of coal found varies greatly. **Lignite**, or brown coal, is usually geologically recent in origin and has not become compacted into a hard form. It is chiefly used for domestic heating and the generation of thermalelectricity. As it crumbles easily, it cannot be stored for any length of time.

Bituminous coal is much harder than lignite as it has been subjected to more heat and pressure. This is a general utility coal that can be used for heating, thermal power, the driving of steamships, and the manufacture of chemicals. Certain grades of bituminous are used in the steel-making process. The coal is heated in ovens; the volatile material that is driven off is the manufactured gas used in many cities. The residue, coke, which is almost pure carbon, can then be added to the blast furnaces of the steel industry.

Why is most coal transported by river instead of by rail?

Embassy of France

Lignite and coal dust are pressed into briquettes for marketing. Why is this necessary?

Anthracite is the hardest of the coals. It is found only in areas where great pressure has warped the sedimentary rocks and caused metamorphosis of these rocks with their organic remains (of plant life) of former ages. This coal, while ideal for domestic heating, is usually expensive as it has to be recovered from faulted and folded strata. The incline of the beds and the lack of continuity in the coal seams all add to the expense of mining.

Petroleum and Natural Gas

These two fuels are usually found together although it is not uncommon for them to be located separately. Anticlines capped with impervious strata are the usual geological formations which collect gas and oil. These fuels are always found in sedimentary rock as they are derived from chemical action on organic matter (plant and animal remains).

As both are lighter than water, they migrate through reservoir rock, either floating on top of water or being forced along by pressure. As a result of this action much oil and gas has probably escaped to the surface and been dissipated by natural forces. Where the geological structure is right, oil collects in the pores of the reservoir rock and can be obtained by drilling. If the oil is under great pressure, it will explode through the drill hole in the form of a gusher. When the pressure subsides, or when there is little to begin with, the oil must be pumped to the surface.

Gas is obtained in a similar manner, but the drill holes must usually be located at the top of the anticline. A hole that penetrates the lower base of such a structure will probably produce salt water. The sedimentary beds of gently folded strata that produce most of the world's oil and gas are found in western North America, the Middle East, Venezuela, and the plains of southern Russia.

In recent years, uranium has become an important source of industrial energy. The radioactivity of this material, when concentrated in one area, produces great heat. Uranium rods are lowered into heavy water until the concentration of heat is great enough to boil the water. The steam, thus generated, is used to produce electricity.

Where does France obtain her pit props for the Franco-Belgian coal mines?

3 MANUFACTURING

Very early in history man learned to make use of the more accessible resources of the land and the sea. He hunted, fished, and practised certain forms of agriculture and herding. The use of wood and stone was confined to the construction of houses or the production of crude tools and weapons. Minerals and metals were used to a limited extent in a few areas even in prehistoric times, but it was not until very recently that man embarked on a programme of manufacturing and mass production. The technological advances which made this possible are many and varied, but one simple economic fact pertains to all cases; that is, the individual must produce more than is required for his own subsistence. If all of man's time and energy must be spent in gaining enough food to survive, he will not be able to engage in the manufacturing of products for someone else's use. This is the chief reason that the most densely populated areas of the world lack large-scale industry.

Many of the products extracted from farms, ranches, forests, and mines are not ready for consumption in their natural state; they must, therefore, undergo some form of processing before they can be used. In its broadest sense, manufacturing includes all forms of processing, from the simpler methods of baking bread to the more complicated production of electronic equipment.

For the purpose of more fully studying and understanding the manufacturing industries, we often group them into several categories. However, because of the complexity of manufacturing, no classification is entirely satisfactory for all purposes. With this in mind, let us look at some of the classifications that have been used in the study of manufacturing.

Types of Manufacturing

In the early stages of development, manufacturing takes the form of handicraft and has been termed a **home industry**. Many of the oriental rugs of Kashmir and Pakistan are produced in this manner. A unique situation exists in the textile industry, for much of the weaving and sewing is still done in the home by highly skilled workers. **Workshops** followed home industry and are exemplified by the furniture and carpentry shops that in earlier times were added to private homes. In most cases, the shop owner employed one or more apprentices to help him in this work. **Factory** industry developed from home industry when water power or mineral fuels could be used to operate the machinery. The change from home to factory manufacturing was known as the industrial revolution.

Industrial manufacturing has also been grouped under the broad headings of **heavy** and **light** industry. Basically, these terms were meant to distinguish between such industries as steel making, where an enormous amount of relatively inexpensive material must be moved about, and watchmaking, where the amount of material needed is much less but the finished product may be just as valuable.

Classification of manufacturing by stages gives us the terms primary, secondary, and tertiary. **Primary** manufacturing refers to such activities as ore refining or flour milling. Steel production and pastry making would be a **secondary** stage in the manufacturing process, whereas the creation of electrical appliances from the steel would be an example of **tertiary** manufacturing.

For the purposes of our study, it is necessary to know in what context we use the word manufacturing. The **extractive** industries are those which deal with the production of raw materials, e.g., farming, fishing, ranching, mining. **Manufacturing** is the processing of these products. **Service** industries are those that result from either the extractive industries or manufacturing, e.g., transportation, communications, trade.

Factors Affecting the Location of Manufacturing

In order to develop manufacturing of any kind, it is necessary to have a supply of **raw materials** to process. Most factories tend to be located as near as possible to their source of supply since this will cut down on the cost of transportation. Good examples of this in northern Canada are ore refineries located beside the mine shaft. Many pulp and paper mills also locate close to their supply of timber. Needless to say, most home and workshop manufacturing is done near the source of raw materials.

Large-scale production requires the use of vast quantities of **fuel**. The source of power is, therefore, often important in the choice of location of a factory. Since the smelting of aluminum requires much electricity, it, therefore, becomes more economical to move the raw materials to the source of power. The U.S. steel industry is also located close to its supply of energy, for the major producing centres have been constructed on the Appalachian coalfields.

Any industry requires an adequate supply of **labour** possessing a variety of **skills** and knowledge. The location chosen will depend on the availability of personnel possessing the necessary skills required for a particular operation. If highly trained individuals are required, the factory will probably be located in or near a large city where people can receive an education in technology. If, on the other hand, manual labour is required, small towns or rural areas can often provide a much better supply. Labour unions may force the cost of production to such a height that plants will either go bankrupt or move to a new location. This consideration particularly affects small town industries that are forced to pay the same wages as for similar operations in the large cities.

Closely related to labour is **market**, for a densely populated area can supply both. Most towns have some industry based on the local market, e.g., dairies, bakeries, newspapers, and bottling works. More specialized industries are located in specific areas because of a particular demand for their product; e.g., glass and paints are needed for automobile manufacturing and, therefore, are located in southern Ontario. Agricultural machinery is most extensively used in western U.S.A. and Canada; hence, manufacturing and assembly plants for such machinery are located in the mid-West.

Much of the above-mentioned production could not be carried on without the availability of **transportation facilities**. Rail, road, and air services are used to concentrate raw materials in an area or to distribute them to distant markets. Some industries, however, are so favourably situated as to be able to take the best possible advantage of all of these facilities. Processing and refinery plants are often located at port sites in order to tap trade routes for their raw materials. Sugar refineries, oil refineries, west-coast lumber mills, and some textile mills fall into this category. Some industries that do not require great quantities of raw materials rely entirely on the transportation systems to bring their raw materials to a central location: e.g., the electronic plants of Ottawa.

It is entirely possible that a nation may possess all of the necessary resources to create a full range of manufactured products, but lack the **capital**, or money, to develop these resources. This is the case in most of the over-populated nations of the world. Only recently have some of these countries been able to obtain outside capital to carry on a programme of industrialization. Unfortunately, much of this capital is invested for monetary, political, or strategic gain with little thought for the welfare of the country involved. In such cases, nations may unwittingly find themselves involved in the east-west cold war.

Tariffs, a device of governments, are sometimes responsible for either the building or the abandonment of factories. Protective tariffs, i.e., a tax on imports, may create a thriving industry such as automobile manufacturing in Canada. Without the import duty which a Canadian citizen must pay on a U.S.-made car, the car producers in this country would be unable to operate. This tariff raises the price of the U.S. car to such a level that the buyer finds it more economical to purchase a Canadian-built or Canadian-assembled car. The lowering of tariffs between nations may result in an increase in the buying of foreign-manufactured products, thereby causing the closing of many local factories.

Local taxes and **municipal policies** are often influential in the determining of the location of an industry. An area which taxes manufacturers heavily will be shunned by industry. On the other hand, some far-sighted communities have lowered the taxes, or even arranged for a tax-free period, in order to attract factories to their area. Land grants and the use of local public utilities are often offered as inducements to manufacturers. By following such a policy a community or municipality can often obtain full employment for its inhabitants plus the income from factory taxes in the years ahead.

Industrial momentum, or **inertia,** often accounts for the present-day location of a plant. Many of the New England textile mills were built in order to take advantage of local water power or the humid climate. Today, thermalelectricity and air conditioning have made it possible to produce cloth in the south. Because of the prohibitive cost of moving or of building a new plant, the factory remains at its old location.

Local **site** is mainly responsible only for the situation of a plant within a community, but occasionally favourable circumstances will concentrate a particular type of manufacturing in a given region. The hydroelectric potential of Niagara Falls has attracted electro-metallurgical industries to that area. On the other hand, further expansion of manufacturing in the Niagara Peninsula is being discouraged as it is using up the best land of Canada's principal fruit-growing area. The choice between Toronto and Hamilton as Canada's main steel-producing centre went to the latter city owing to Hamilton's better harbour facilities. Stream and river sites are preferred over inland locations as most plants require a considerable quantity of water. Level land is essential where storage of raw materials may require as much as fifty acres.

Many of the factors influencing manufacturing are interrelated and it is only by a careful analysis of the situation and all related circumstances that the industrialist can choose his site wisely. It is in the capacity of adviser to the manufacturer regarding the location of factories that the geographer plays his most important role.

World Manufacturing Regions

Three major manufacturing regions can be distinguished in the world today: one in western Europe, one in North America, and a decentralized one in the U.S.S.R. Japan is probably the next best-known manufacturer, while India, Australia, Brazil, Argentina, New Zealand, and South Africa are all engaged in this activity to some extent. Each of these areas is marked by various degrees of specialization within the region itself.

Western Europe

The continent of Europe is highly industrialized and it was here, because of a number of human and physical conditions, that the Industrial Revolution took place. The rapid expansion of factory industry was due to an abundance of raw materials. These included Ruhr coal, Lorraine iron, German potash, and British natural gas, coal, and iron. Hydroelectricity and nuclear power have been more recently added as sources of fuel.

The dense population provided both a good supply of labour and a market. The technical skills necessary for industrialization were partially developed in

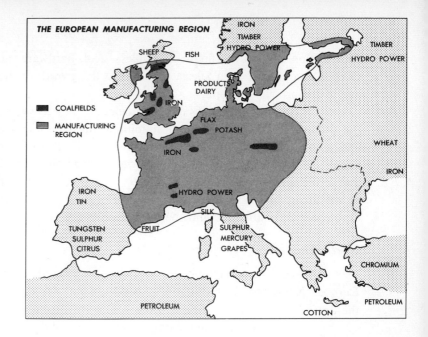

THE EUROPEAN MANUFACTURING REGION

IRON
TIMBER
HYDRO POWER
SHEEP   FISH
TIMBER
HYDRO POWER

PRODUCTS
DAIRY

■ COALFIELDS
IRON

■ MANUFACTURING
   REGION
FLAX
POTASH

WHEAT

IRON

IRON

IRON
TIN
HYDRO POWER

SILK

FRUIT
SULPHUR
MERCURY
GRAPES

TUNGSTEN
SULPHUR
CITRUS

CHROMIUM

PETROLEUM

PETROLEUM

COTTON

Which countries in the manufacturing region do not belong to the European Common Market? What benefits can be derived from an economic union? Why is the edible-oil industry centred at Marseilles? silk at Lyons? stainless steel at Sheffield? furniture in Scandinavia?

Europe because of the number of, and specialization in, many household and workshop industries. As well as this, Europe had the advantage of the most highly developed transportation system in the world. Highways, canals, and ports had been constructed and used for many years. Recently, the nations of central Europe have united in an economic union with the professed aim of lowering tariffs and increasing prosperity.

The continent of Europe is easily accessible to trade, enjoys a climate favourable for industrial activity, and possesses a large foreign market. Inventions and the introduction of new manufacturing techniques added efficiency to the industrialization of this area. England early sprang into prominence as she had vast coal deposits and initially had considerable iron-ore reserves. Heavy industry is concentrated in the Scottish lowlands, the Newcastle area, and the Midlands. Much of the steel produced in the first two areas is used for shipbuilding, whereas the Midlands concentrate on making machinery and motor vehicles. Manchester is world renowned for its cotton industry, whereas woollens are the chief product of the Yorkshire district. Northern Ireland is noted for its production of linens from locally grown flax.

The French manufacturing industries are located in the northeast on the Franco-Belgian coalfield. This manufacturing district extends into Belgium and the Saar Basin. Valenciennes, Lille, and Nancy are large textile centres, while the Belgian cities of Namur, Liège, and Brussels engage in such industries as iron manufacturing and the production of chemicals.

The Ruhr valley is Germany's, and Europe's, leading manufacturing area. A dozen or more cities in this area produce a full range of manufactured goods from

353

construction steel to the finest of stainless steel, hardware, and textiles. Deposits of coal, zinc, and iron in Silesia have led to the growth of metallurgical industries and textile production there.

Southern Europe enjoys the hydroelectric power of the Alps and leads in the production of aluminum and aluminum alloys. As a result of this, airplanes and automobiles are the principal products. The Swiss have engaged in watch- and clock-making since the first clocks were carved out of Alpine wood. Marseilles and Lyons are centres of the silk industry, for mulberry trees can readily be grown in the area. In this region, too, the processing of Mediterranean foodstuffs has developed the edible-oils and margarine industries.

North America

American manufactures are exceeded in world importance by those of Europe. Nevertheless, this continent is remarkable for the variety of its products, the degree of its specialization, and the volume of its mass-produced goods. Based on the diversity of its manufactures, it may be subdivided into several regions, each having its own distinctive characteristics.

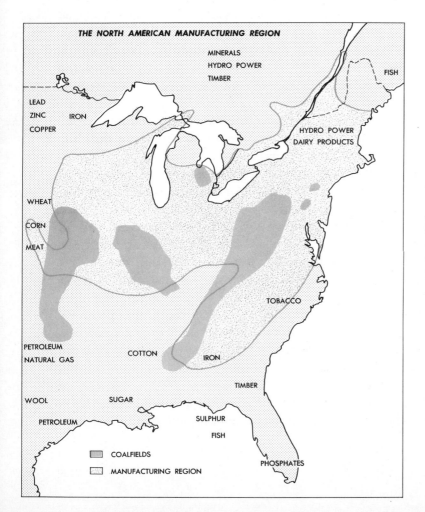

Why have Canada and the United States not united to form a common market? What resources not shown here occur within the manufacturing region? Why is the steel industry located on the coalfields and not on the iron-ore deposits? Why is Sault Ste. Marie included in this belt?

The New England district specializes in textiles, leather goods, and light metallurgy. The textile mills were attracted here because of the moist climate suitable for spinning and weaving and the numerous waterfalls that provide power. The leather industry is an offshoot of dairying, which is carried on in the region to provide milk and butter for the large cities. The southern part of the New England states produces electrical equipment and light metalware such as firearms, keys and locks, motorcycles, etc. These industries owe their existence to the local supplies of hydroelectricity.

The middle Atlantic district includes several large cities. The industry of New York is mainly based on the import-export trade. Textiles produced in New England are made into garments here. Though obtained from other areas, sugar, vegetable oils, copper, and petroleum are refined here. While a considerable quantity of machinery is manufactured in Baltimore and Philadelphia, these cities concentrate on shipbuilding and steel production.

The Hudson-Mohawk district has developed along the Erie Canal and the New York Central Railroad. As there is little coal in this area, the factories tend to produce lighter, more valuable, goods. Rochester specializes in photographic equipment, Rome in copper and brass, Syracuse in typewriters, and Schenectady in electrical equipment.

The Niagara-Ontario region includes Buffalo, Hamilton, and Toronto. Cheap lake transportation, a good supply of electricity, and a rich agricultural soil are the chief assets of the area. Buffalo and Hamilton produce steel used in the production of automobiles, agricultural machinery, and lake boats. Niagara Falls specializes in electroplating and flour milling. St. Catharines produces automotive parts and Welland is the centre of stainless-steel and metal-pipe production.

The Pittsburgh region has the advantage of enormous coal and natural gas supplies. It is the centre of the blast-furnace and steel-production industries for the entire U.S.A. The iron is obtained from the Lake Superior mines and brought in by barge. Associated with the steel mills are steel-pipe plants, structural-steel factories, and a glass-manufacturing industry.

Detroit is the automotive centre for the United States, and Canadian branches of the industry are found at Oakville and Oshawa. Associated industries include the making of glass, rubber, and paint. Inland from this area lie Cincinnati and Indianapolis, which specialize in agricultural machinery and food processing.

Chicago and Milwaukee are the principal cities of the Lake Michigan region. Blast furnaces and steel mills are to be found here, too, but the processing of agricultural and forest products reaches exceptionally high proportions. Large meat-packing plants, flour mills, and tanneries process the farm products of the Great Plains. From the north comes timber for furniture and paper.

The Montreal district includes the area from Quebec City to Ottawa. An abundance of hydroelectric power, an inland seaway, good agricultural land, vast timber reserves, and accessible minerals make this area one of the most productive of the manufacturing subdivisions. Pulp and paper production, aluminum refining, textile fabrication, shipbuilding, and aircraft manufacturing are only some of the industries located in this area, but they serve to illustrate the diversity of its production.

The U.S.S.R.

Manufacturing in Russia is much less concentrated than in either Europe or America. Instead of one major region there are five distinct manufacturing belts and many smaller areas centred about a particular city or town. Owing to the great distances which separate these areas, each one has become partly self-sufficient and uses mainly the resources within its area. Leningrad, for instance, specializes in wood and paper products; Moscow is the centre of Russian textile production; the Donbas is the nation's principal supplier of steel; the southern Urals produce iron and several other minerals; while the Kuzbas supplies central and eastern Russian with coal and steel products.

The Leningrad area began as a window on the Baltic through which Russia could obtain supplies of coal, cotton, and machinery. Today this area has turned to manufacturing and the development of its own resources. Thus, from agriculture come flax for the textile industry and wheat for the flour mills. The forests provide lumber, pulp and paper, matches, rayon, and wood alcohol. Bauxite mined nearby, in addition to the hydroelectricity of the Neva River, is the source of aluminum production. From the Kola Peninsula come nickel, iron, potassium, and phosphate salts. These latter two provide the basis for a thriving chemical and fertilizer industry.

Why is it cheaper for Moscow to purchase steel from the Donbas area than to buy it from the Urals? What are (a) the advantages, (b) the disadvantages of several dispersed manufacturing belts?

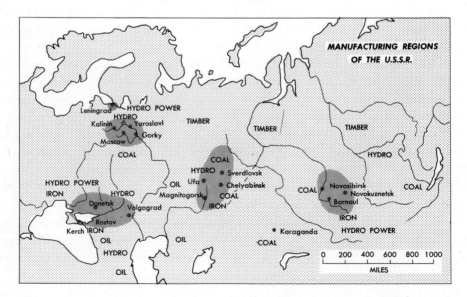

In Russian industry the Moscow, or central manufacturing region, is the exception to the rule. Unlike the other districts, most of Moscow's manufacturing is based on products which must be imported into the area. For many years a leader in textile production, this area receives cotton from Transcaucasia and central Asia, wool from Kazakstan and the Urals, rayon from the northern forests, and silk from the Black Sea area. Machines and precision tools are manufactured from steel obtained in the Urals or the Donbas basin. From the Leningrad region come the chemicals for the textile dyes and the pulp industry. Almost the only raw materials that this area possesses are lignite coal, flax, timber, and water power. It is a tribute to the people of this area that they have developed manufacturing to such an extent that they lead the Soviet Union in the value of goods produced.

The Donbas, or Donetz Basin as it is often called, has a natural setting for the production of steel and heavy equipment. Coal, both anthracite and coking, are abundant and easy to mine, while iron and manganese can be brought from nearby Krivoi Rog by either rail or water. Water power and petroleum can be easily obtained and the Sea of Azov provides an outlet to the sea. These natural advantages have been utilized by the Russians to create an industrial complex similar to that of the Ruhr or the Pittsburgh producing region. Besides the steel that is shipped to other parts of the country, much is used locally for agricultural machinery, mining equipment, shipbuilding, and rolling stock for railways.

The southern Urals probably contain a greater variety of mineral wealth than any other area of comparable size in the world. Rich in iron ore, the Kuzbas for many years supplied coal for these steel mills; but the coal had to be transported over a thousand miles! However, the discovery of a large deposit of coking coal at Karaganda has eliminated the necessity for this expensive haul. In addition to iron, the southern Urals produce copper, gold, nickel, tungsten, and aluminum in considerable amounts. From the surrounding area come oil, salt, potassium, and timber. These raw materials form the basis for the products of smelters, refineries, steel mills, blast furnaces, fertilizer plants, and pulp mills. Though this area is a relative newcomer to the manufacturing world, it possesses two distinct advantages: modern equipment and easily accessible resources.

The last, and most recently developed, industrial area is that of the Kuzbas, or Kuznetz basin. Here, the Tom River has cut through beds of sedimentary rock to expose coal beds beneath. During World War II the industrial complex of the Donbas was almost completely destroyed. However, Ural iron ore and Kuzbas coal teamed up to create steel mills at both ends of a 1,200-mile stretch of railway. When the discovery of coal at Karaganda cut off the supply of iron ore for the Kuzbas, an intensive search for new iron deposits was initiated. Today low-grade ore from the Gornaya Shoria Mts. to the south is supplying the bulk of the iron required. The steel produced here is mainly used for railway equipment and repair on the Trans-Siberian Railway. Agricultural machinery, lumbering and mining equipment, and also shipping equipment used in river navigation are all manufactured in this area.

The Steel Industry of Sydney, N.S.

In the foregoing sections, we have been dealing with the factors that influence selection of sites for regional manufacturing and also for world-manufacturing conurbations. Let us now turn to a more detailed study of how these location factors affect a particular industry, namely, the steel industry of Sydney, Nova Scotia.

The **raw materials** needed for this industry come from Cape Breton Island and Newfoundland. Good coking coal for smelting and thermal **power** is obtained from nearby Sydney Mines, New Waterford, and Glace Bay. High-quality iron ore is imported into the area from Bell Island, Nfld., while limestone, which must also be shipped into Sydney, is quarried at Aguathana, Nfld. The common factor that makes the assemblage of raw materials economically possible is the Dominion Steel and Coal Company, which operates the steel plant, several collieries, the Bell Island iron mine, and the limestone quarry.

The **local site** of Sydney encloses a large, deep harbour that is open for most of the year. This location, plus the fact that the coal, iron, and limestone are all found close to tidewater, has been responsible for keeping **transportation** costs down to a workable level. In addition, the company owns and operates its own fleet of barges for the movement of the bulky iron and limestone.

Labour, a prime requisite in any type of industrial activity, is particularly plentiful in the Atlantic Provinces. This area has the highest density of population of any region in Canada. Many of the people engaged in agriculture, fishing, or lumbering, while obtaining a fair livelihood, do not have a high cash income.

Iron ore from the world's largest subterranean mine fills seagoing ore corries at the rate of 100 tons per minute. How have the natural features of this area aided in loading operations?

Dominion Steel & Coal Company

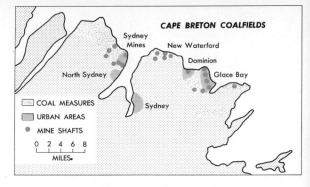

Account for the fact that the steel plant is located at Sydney and not on one of the coalfields. How is the coal transported to Sydney? What method of transportation would be used to transport the finished steel to Halifax?

These two factors help to keep down costs and allow this industry to compete in world markets.

The integrated iron and steel mill at Sydney produces ingots, rails, rods, bars, wire, and even nails. Much of the steel produced is shipped in the ingot or bar state to be processed elsewhere. **Markets** for the steel goods are provided by the steel works at Trenton, which supply the basic steel for railway rolling stock, the railway repair shops at Truro and Moncton, and the shipbuilding industry of Halifax, Pictou, and Saint John. The more heavily populated and industrialized regions of Quebec and Ontario are too remote for Maritime steel to compete effectively in that market, but the Dominion Steel and Coal Company has established steel-processing plants in Montreal and Toronto. The United States and European markets are also difficult to enter as they are protected by tariff barriers.

With respect to steel, the Canadian Government has played an important part in encouraging this industry. **Tariffs** have been placed on imported iron and steel in order to promote Canadian production. **Subsidies** have been granted to certain collieries so that they may maintain a more competitive price for coal. The steel industry benefits indirectly from this as it can, consequently, market its product at a lower price. Canadian participation in world affairs and the extension of Canadian trade legations are expanding the market for Sydney steel.

Capital to finance this extensive and costly operation is obtained mainly in Britain and Canada. Hawker Siddeley of Canada, a branch of the British company which produced the famous Hawker fighter planes of World War II, holds 77% of the shares of the Dominion Steel and Coal Company. Other moneys are raised through the selling of stocks on the world's stock exchanges. Some indication of the vast amount of capital required and the extensiveness of the company's operations may be obtained from the names of subsidiary companies, e.g., Nova Scotia Iron and Steel, Eastern Car, Acadia Coal, Scotia Rolling Stock, Halifax Shipyards, Old Sydney Collieries, Trenton Steel Works, and Trenton Industries.

UNIT REVIEW

Questions

1. What physical characteristics of streams favour their use for hydroelectric development?

2. Under what conditions might it not be possible to use a good stream and power site for hydroelectric production?

3. In what respects are the conditions on the Niagara River excellent for power production?

4. What is the difference between water power and hydroelectric power?

5. What is meant by the following terms: mineral fuel, coking coal, nonmetallic mineral, alloy, lignite?

6. Why are metallic minerals more commonly found in highlands than in plains?

7. What minerals are found mainly in association with sedimentary rocks? Account for this phenomenon.

8. How and why do coal seams differ in the ease with which they can be mined?

9. Describe the geological formations in which petroleum and natural gas may be found.

10. Name the chief mineral fertilizers and state the most important source of each.

11. Discuss the importance of governmental policies in industrial development.

12. What are the chief reasons for the rise of the textile industry in the southern United States?

13. Which of the important manufacturing regions of Europe are under the direct or indirect control of the Soviet Union?

14. Endeavour to explain why the Canadian textile industry is mainly centred at Hamilton and Montreal.

Research Assignments

1. Prepare a map showing the potential sources of hydroelectric power in Canada.

2. Locate the power dams on the Ottawa River and discuss the possibilities of future developments.

3. The construction of dams for hydroelectric power generation may have beneficial side effects. Investigate this field and report on any effects which have proved beneficial to man.

4. List the world's two leading producers of each of the following minerals: coal, petroleum, iron, chromium, nickel, tungsten, tin, zinc, magnesium, silver, platinum, and mercury.

5. Consult an economic geography or an encyclopedia to determine three important uses of the following minerals: potash, titanium, asbestos, mercury, mica, zinc, nickel, vanadium, manganese, and tungsten.

6. Prepare a report on the geography of a mineral for the world or for a selected country. Include a map showing its distribution and transportation routes. Discuss the geological structures associated with its occurrence, the methods of mining and transportation, the problems of marketing, and the uses of the mineral.

7. What factors have contributed to the location of an iron and steel mill at Kimberley, B.C.?

8. Prepare a report on a manufacturing industry in your locality. Be sure to include a map to illustrate the sources of raw materials and the markets for the finished products. Account for the presence of the industry in your area and discuss any problems associated with transportation, raw materials, competition, etc.

9. Investigate the chief manufacturing industry of Japan, India, or Brazil. Prepare a map of the resources of the area chosen and account for the type of manufacturing carried on.

10. The nitrate beds of Chile are world famous. What can you tell of their formation from the shape and size of the deposits? What can you deduce regarding the terrain from the position of the deposits? Why are nitrate beds found only in desert regions? Prepare a report on the industrial uses of nitrates.

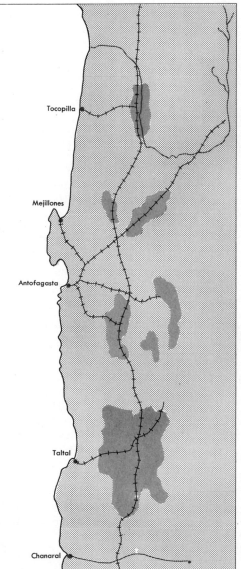

361

Transportation

1 OVERLAND TRANSPORT

Modern industry and commerce would rapidly come to a standstill without our efficient transportation systems. Indeed, our whole way of life would soon undergo drastic changes if we were suddenly deprived of planes, locomotives, ships, and automobiles—things we so easily take for granted. Some authors have pointed out that the history of the progress of civilization and of technical advances can be exactly paralleled by a history of improvements in transportation. As we read of man's miraculous journeys into space and of plans to visit the moon and more distant bodies, we realize that even many of the greatest achievements of our own time are advances in the field of transportation.

If the history of civilization and of transportation is so closely linked, we might well expect to find varying forms of transport in the different civilizations of the present. Usually, the more primitive the culture, the more primitive the transport.

Primitive Forms of Transport

The first means man used for moving an object from one place to another was simply to carry it, and in many societies this is still the custom. In most cases, the women are the carriers of household and bulky goods, men bearing only their weapons. However, there are wide areas in Africa and in the mountains of Asia where terrain is particularly difficult and where the male porter is the only practicable means of transporting goods. If you have read the exciting story of the ascent of Mt. Everest, you will know the important role the Sherpa porters played in that achievement.

In most regions of the world, man soon realized the value of training certain local animals to carry his goods. The animals varied with the climatic conditions. The dog was used but soon abandoned because of its limited strength except in the Arctic regions in which it has the advantages that it does not eat so much as a larger animal and that its relatively light weight allows it to run over deep snow. In Siberia and some other parts of the Arctic, the reindeer is highly prized both as a beast of burden and as a source of meat, milk, and skins.

Throughout most of the temperate lands of the world, the horse has played an important part in the history of transport. These areas, however, include many of the most advanced countries on earth and thus the horse has largely been replaced as a means of transport except in the more backward regions. The horse was probably first domesticated in central Asia and here its place is still unchallenged. Introduction of horses to this continent from Europe profoundly affected the way of life of the North American Indian.

Perhaps the most widely used beast of burden in history is the ox, which has played a role in transportation in Europe, Asia, the Middle East and, in later centuries, in South America and South Africa. In the lands around the Mediterranean and the monsoon regions of Asia, the oxcart and ox-drawn plough have become traditional parts of the landscape. Other important animals include the yak in the mountains of Asia, the elephant in India (but not in Africa), the llama of the Andes, and the buffalo in several areas. The remarkable qualities of camels have made them essential to the traditional life of desert lands, and the story of the exploration of the world's great deserts has recorded the feats of these animals. A sturdy camel may travel as much as 150 miles in a day under conditions that no other large animal could survive. Among the smaller animals, the donkey still has some importance, but this is usually limited to very short distances; therefore, we may say that its importance is purely local. The mule, with its great stamina and agility, is still invaluable in difficult mountain country but it is only a hybrid animal and its numbers have never been great.

The camel has survived into the present century as the best method of transportation in desert areas.

Pan American Union

An Amayran Indian builds a balsa boat on the shores of Lake Titicaca. Such distinctive forms of transportation survive only in the less accessible parts of our modern world.

In many regions of the world, travel between communities is easier by water than by land. Generally speaking, transport by water is less difficult than that by land, so many of the primitive peoples have made their greatest advances in boat-building. The earliest boats were usually rafts of logs, reeds, or grass tied together and these have been used in Africa on the Nile, in South America on Lake Titicaca, and in countless other areas. The famous Kon Tiki expedition, led by Thor Heyerdahl, gave us a modern proof that even a simple raft can carry men for thousands of miles at sea.

Logs, which have been hollowed out to form dug-out canoes, are still widely used on the rivers of South America and in primitive societies elsewhere. These may be as large as 50 feet long and can carry many people and much merchandise. Probably the largest dug-outs are those of the Pacific where the Polynesians fit them with outriggers for better balance and control. In some areas, the most skilled boatbuilders use skins or bark in their craft. The clumsiest of these are perhaps the ancient coracles of Ireland and Wales, very seldom seen nowadays. Much more advanced are the kayaks and larger umiaks of the Eskimos—skin boats used for hunting and fishing as well as for transport. On the rivers of the Middle East, one might still see inflated skins being used as primitive boats in just the same way as they were used here in the days of Alexander the Great. Finally, canoes formed by the sewing of bark—birch, spruce, cedar or eucalyptus—over a light wooden framework have long been well known in North America and Australia. Basically, these craft are of the same type as those of the Eskimo.

The student interested in the early forms of water transport will find his best area of study in the Pacific. In the south of that great ocean are many tiny secluded islands where the skills in the building and navigation of small boats have probably reached their peak.

Land Transportation

Most of us have done little travelling beyond the confines of Canada, or at least, of North America. In this case, we have probably experienced several forms of land transportation and can understand this form most easily. At present we are not concerned with the forms of locomotion, by automobile, airplane, and ship, that do not lie within the field of geography but with the major arterial systems of human transport and trade.

Road Systems

The word *road* can signify very different ideas in different settings. Basically, it means an improved overland pathway, a narrow winding track in the mountains, an ill-defined jungle footpath, or a broad six-lane highway. The different conditions within which roads are thus found is reflected in great differences in their quality, but one should bear in mind that most of the world's traffic is still carried on rather poor surfaces and that the magnificent throughways, marked out so clearly on road maps and of which North Americans are so proud, are still rather exceptional.

A number of physical and social factors determines the precise route of any road. Prominent among these is the **relief** of the land, e.g. roads threading their way through the narrow passes across mountain barriers. Other natural **barriers** play an important role. Areas likely to flood easily at certain seasons are usually avoided. Rivers will be followed to a convenient fording or bridging point. In the older settled areas of Europe, important roads often steer away from dense forests providing easy ambush. Population centres or **markets** played a major role in the routing of roads because communication between these is the very reason for a road's existence. Particular **political** ends often played a key role in the creation of a new highway or in determination of its route. France's fine road system was deliberately centred on Paris to enhance the importance and power of the capital. In World War II, the Burma and Alaska highways were constructed with strategic objectives in mind. The great Soviet military highways in the Caucasus and, more recently, linking Moscow with Peking were explicitly constructed with political and military factors paramount. In recent years, the more detailed outline of major arterial roads has often been altered with a view to making greater **speeds** possible. For this reason, main roads will now by-pass small towns or will be characterized by the presence of long gradual bends instead of the sharp turns forcing drivers to slow down.

Roads can be classified into those having a purely local function and those serving long-distance traffic. The Romans built the first road system of continental proportions, and the success and magnificent achievements of this empire were in large measure due to the work of the Roman engineers. From the fall of Rome until little more than a century ago, the world lacked any similarly integrated road network and most of the world's roads were fit only for local traffic. Road systems may be classified into those that are dense and those that are fragmentary or sparse. Generally speaking, those areas that are economically self-sufficient and, therefore, are geared to a subsistence economy have fragmentary road systems. Areas of great industrial and commercial activity are those with the densest road networks.

In recent years, the development of the internal combustion engine suddenly gave the world's road systems a new importance. The family automobile has revolutionized the North American way of life and has had far-reaching effects in most parts of the world. Long-distance trucking, too, has played a great part in the internal trade and in the growth of industries in countries such as Canada, the United States, and several European countries. An interesting round in the keen struggle between road and rail transport systems has now been reached in which the railways are carrying long-distance trucks *piggy-back*. This would suggest that, over long distances, road transport is no match for the railway, but the struggle is not yet over.

Over short distances and with light loads, the road is still the best means of overland transport, the dense network of roads and streets providing an invaluable diversity of routes. Modern road costs, however, are high. A major throughway or national highway requires a great deal of land, vast quantities of material, and many man-hours of labour; in addition, there is the need for constant maintenance.

The Railroad

The building of a railway system is a very costly undertaking and, once constructed, it is fixed and can only serve the area within the immediate vicinity of the tracks. Many of the main rail systems, however, were first built in a period when costs were much lower and sufficient capital available to permit continued expansion and improvement. Those early days of the railway era are amongst the most romantic in the history of Canada and the United States, and it was the steel road that made possible the rapid growth of these and other countries. In Europe and in the industrial northeast of the United States, the railway was itself the child of the industrial revolution and yet it in turn made possible the full industrial development of vast areas. The great mining and industrial concerns of these regions grew on the basis of the rapid carrying of heavy loads, which the railways alone could manage at that time. Military purposes also dictated the construction of many of Europe's main railway lines. The political desire to bring British Columbia into Canada led to the building of our first transcontinental railway and in a broadly similar way political considerations lay behind the construction of the world's longest railway, the Soviet Union's Trans-Siberian Railway.

THE NORTH AMERICAN
RAILROAD NETWORK

LAND WITHIN 10 MILES
OF A RAILWAY

Notice the concentration of rail services on the industrial east and on the southerly location of Canada's railway network.

It would appear, however, that the era of vast railway projects is over, and most of the future growth in this respect will probably be in the form of tracks measured in mere hundreds of miles.

With about 45,000 miles of track, Canada's railway network is exceeded in mileage only by that of the United States and the Soviet Union. Both the Canadian National and the Canadian Pacific railways are transcontinental lines ranking amongst the largest in the world. A significant difference between these two systems lies in the fact that the former is a government-owned company operating a number of branch lines, which are quite uneconomic but provide a public service. One of the major problems of both companies and of others elsewhere in the world is the inescapable fact that to reach many of our most important mining and agricultural areas the railways must run through hundreds of miles of almost empty land where there is no possibility of trade. This is reflected on maps in the long, narrow tentacles of track spreading thinly over the map. The Ontario peninsula and the area around the St. Lawrence as far north as Quebec City are the only really densely populated regions in the Canadian railway network.

The traffic carried on Canadian railways is largely industrial. Vast quantities of Appalachian coal are carried on the tracks of southern Ontario, into the industrial plants of this region and between Buffalo and Detroit. The iron ores of Knob Lake, Lake Superior, and elsewhere also utilize many Canadian lines. Minerals provide about 35% of Canadian railways' freight tonnage. Agricultural products account for a further 20% of the total. Wheat is a main source of railway revenue and the wheat trains alone would be sufficient to make Winnipeg one of the largest and busiest rail centres. Canada's vast exports of wheat and other grains are carried from the Great Lakes ports, to Montreal, Vancouver, and Churchill; to reach these points they are carried by hundreds of long, thundering trains some of which contain as many as 80 freight cars.

Almost a third of the world's total rail mileage lies within the United States where there is far more freight carried by rail than in any other part of the world. U.S. rail activity is at its maximum in the northeastern industrial region north of the Ohio river and east of Chicago and St. Louis where about half the nation's freight and two thirds of the passengers are carried. The rail net of the south and west is much less dense, and only the Pacific Coastal region shows any comparable development. In the west, extensive farming and grazing coupled with difficulties of terrain reduce the possibilities of any dense network ever being built. There is no U.S. parallel to the great annual trek of trains from interior Canada to the coast, but there is a marked dominance of traffic movement towards the Atlantic ports from the many cities between Chicago and the east coast.

Boston, New York, Philadelphia, St. Louis, Kansas City, Salt Lake City, and several other U.S. cities rank among the busiest rail centres in the world. Chicago owes much of its importance and enormous size to its magnificent position on the main U.S. lines, and the increases in rail traffic relate very closely to the city's early growth.

Europe's early rail network was built in quite different circumstances from those of North America. There the cities and industrial centres were already in existence and the railway system was planned to link them. The dense population, intensive agriculture, and numerous manufacturing centres of Europe provide practically ideal conditions for efficient railway operations. The only serious physical barriers in the area are the Alps, Pyrenees, and Apennines where tunnelling is often necessary in their most difficult stretches. Excessive political fragmentation of such a small area and the ensuing customs and tariff barriers, however, were long a major handicap in western Europe. A map of Europe's railroads would show an extremely dense network west of central Poland but less development in Scandinavia, Spain, the Balkans, and eastern Europe. France and Britain each have over 20,000 miles of track; West Germany, Italy, Spain, Poland, and Sweden each have over 10,000 miles. Compare each of these countries in terms of area and track mileage with Canada.

There is much less transcontinental traffic in Europe than in North America and long-distance services are fewer. Minerals, carried on a short haul, are important but proportionately less so than on this side of the Atlantic. Passengers, however, in numbers and in relative importance are much more important on European railways than on ours.

The numerous marine inlets and the irregular coastline have imposed a certain pattern on European railways. The cheapness and the efficiency of coastal shipping have resulted in particularly dense traffic between inland centres of population and production, and the sea. Ports such as Hamburg, London, Rotterdam, Antwerp, and Le Havre have a rail importance as great as that of cities such as Berlin, Paris, and Milan. In addition to a constant stream of bulky goods for the sea, European railways also carry great quantities of purely local traffic.

Australia, with an area similar to that of the United States, has a very much smaller population. Settlement is largely coastal, there being no city of national importance more than 50 miles from the sea. Only 13% of the land has as much as 20 inches of rain a year and aridity will always preclude settlement in large areas of the interior. All of these facts are reflected in that country's railway system. Early railway building in Australia seemed to hold out little possibility of profit or success and each of the state governments was responsible for its own system. Unfortunately, three different gauges—or widths between tracks—were used in this early work with the result that the systems could not be unified and people and freight had to change trains at state boundaries, a situation now being remedied at great cost. An examination of Australia's railroads reveals a fairly dense network around Sydney and Melbourne, one transcontinental railway running east and west (and containing the world's longest stretch of straight track), but no track running from north to south across the continent. There is, moreover, no likelihood of such a north-south railway being built.

This map shows the multiplicity of gauges in use until recently in the populous part of Australia. Government action is now helping to remedy the situation.

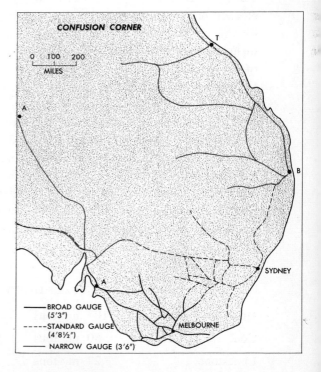

From the cases already quoted, it should be clear that railways are most economic when they are able to carry a great volume of heavy freight over great distances at fairly fast speeds. These are the optimum conditions and they are most likely to be found in areas of dense population or extensive industrialization. At the present time, the position of the world's railways is under serious challenge from other forms of transport, but for the overland carrying of minerals, agricultural produce, machinery, and heavy, bulky equipment they still have no rival.

Inland Waterways

The Indians and early traders in Canada developed a way of life dependent in large part on the existing arteries provided by our broad lakes and long rivers. On a commercial basis, inland water transport is still of very great importance in Canada and in many other countries. Such transportation is probably the cheapest of all for heavy, imperishable goods. It is, however, very slow and often involves very circuitous routes between places and it is much more restricted by the nature of the terrain than either the road or the railroad. A further limitation lies in the great cost of major canal construction and the extra cost of locks and tunnels can often prove prohibitive. Inland waterways, however, include also rivers and lakes that do not require such an initial outlay of capital but may involve large sums in keeping channels clear and in other forms of maintenance.

There is no inland waterway in the world comparable to our Great Lakes in the volume or value of the freight carried each year, and this in spite of the fact that navigation is normally limited to an eight-month year by the winter freeze-up. The excellent location of the lakes, their great area (95,000 square miles), and the efficient organization of surrounding industrial and agricultural areas help account for this heavy traffic. Other factors include the good management of Lakes ports including the building of huge grain-storage facilities, and the design and operation of the eminently practical long lakes vessels with their loading and unloading techniques and equipment. The long Great Lakes vessels are designed to carry large loads of wheat, coal, iron, etc. in bulk and yet have a maximum draught of only 21 feet because of the canals they must pass through. These vessels may be as long as 600 feet and have a capacity of half a million bushels of grain or more than 15,000 tons of iron ore or coal. Loading is done by gravity and unloading by clam-shell buckets, each with a 20 ton load, or by suction pipes. The speed of these operations can be excelled nowhere in the world and a large cargo of iron ore, for example, can be unloaded in 4 hours. Over 95% of the traffic on the Lakes is concerned with iron ore, coal, limestone, petroleum, grain, and similar cargoes. The movements of these various commodities are depicted in the maps of Lakes traffic.

AN AVERAGE YEAR'S HEAVY FREIGHT ON THE LAKES

Iron Ore	107 m. tons	Petroleum Products	17 m. tons
Coal	50 m. tons	Grain	14 m. tons
Limestone	27 m. tons	Anthracite	.3 m. tons

Embassy of the Federal Republic of Germany

This scene of activity can be duplicated for many miles along the Rhine and along several other European rivers. What are the chief cargoes carried by barges on the Rhine?

Many decades passed before the obvious extension of the Great Lakes waterways—namely the St. Lawrence Seaway—was finally opened on June 26, 1959. As a multipurpose project providing power, recreational facilities, and a navigable channel, the Seaway is one of the world's greatest engineering feats but in terms of navigation alone it still leaves much to be desired. The channel between the Lakes and Montreal is now 27 feet deep but some of the upper canals are much shallower than this. Several canals still carry single locks and act as bottlenecks to shipping. Nevertheless, the opening of the seaway provides our continent with a navigable waterway for 2,347 miles from the Atlantic to the heart of the continent. One great advantage of the seaway is that it now enables the Lakes ships to proceed all the way down to Montreal. Another lies in the fact that the newly developing iron-ore fields of Quebec and Labrador now have direct water transport to the existing steel plants of Hamilton and the United States.

Among the historic canals of North America are the Erie Canal and the Rideau Canal. The latter joins Kingston to Ottawa and was originally planned for military purposes; its sole value now is as a tourist attraction. The New York Barge Canal system, the successor to the Erie Canal, still has some economic importance.

For many years America's longest river, the Mississippi, was of declining significance as an inland waterway. This was due to the lagging commercial activity of the south and, indeed, of vast areas throughout the whole basin. Now bauxite, oil, timber, sulphur, and grain provide large cargoes and, in recent years, the automobile plant at St. Louis has been sending its products by barge to New Orleans whence they are shipped by sea.

371

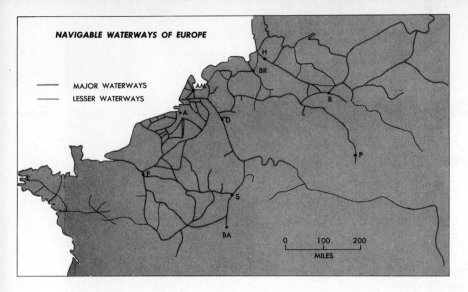

NAVIGABLE WATERWAYS OF EUROPE

MAJOR WATERWAYS
LESSER WATERWAYS

0   100   200
MILES

Name each of the cities indicated by an initial. Trace the Seine, Rhine, Elbe, and Danube rivers. Notice the concentration of water routes in the Great European Plain. Explain this concentration.

Europe, too, has a long river whose position restricts its trade possibilities. The Danube winds through south and eastern Europe towards the Black Sea and is remote from the densely populated parts of the continent. The interruption of trade caused by the cold war and the iron curtain has further diminished the possible trade carried on the river. Farther north in the great European Plain where population is dense, the conditions are excellent for the cheap water transportation now playing an essential role in the vast industrial complexes of western Europe. The Rhine is navigable to Basle 513 miles from the sea and hundreds of barges, each with a capacity of about 2,000 tons, ply these waters between the North Sea and the Ruhr, Alsace, the chemicals plants of Mannheim, and the light industries of Switzerland. The few difficult stretches of the Rhine have long been supplied with canals, and the river is remarkable for the fact that there is ice for only about 17 days and the flow is regular for all but 25 days of the rest of the year. From Czechoslovakia to Hamburg flows the Elbe, an avenue for grain, sugar, coal, and chemicals and it provides a funnel into one of the world's greatest ports.

Joining these and many other rivers, western Europe has a canal system that, for its traffic and mileage, has no equal in the world. Study the map closely and, after identifying each of the major cities marked, find out what products are probably carried on each waterway.

Elsewhere in the world, with the exception of the U.S.S.R., inland waterways are largely limited to rivers and lakes, and traffic is very small. The Soviet power and navigation projects along the Volga and other rivers have augmented the already great mileage of navigable waterways in that country. On the Volga alone, one can travel over 2,300 miles by boat. However, the volume of traffic carried on Soviet inland waterways is still not large and the long winter freeze-up followed, in many cases, by a critical loss of volume during the dry months, seriously handicaps their waterways system.

2 OCEAN AND AIR TRANSPORT

Until the present century, the oceans were the great avenues of international exchange and trade. Even in recent decades, most countries have attached a great deal of importance to having an ocean frontage and the facilities for opening a port; witness the difficulties of Hungary and Czechoslovakia prior to 1939 and the friction between Germany and Poland over Danzig. The attractiveness of ocean transport is associated with the wide variety of routes provided by the oceans and with the cheapness of such transport. The cheapness of water transport is explained by the buoyancy of water, which permits actual movement without having to overcome friction. As an example, whereas a horse can pull a one-ton load on a level road, the same animal could pull 40 tons on a canal barge. Ocean transport involves no highway maintenance costs. Finally, for many years, the shipping business has been intensely competitive, and low rates result from such competition. Although this is undoubtedly the cheapest way of transporting great quantities of heavy, bulky goods, the fact remains that such transportation is slow and does require the construction of large and costly port facilities.

By far the busiest ocean route in the world is the North Atlantic, linking the vast industrial units of North America and western Europe. Both of these coast-lines are broken by large bays and inlets providing good conditions for the build-ing of ports as well as for permitting ships to penetrate far into the continents. This route, too, is relatively free from navigational hazards. The sandbanks of Cape Hatteras, Sable Island, the fogs of the Grand Banks, and a few dangerous rocks near the two coastlines are all well known to mariners. Icebergs floating into the shipping lanes between March and July are a less predictable hazard, particularly in the area south of the Grand Banks. Since the loss of more than 1500 people on the liner *Titanic* in April, 1912 because of collision with an ice-berg, the main shipping lanes have been moved 2°30′ further south during the most dangerous months. The international ice patrol provides a further important safeguard.

Pick out on this map the five busiest ocean routes. Locate the Panama and Suez canals.

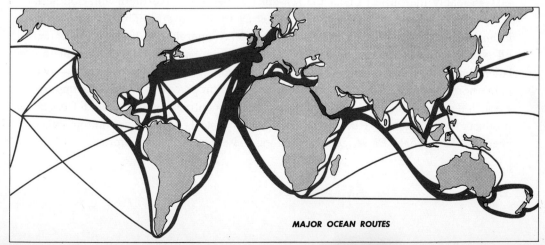

MAJOR OCEAN ROUTES

The enormous traffic that the map indicates for the North Atlantic route is partly due to the fact that the great circle routes followed by ships result in a convergence of shipping in the sea waters. The southwest-to-northeast strike of the American coast between Florida and Newfoundland is astonishingly close to the great circle line between Florida and industrial Europe. As a result, most of the shipping between Europe and the southern United States, the Gulf of Mexico, and Caribbean areas follows the same general lanes as that from more northern latitudes. In addition to this being a shorter course than that directly across the Atlantic, it has the advantage of allowing vessels to carry trade between ports on this eastern seaboard. For the large number (over 80%) of the world's merchant ships using oil this route has the further advantage that fueling can be done at a wide variety of ports drawing on Caribbean and Gulf oilfields.

Normally, the eastbound freight on the North Atlantic is three or four times the westbound. Oil, iron ore, grain, wood pulp, sugar, fruit, and phosphates are exported in enormous quantities to Britain and the rest of Europe. Return shipments consist largely of manufactured goods having a high value for small bulk. There are two basic types of vessel that carry trade, namely the large liner and the tramp. The former runs on a previously announced route and timetable and so must often return to North America with most of its cargo space empty; this in turn means that often these liners are compelled to charge higher rates on eastbound routes than would otherwise be necessary. The tramp, however, will often follow its cargoes around the Atlantic, carrying British coal or Swedish paper to Brazil where it may in turn pick up a load of manganese for the United States and there pick up a cargo of phosphates for Britain.

More widely publicized than the busy cargo liners of the Atlantic are the magnificent passenger liners, the *Queens of the Seas*, such as the Queen Elizabeth, carrying mail express items and small quantities of high-value freight. Transatlantic passenger traffic is definitely seasonal, and many of the vessels designed for this service are now used on special cruises in the winter months. Airline competition is also a problem for the passenger liners, and now half of those who leave North America to vacation in Europe do so by air. The great cost of building and maintaining these great liners seems prohibitive, and it would appear that few more will be built. The S.S. United States alone cost over $70 million.

Probably the busiest of all the sea-lanes between the Northern and Southern hemispheres, are those leaving South America for the north. This traffic results in an oceanic crossroads near Cape Sao Roque comparable with the busy waters off Newfoundland. Off this Brazilian cape, the grain-, meat-, coffee-, or mineral-laden fleets from Argentina, Uruguay, and Brazil divide into two streams—one going north to the U.S.A., the other crossing to Europe. North America imports wool, hides from the far south, and enormous quantities of coffee and tropical products from Brazil. Returning vessels carry steel, machinery, automobiles, chemicals, and coal. Passenger traffic along these routes is very limited.

Two vessels in Oslo harbour depict the grandeur of the sailing ship and the beauty of modern motor vessels. The demand for speed doomed the sailing ship and is now reducing the importance of the other.

Caribbean shipping presents a very confused picture. Here, there is a maze of intersecting sea-lanes with no main route but with a general funnelling of traffic towards the United States. The area is dominated by the Panama Canal that is both a front door and a back door depending on the direction of the trade. Liner traffic in these waters tends to be expensive due to the many small ports of call and the short distances between them. Outgoing trade consists of oil, bauxite, sugar, tobacco, iron ore, coffee, tropical timber, and fruit, and these cargoes far exceed imports in value and volume. Once again, manufactured goods dominate the imports of these lands.

The Panama Canal, which plays an important role in Caribbean shipping, is also of enormous importance to the trade of the west coast of South America. Very little traffic now sails round Magellan Strait. This canal brought Europe and eastern North America much closer to the west coast of the two Americas and also reduced the sailing distance between the industrial northeast of North America and much of the Far East. Some examples of the miles saved include 7,900 between New York and San Francisco, 5,705 between New Orleans and Yokohama, and 1,540 between Liverpool and Valparaiso. In practice, however, the canal has become overwhelmingly U.S. in its trade, that country owning over a third of all ships passing through. A few points of comparison between this canal and the Suez follow later.

The undoubted supremacy of the North Atlantic, in terms of number of ships and passengers and volume of freight, has in no way diminished the busy traffic on the Mediterranean whose waters have been carrying hundreds of vessels daily since before the dawn of recorded history. Penetrating deep into a block of land—Europe, Asia, and Africa—accounting for a half of the earth's land surface, this sea occupies a position the importance of which will never decline. Indeed, the progressive industrialization and political growth of the new Asian countries are adding daily to its significance. When you examine a world map, you will see that routes fan out at both ends of this aptly named sea: to Europe and North America on the west, to the Far East and Australasia on the east. Although there is always a great deal of shipping entering or leaving Mediterranean ports, most of the traffic on the Mediterranean is essentially through traffic. One advantage of the route, however, is that these vessels passing through can stop at any one of a number of ports to pick up extra cargo and passengers.

It should be clear that much of the importance of the Mediterranean today can be attributed to the short Suez Canal at its eastern end. This waterway saves 4,500 miles on a voyage between Liverpool and Bombay and about 1,000 miles between London and Sydney. About a third of its total trade is of British origin but large numbers of Norwegian, French, Italian, and other vessels also use the canal. Oil tankers from the rich oilfields of the Persian Gulf and Saudi Arabia now form a very large proportion of the total tonnage on the canal. Indeed, the world's first oil tanker was specifically designed to meet the requirements of this canal.

The strategic importance of the Suez and Panama canals can hardly be exaggerated; they became major life-lines for Britain and the United States in World War II and they undoubtedly saved the lives of thousands of seamen. Since 1945, however, traffic on Suez now outweighs that on the Panama by about 3 to 1. This difference can be accounted for by

> The enormous oil-tanker traffic on Suez,
>
> The large number of trading nations on the trade routes fanning out from Suez,
>
> The fact that much North American traffic now crosses the continent cheaply and swiftly by land.

The water hemisphere—the vast Pacific ocean—plays perhaps a surprisingly small role in world ocean trade. To explain this, you merely have to compare the small commercial activity of the countries around this ocean with those of America and Europe. A close examination will reveal that few of the exports of the Asian countries are bought in great quantities by North America, and vice versa.

The World's Shipping Industry

World War II had a more disastrous effect on the shipping services of the world than on any other single service. The large merchant fleets of Japan, Germany, and Greece ceased to exist altogether, and British, Norwegian, French, Italian, and other fleets were ruthlessly decimated. Intense shipbuilding activity began in 1945 and by 1953 there were already 47% more merchant vessels in the world than in 1939. The United States, Britain, Norway, and Panama now have the world's largest fleets. Most governments in the world now give financial assistance to their merchant fleets, but Britain is an outstanding exception to this rule.

A major trend in shipping, begun prior to World War II and since become firmly established, is the steady increase in specialized liners—passenger liners, oil tankers, ore-carriers, refrigerator ships, timber carriers, and dozens of others. The formerly ubiquitous tramp steamer immortalized in Masefield's words—

> "Dirty British coaster with a salt-caked smoke stack
>
> Butting through the Channel in the mad March days,
>
> With a cargo of Tyne coal,
>
> Road-rail, pig-lead,
>
> Firewood, iron-ware and cheap tin trays."

—is now a thing of the past and is disappearing from the shipping lanes and being replaced by faster ships that carry specific loads on a course and operate on a timetable not unlike that of the great passenger liners.

Air Transport

The youngest of our major forms of transportation is unquestionably the most exciting and most progressive of all. Only in 1918 was the first commercial air-line—a Danish one—established, and it was not until the 1930's that the first transatlantic and transpacific routes were established. Already the major advantages and disadvantages of air travel are quite clear. The airplane has the advantage of being unhampered by obstructions on land or sea. The expenditure involved in building international airports is sometimes cited as a drawback, but such costs are normally no greater than those involved in constructing a major rail network or in building port installations. Air transport, above everything else, is fast and it is excellent for the carriage of passengers and fairly light commodities. On the other hand, the airplane is relatively small and it is also normally more limited by weather restrictions than other forms of transport. Perhaps the greatest advantage of air transport is the fact that the plane can always follow great circle routes.

In 1954, Scandinavian Air Lines established the first transpolar air route. The service saves 700 miles between Copenhagen and Los Angeles, and 1000 miles between Copenhagen and Tokyo.

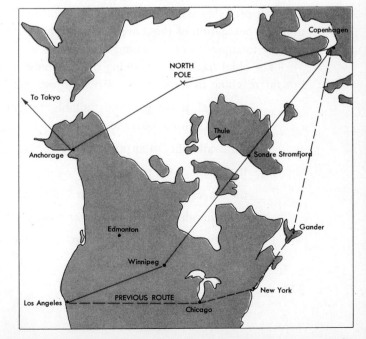

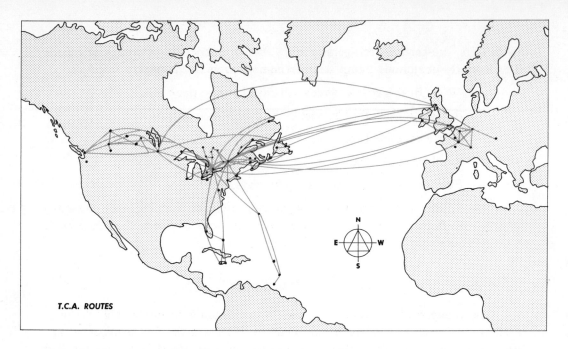

T.C.A. ROUTES

Often, however, it is more economic to follow a route linking large cities where trade and passengers create more business.

Four major areas of airline activity can easily be identified on a map of world air traffic. These are

> North America,
>
> Europe and adjacent North Africa,
>
> the U.S.S.R.,
>
> and the rest of the Asian countries.

Efficient airlines do operate in Australia, Africa, and South America but much of the trade of those areas is in bulky raw materials or heavy mechanical equipment that will probably continue to move by land or sea for several decades; in addition, the population of these areas is either not sufficiently numerous or sufficiently wealthy to support heavy passenger air traffic.

The chief factors determining the economic efficiency of an air route are few but far reaching in importance. Briefly these can be stated as follows:

> potential passenger and suitable freight traffic between terminals or points along the route,
>
> the availability of airport facilities,
>
> the length of the route,
>
> the longest stretch of non-stop flight, and
>
> the generally prevailing weather conditions along the route.

Large jet aircraft, their servicing, and the necessary facilities now cost

378

enormous sums of money and this has led to a sharp division of the world's more than 250 airlines into a small group of huge international airlines and a large number of smaller but independent companies often providing excellent service but restricting themselves normally to local air routes with perhaps a few international runs. Here, in Canada, we have excellent examples within each group. Trans-Canada Air Lines, like many of the other major airlines, is a government-sponsored company, which now ranks eighth in the world. This company is 25 years old and in 1961 it carried over 3,700,000 passengers who paid a total of $143 million. In addition, mail and freight added a further $20 million to this annual revenue. The fleet of aircraft carrying this traffic consists of 83 large aircraft—the huge all-jet D.C. 8's and the slower Vanguards and Viscounts—and the plan is to increase this to 87 in the next few months and to employ a total of 12,000 people. Although this company, as the map shows, is Canada's major carrier of overseas air traffic, it also serves a large domestic market within Canada. As a public service, T.C.A. continues to operate local services some of which are hardly paying their way. Herein lies the greatest handicap of the government-owned company.

The privately-owned Canadian Pacific Airlines is another international Canadian air carrier, which now operates 44,700 miles of routes including 7,500 miles within Canada. In 1955, C.P.A. was one of the first airlines to launch a transpolar route between Vancouver and, in this case, Amsterdam. This is now a particularly popular service. The map shows the major services provided by this expanding company.

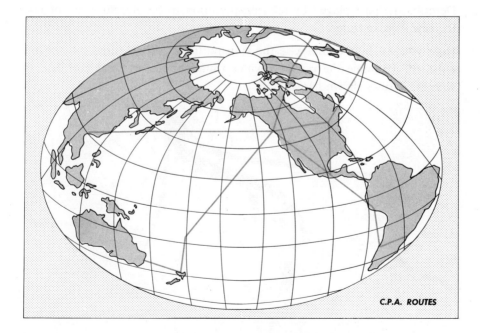

C.P.A. ROUTES

379

UNIT REVIEW

Questions

1. Describe and explain, with reference to specific examples, the geographical factors which (a) encourage and (b) hinder the construction and maintenance of railways.

2. Examine the conditions under which canal and river transport can compete with rail.

3. Outline the value of the Sault Ste. Marie canals to Canada, the Panama Canal to the United States, and the Suez to Britain.

4. Explain and give examples of the following:
   transhipment point,
   nodal town,
   canal locks,
   international airport,
   head of navigation.

Research Assignments

1. Examine the importance of transport facilities in the localization of any one industry. Illustrate your answer with a specific example.

2. Describe the part played by air transportation in the development of one of the new African states.

3. Here you see how complex is the transportation service used by one major industry. Examine the rail and water routes of Europe and correlate them with the arrows shown here.

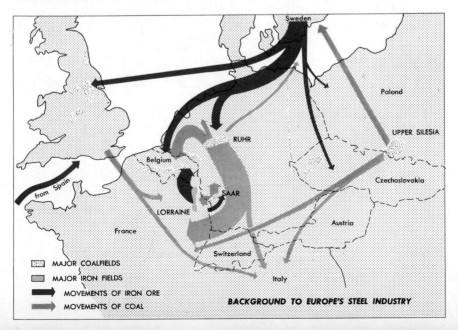

MAJOR COALFIELDS
MAJOR IRON FIELDS
MOVEMENTS OF IRON ORE
MOVEMENTS OF COAL

BACKGROUND TO EUROPE'S STEEL INDUSTRY

4. Prepare a report, complete with sketchmaps, to describe the water, rail, road, and air transport in South America. Pick out the areas with the poorest facilities and explain why their development is so slow.

5. Name each of the ports on the adjoining map of the Great Lakes. Prepare lists showing ports that are primarily exporters and those that are importers. Using a good reference work, name the chief cargoes entering or leaving each port.

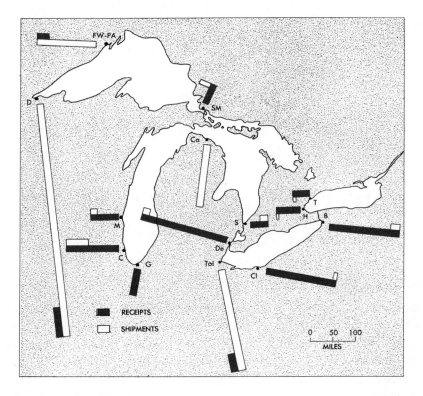

6. Discuss the position of either Montreal or Winnipeg in relation to Canada's railway systems. Illustrate with a clear sketchmap.

Unit Four

Social Geography

1 THE STUDY OF SETTLEMENTS

Homes and Villages

The interrelationship between man and his environment is clearly expressed in the type of home in which people live and the patterns in which the homes are arranged. In former centuries a home reflected not only the taste and standard of living of its owner but also the climatic conditions under which he lived and even the local geology or type of vegetation as revealed in the building materials used. In our industrial society with its efficient and cheap forms of transportation, it has become possible for us to build our homes of brick and other materials that may have originated hundreds of miles away.

The materials out of which men construct their homes vary to suit every type of terrain and every climatic region. Igloos of arctic ice, mud-built dagga huts of Africa, timber dwellings of the Canadian north, stone buildings of limestone regions, all illustrate man's effective use of local materials. The use of timber for buildings in many medieval towns where stone was scarce often resulted in disastrous fires such as the fire of London in 1666. In the loess lands of China it is easy to dig large and comfortable caves in the soft rock; today such caves constitute the homes of thousands of people. Unfortunately, cave-ins produced by earthquakes in this area can result in enormous loss of life.

A study of the traditional design and construction of men's homes throws light not only upon the materials used but also upon the local climatic conditions

382

and the skills acquired by man in a particular region. Heavy snowfall or rainfall often leads people to construct homes with steeply pitched roofs. In tropical areas where timber is scarce the flat roof requires a minimum amount of lumber and at the same time provides a family storage place or drying floor. The strong winds of the Tyrol are countered by large stones on the roofs of the picturesque Tyrolese dwellings. Thatched houses built on piles above river banks or on marshy terrain furnish excellent living quarters for people in Amazonia and in Borneo. The tent of the Bedouin, consisting of a goat-hair cloth stretched over thin poles and facing downwind, serves its purpose in the desert. Wooden supports form the skeleton of the Mongol yurt, which, with its warm covering of felt and fur, is perfectly adapted to living conditions of the Kirghiz and other nomadic tribes of Siberia.

This is a summer dwelling on a high Norwegian saeter. In what ways can you relate it to its surroundings?

Royal Norwegian Embassy

The culture and social conditions of a people are often reflected in the design and decoration of their homes. A stranger travelling in Canada might be impressed by the Norman baronial style of many of the older buildings in Quebec or by an occasional chateau-like structure typical of older French architecture. Edifices of a staid and heavy Victorian style are to be found in Toronto and elsewhere in Ontario. In Toronto, however, and perhaps even more in the Prairies and on the B.C. coast, much of the planning and buildings shows strong U.S. influence. At any rate, buildings are indicative, or symbolic, of something very important in our environment and not easily measured.

Rural Settlement

When we think of the hundreds of millions of people in India, China, and other countries of the world, we usually conjure up mental pictures of crowded city streets and miles of densely packed houses. We probably do so because most of us are town dwellers prone to project the North American picture into other areas. In truth, however, most of the vast populations of the world consist of countryfolk or rural dwellers. An examination of rural settlements reveals three fundamental patterns of dwelling distribution: that in which individual farmsteads predominate, that characterized by numerous scattered tiny hamlets, and that distinguished by large nucleated villages.

The form that settlement in any region will take depends largely on certain geographical factors. In regions of widespreading rich soils, farmers are usually prosperous; accordingly, the social advantages of their communities often result in the growth of large nucleated villages. Where security from attack is of cardinal importance, people also tend to become grouped in large villages. This happens, too, where water is in short supply but where individual good wells become focal points for villages. Dispersed farm settlements are most common in more difficult areas where people seek out small isolated pockets of good soil. It should be clear that fertile soil, a suitable climate, good drainage, a sunny aspect, a defensible site, as well as other favourable factors, enter into the choice of sites that, taken together, form one of the fundamental dwelling patterns, be it of individual farmstead, tiny hamlet, or nucleated village.

PRAIRIE FARMS IN THE U.S. CORN BELT

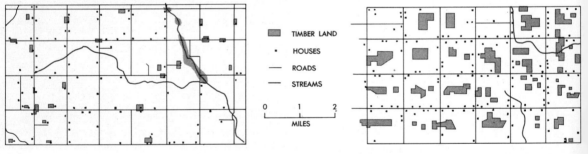

TIMBER LAND

HOUSES

ROADS

STREAMS

0 1 2
MILES

DISPERSED RURAL SETTLEMENT IN TWO FARMING REGIONS

Note the small clumps of woods around the farmhouses and a little galeria forest along the river.

Here is farming in a forested region. Large clumps of forest remain among the farmed lands here. The rectangular settlement pattern is typical of much of North America.

Dispersed Settlement

The tradition of individual family farms owned in many cases by their operators, produced in western Europe a characteristic pattern of single family dwellings standing in the centre of the adjacent farmlands. This manifestation of

384

individualism followed the breakup of the feudal system and contributed to the decline of village life in wide areas of Britain, France, Germany, and the Low Countries. Large numbers of the early settlers in America came originally from such areas and, of course, they brought their way of life with them. The availability of good land overseas further encouraged the dispersal of these self-reliant farmers with the result that the dispersed-settlement pattern is now the dominant one throughout the major farmlands of Canada and the United States; indeed, it is especially prevalent in the older settled parts of Ontario.

It should be borne in mind that while a widespread distribution of individual prosperous farms precludes the development of vigorous village life, it does usually demand the presence of prosperous market towns as centres of social, commercial, and cultural activities.

The line of villages along the northern side of the valley takes the advantage of a southward aspect— greater sunshine. What effects will this have in terms of the snow line, vegetation, and agriculture?

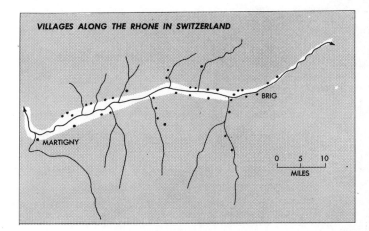

VILLAGES ALONG THE RHONE IN SWITZERLAND

MARTIGNY

BRIG

0   5   10
MILES

Nucleated Settlements

For a number of reasons people have long grouped themselves into units larger than one family, but the resultant village groupings have assumed different shapes. Some villages have cleared a central space around which the homes are built to form a **rough square or circle**. Often the centre of one village is a market place or village green; of another it is a church; of another it is a wealthy person's house. In Europe this type of village was often surrounded by some form of rampart or other defence. A crossroads or bridging point often led to the growth of a **star-shaped village** that tended to spread out along the intersecting highways. The forested lands of Germany and the narrow valleys of Switzerland, Norway, and other mountain regions imposed serious physical limitations upon possible village patterns. In some areas, **long villages** grew along a main highway, each village seldom having more than three or four lines of buildings. Sometimes such villages spread for miles until they linked up with one another and the traveller could no longer distinguish the end of one village from the beginning of another.

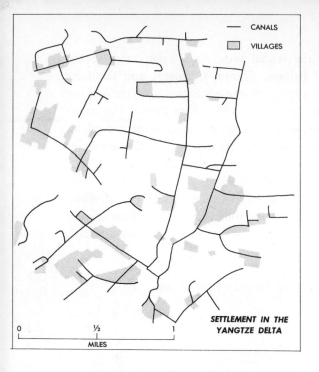

Here we see an extremely dense rural settlement. Farms average less than one acre in area. Canals are used for transport so that all available land can be farmed. Not far away, millions of people live entirely on boats—an eloquent testimony to the pressure of population on a limited land area.

SETTLEMENT IN THE YANGTZE DELTA

0   ½   1
MILES

Nucleated villages of a special type are found in the **plantation settlements** of the United States and the **haciendas** of Latin America. In both cases, one person owned a large area of land for which he needed workers; he, therefore, built permanent accommodation for these people and their families at a convenient site on the farm. Eventually the land may have been parcelled out and changed ownership, but the original settlement pattern remained unaltered. In the Soviet Union, where all land is owned by the State, thousands of **collective** villages have been built on the nationalized farms, yet in most cases these are merely newer buildings on the site of long-existent villages.

Throughout the western world the *dormitory* village has assumed new importance in the past thirty years. It is a small residential settlement sufficiently close to a large city for most of its inhabitants easily to commute daily to the nearby city where they work.

Legation of Finland

This is a picturesque area of rolling country in southern Finland. What type of settlements is shown here? Describe the location of three of the settlements shown.

386

2 URBAN SETTLEMENT PATTERNS

Once a village has been established it will normally grow for some time by the adding of such services as are provided by more stores, schools, churches, etc.; any one of these can at some time be either the cause or the result of further growth. There will come a point, however, where the presence or absence of certain natural advantages will result in the village's growing into a town or else ceasing to grow altogether. A town differs from a village not only in its size but also in the variety of its services.

A large number of the cities of Europe date their origin from the days of the Roman Empire when they were primarily important as military camps protecting a strategic location or guarding the population of the surrounding farmlands. (Similarly, many of the first settlements in North America originated as military or naval bases and eventually grew into great cities.) Later, in the mediaeval period of Europe, certain of the towns acquired a new importance as centres of trade or of education or of religious significance. As long as transportation facilities remained inadequate and people for the most part moved about on foot, the towns tended to be small, numerous, and close together. Improved transportation, however, resulted in the growth of many centres and the decline of others. During the sixteenth and subsequent centuries the presence of a royal family and the accompanying nobility, added a new importance to capital cities, which then became centres of international trade and early industrial activity. The industrial revolution added a new growth dimension; cities with access to coal or other forms of power or to raw materials, received an impetus to expansion which, in many instances, is still operative today.

In many countries there is a persistent trend of population away from the rural districts and towards the cities. This *rural depopulation* is the result of the interaction of factors, namely:

   the greater job opportunities present in most city areas;

   the generally better social facilities of urban centres;

   mechanization on the farms (which has reduced the need for so many
       workers in certain areas);

   better educational facilities in cities for growing families;

   the snow-balling effect of population in cities, viz., the mere presence of
       large numbers of people, thus creating the need for workers in a variety
       of service industries.

Within the cities themselves there have been distinct changes in growth in the past century. The tendency of people to move out to the suburbs has created wide belts (and in some cases long ribbons) of residential building around cities; the resulting condition is often denominated *urban sprawl*. Such sprawling of homes over the countryside can seriously impair the amenities that open farmland provides, reduce the area of good agricultural land on which a country relies, and produce unsightly conglomerations of unplanned growth. In some instances, the wealthier part of the population moves outward to establish a separate small community at some distance away, thus creating a *dormitory* town. The upshot has been that many North American towns have been left with a dead heart as the result of the growth of shopping centres and other facilities in the suburban residential areas.

Already in some parts of the world a counter-suburbia trend is well under way; in fact, many families today are moving into new apartment buildings nearer the heart of the city. Suggest what advantages these people will now enjoy as compared with those enjoyed by the bungalow dwellers of the outskirts.

Within the past century town planning has grown from being the pleasant hobby of a few wealthy men into a branch of work of vital concern to the national economy; indeed, it is today exerting a marked impact on the happiness of millions of people. Most cities, and even small towns, now have full-time staffs of experts studying living conditions, traffic problems, future industrial growth, need for recreational facilities, and a complex of related problems. In some areas planners have established *satellite* towns to drain off part of the population and industrial activity from cities that are already too large. A few rapidly growing cities such as Ottawa have established a *green belt* of land which will provide a temporary limit to the outward growth of the city but beyond which the city will eventually expand. In time such a green belt would become a wide area of unspoiled countryside within the city itself. This measure is far-sighted since it recognizes the fact that once a city has expanded across a particular zone, it would be very costly later to purchase the land involved and remove the buildings on it.

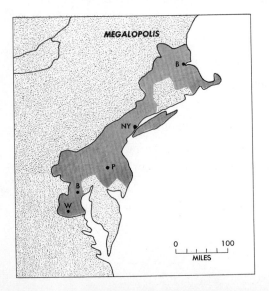

Here we have a huge cluster of metropolitan centres. Name each of the cities indicated.

The terminology employed in the study of urban settlement is undergoing certain changes. To use the term *city* to describe a centre with a population of a quarter of a million and also one of five, six, or seven million, obviously implies that the term is in some respects inadequate. Continued rapid growth has resulted in an administrative change that has provided us with one useful term, namely, metropolitan area. The term *metropolis* has several definitions, but essentially it designates a major city with its suburbs and adjoining cluster of small towns. Toronto and Montreal are outstanding examples of metropolitan areas in Canada. Another term used to designate an extensive fairly continuous, built-up area around a large city or group of cities is *conurbation*; it signifies an area that has several millions of people but no unified form of local government. On the eastern coast of the United States there are a number of cities that virtually coalesce; to these has been given the name *megalopolis*, a term denoting a chain of large metropolitan cities.

Analyzing a City

In analyzing the growth and importance of a city, we must use a number of terms whose import should be clearly grasped. To illustrate, let us consider the evolution of a city. An historical approach to the analysis will begin with the noting of the precise location where the first settlement began, e.g., at a bridging point, or on a ridge of dry gravel overlooking an adjacent lowlying swamp. The choice of this *site*, as the original location is called, plays a key role in determining whether continued growth is to follow. Eventually, of course, if the site is strategically chosen, the city grows beyond its original site and may indeed extend so far that one finds difficulty in locating the original site. In such an outcome, the dominant factor will have been the position of the city in relation to the surrounding region, country, or continent on which it stands. This regional position upon which the city's transportation and industrial facilities depend is called its *situation*. Using the topographical map of Vancouver provided and your own atlas, briefly describe the site and situation, respectively, of that city.

There are many varieties of site: a bridging point, a defensible position, a ford, a centre of water power, a head of navigation, a good deep harbour, the confluence of two rivers, the entrance to a mountain pass or major valley—these are just a few of the natural sites around which a large city may grow. In the study of a city's geography, one looks for the reason behind the choice of site. Unfortunately, certain sites are chosen arbitrarily; such are those of many railway towns in North America; these could not have possibly developed into great cities.

The original site that fostered the early growth of a city may eventually prove a handicap to its further growth unless the merits of its situation overrule this handicap. San Francisco at the tip of a narrow hilly peninsula, constricted Manhattan Island in New York, and the island of Montreal are examples of advantageous sites that ultimately presented difficulties.

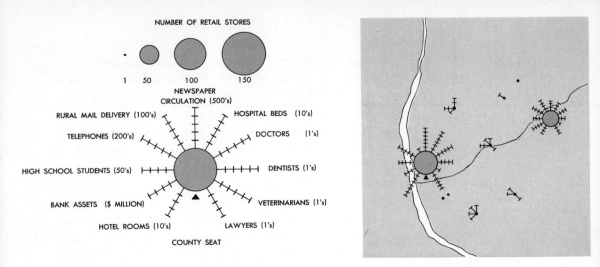

This way of studying the service of towns is obviously a better way to judge the importance of small settlements than using population as a guide. Prepare a similar map for a few small settlements in your own district.

Urban settlements are classified as to size, site, situation, and function. The *function*, which comprises the major roles played by a city, is generally the best indication of its importance, and often of the significance of its situation, in terms of human activity. Changing conditions of modern life and new forms of society are reflected in the function of cities; however, we still have a few examples of cities whose functions are being carried over from a previous age. Thus Oxford in England, Heidelberg in Germany, and Kingston in Canada are towns whose importance has been, and still is, due to their educational institutions. In all three, fortunately, industrial importance has now been added to the more historic role. Military towns are to be found commanding strategic locations or serving the needs of vast military bases. Nevertheless, the dispersal of modern armed forces in the light of possible missile warfare seems to preclude the further building of any towns of this type. Rome, Lhasa, Mecca, Benares and many other cities have attained major significance as centres of religious worship or pilgrimage; around each a whole structure of administration and essential services has grown up. Many small towns have achieved importance as transshipment points for cargo from rail to ship or vice versa and also as focal points of communication lines; yet these two facilities now normally serve as merely routine functions of any major city.

In the following pages we will briefly review some of the chief characteristics of commercial, mining, industrial, administrative, and recreational centres with reference to specific examples. It must be stressed, however, that every large city combines a number of distinct functions and it would be incorrect to picture any city as serving but one predominant function. Indeed, it is virtually impossible even to say which is the chief function of a city such as London or New York. The examples that follow are merely clear exemplifications of a particular function among others.

Montreal had its origin in a French settlement founded in 1642 at a defensive site on an island a thousand miles from the sea. Protection from attacking Iroquois Indians and access to the sea were of prime importance in this choice of site. The value of its situation became apparent when the movement of trappers along the Ottawa River, on the St. Lawrence to the Great Lakes, and via Lake Champlain to New York made the site a focus of routes in this part of the continent. Railway expansion into the vast prairie lands added a new importance as the city became one of the major railway centres on the continent. Finally, the opening of the St. Lawrence Seaway, which seemed at first to threaten the city's importance as a transshipment point owing to adjacent rapids, has actually made it the chief port and industrial centre on a busy shipping lane. It is now the meeting place of oceanic and Great Lakes shipping. A navigational handicap is the fact that Montreal's port is closed by ice from December to April each year, but already research is in progress to solve this problem.

Having a huge population and being already an accumulation centre for great masses of raw materials meant for export, it was natural that industrial processing soon became a major activity of Montreal. The chief oil-refining centre in Canada, it is also the chief manufacturing centre, busiest port, and largest city in the country. Its universities attract students from many parts of the world. Its religious shrines are major centres of Roman Catholic Quebec. Large hotels attest the importance of the city as a centre of conventions and of tourist activity.

Owing to its political significance, Hong Kong has recently been one of the most rapidly growing cities in the world. Here we find an excellent, sheltered deep-water harbour situated at the mouth of one of China's populous river valleys on the main route between Singapore and industrial Japan. Originally a fishing port, the town was selected by the British as a major military centre and coaling station for their former Pacific Fleet. The city became commercially important following the establishment of a sizeable European population on the island. When China became a Communist state, Hong Kong assumed a new role as a major link between this vast state and the rest of the world. As China became more and more a huge market, many industrialists found it convenient to set up plants here to produce articles for export to the mainland. Soon the low overhead costs and cheap labour of Hong Kong enabled many of these products to be sold economically on the North American and European markets. Cheap textiles, rubber shoes, flashlights, plastics, etc., now flow out from densely crowded Hong Kong to markets all over the world. Shipbuilding and repairing, too, are major activities at a port which has no rivals for many hundreds of miles.

The fact that Hong Kong is politically the main gateway between China and the western world is demonstrated by the industrial and commercial activity that makes it today the most valuable link between Oriental Communism and the western democracies.

From an examination of such ports as Montreal, Hong Kong, Vancouver, and New York, we can draw certain conclusions about the major facts operating in their growth. A port must have a productive hinterland and must command important land as well as sea routes. A large population in the hinterland is also a great asset since it will stimulate import traffic through the port. Given these advantages others may also follow. Industrial activity around the port, shipbuilding yards, a naval base or fishing fleet, and administrative or other activities all further stimulate the growth of the port itself. Serious deterioration in the importance of a port can result from the silting of its harbour, economic depression in its hinterland, and even a changing political situation.

Commercial Centres — Inland

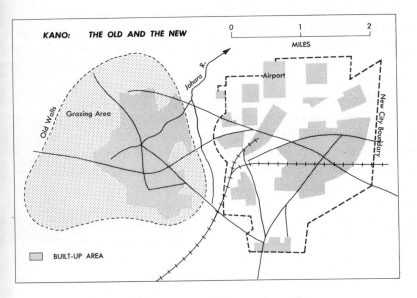

Notice *the convergence of transportation routes in the new city. This map shows only site; prepare a map of Kano showing its situation in West Africa.*

Kano in Nigeria is an example of an inland centre which fulfils many of the essential functions of a port. An ancient Hausa city, it has for many centuries been a meeting place of desert caravans from the north and of traders bringing tropical products from the Guinea coast. The original city grew up on a rocky hill close to a small stream, but much of the water supply comes from deep wells. For centuries a flourishing city of mud and adobe homes stood here within the protection of its walls.

Improved road and rail transport services, inaugurated under the authority of the British colonial office, has increased the volume of traffic flowing into this city, which at first functioned primarily as a market. New growth, however, has resulted in the building of a new town complete with an airport, which has now become one of the busiest in all Africa. Besides having a large trade in peanuts, the city has also become a centre of the hide and leather industry, of textiles (using local cotton), and of service industries such as those provided by weavers, smiths,

392

tailors, etc., for the huge surrounding region. For a considerable period under the British it also had importance as an administrative centre; this importance has not lessened as a result of recent political developments.

The requirements for a major inland commercial centre are similar to those of a port. It must have access to two productive but contrasting regions between which there is an encouragement to trade. Good communications are desirable, as well as a stable political situation which will permit easy movement and trade. Local functions, such as industries and administration, add to its significance and usually attract still more trade.

Industrial Centres

Shown here is the main steel-producing centre at Hamilton. In the background is a bar carrying the Burlington skyway and beyond that is Lake Ontario. List four major advantages of this site for a large steel industry.

The Steel Company of Canada, Limited

Hamilton is the most industrialized city in Canada with a variety of manufactured goods including textiles, electrical equipment, rubber goods, chemical products, tobacco, soap, and processed foods as well as its basic iron and steel and heavy machinery industries. The city has developed on a narrow lowland on the shores of Lake Ontario along which traffic flows between the U.S. frontier and the Toronto region. Although the Niagara escarpment limited the area of flat low-lying land, there was enough for the building of large plants close to the lake level and to the main rail and road services. Thus, added to the advantage of a good situation, the city enjoys excellent tranportation facilities by road and rail, and, more important, by water for raw materials which are shipped in great quantities. Iron ore comes from Lake Superior and Labrador, coal from the Lake Erie ports, and limestone for fluxing from the Niagara escarpment. Power for other industries is derived from the local electricity supply and imported coal. The facilities which make possible the import of raw materials also help in marketing the finished products, although the local and Toronto markets alone account for much of the trade.

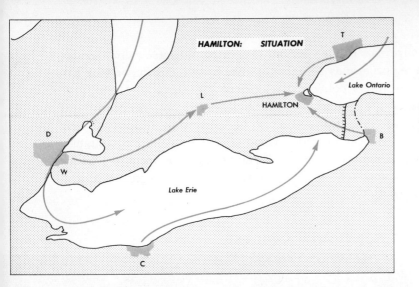

HAMILTON: SITUATION

T

Lake Ontario

L

HAMILTON

D

W

B

Lake Erie

C

Name each city shown here. Notice the convergence of routes on Hamilton. What are the chief products moving along each of these routes?

While over half of Hamilton's population is engaged in industry, a large percentage of the people is employed in such essential services as wholesale and retail trade, finance, education (McMaster University), and entertainment.

In Brazil, Sao Paulo is a flourishing city of over 3 million people founded originally as the centre of a rich farmland in the 16th century. Industry began here with the preparing and export of the vast coffee crop from the region and with the processing of the cotton in local textile mills. Standing in the tropics at about 2,500 feet above sea level, it has a healthy bracing climate that has encouraged the settlement of a large population while at the same time producing no serious enervating effects from tropical heat. The huge Cubatao power plant provides vast power resources within a 35-mile radius. Excellent overland transport exists to the Brazilian sources of raw materials.

Sao Paulo's location ensures a pleasant climate, rich soil, plentiful power, and an excellent outport. These advantages, plus raw materials and available labour, can mean immense industrialization.

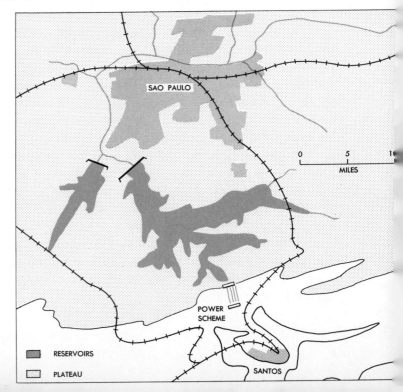

SAO PAULO

0   5   1
MILES

POWER
SCHEME

RESERVOIRS

PLATEAU

SANTOS

394

Of outstanding importance to Sao Paulo and Brazil generally is the port of Santos, which has connections with all parts of the world. The largest industrial centre in Brazil, Sao Paulo has over 400,000 workers employed in 15,000 plants producing textiles, chemicals, steel, tires, machinery, and processed foods. It is a state capital, as well as an educational and resort centre of importance.

All cities are industrial centres, but many resemble Sao Paulo and Hamilton in the preponderance of industry among their multiple functions. In such cities we usually find good transport facilities, an easily accessible source of raw materials, a large market, considerable power resources, and a good number of light industries and service industries bolstering the essential major industries.

Mining Centres

At an elevation of about 3,500 feet on the vast African plateau and almost in the centre of the continent, stands a city which has figured prominently in the news for the past two years (1959-1961), namely, Elisabethville. Here in 1910 the first European settlement on the rich Katanga mineral field was established to work the rich high-grade copper deposits that abound in the vicinity. In time, besides being a major source of copper, Elisabethville became also a supplier to world markets of gold, diamonds, uranium, tungsten, cobalt, and tin, and thus grew to be a thriving city of 200,000 people possessing every modern facility. Of major importance is the transport network to carry the copper ore to the sea, the first part of it being a railway through Rhodesia to carry minerals to the port of Beira. Later, the Benguela Railway was constructed to the port of Lobito, thus providing a much shorter sea route to Europe. Cheap transportation of bulky minerals is essential for the continued prosperity of Elisabethville.

Already the main centres of mining in Katanga province have shifted from Elisabethville as older mines have become worked out and newer ones have opened up. Kambove to the northwest is now the chief centre of copper mining. However, Elisabethville is still at once the administrative headquarters of all the mining operations, the provincial capital, and the major commercial centre of the whole region. Here, employing local coal and hydroelectricity, copper smelters have been built in order to reduce the cost of transportation of ore to the sea.

Many mining towns have proved to be highly ephemeral creations; hence, one of the favourite topics of the storyteller is the *ghost town*, as an abandoned mining centre is called. If, however, the deposits are sufficiently rich to allow a large population to become established in the place, various commercial concerns and service industries may be set up so that as the centres of mining move away from the town it takes on a new role as financial and industrial capital of its region. It has been thus with Elisabethville.

Canada has a large number of mining towns of all sizes. Choose one in the east and one in the west and compare their development, noting especially the influence of transport facilities upon the prosperity of each.

Capital Cities

Capital cities and administrative centres include many of the world's largest cities, but in these the city has grown as a result of a number of important functions. We shall consider two smaller capitals where as yet the administrative function is overwhelmingly the major one.

Ottawa, our own Federal capital, was chosen by Queen Victoria at a time when Canada's population was even more concentrated in the Quebec City to Hamilton areas than it is today, and being near the main areas of population was an asset from the standpoint of communications. Ottawa has always had good transport links with Montreal and Toronto, Canada's two chief cities; and yet it was at a safe distance from what was considered in earlier times to be a vulnerable frontier, namely, the U.S. border. This latter fact gave it an advantage over a similar city to the south, namely, Kingston. On the basis of local timber industries, especially Hull, settlement had already occurred in the area; it was not, therefore, necessary to begin building a completely new town as a capital.

Being the meeting place of French Quebec and English Ontario, Ottawa could assume a certain impartiality between the two cultures and could attempt to be more truly bilingual than most other centres of its size.

Over half of the workers in the city are employed directly or indirectly by the Federal Government. Not only are the headquarters of the government itself here, but also those of the armed forces, the R.C.M.P., the National Research Council, the Defence Research Board, all branches of the Civil Service including even (in the Hull area) the government printing establishment, the Mint, the National Museum, the Art Gallery, and a variety of other cultural centres. As a result, the city is now becoming a centre of tourist attractions of no mean importance.

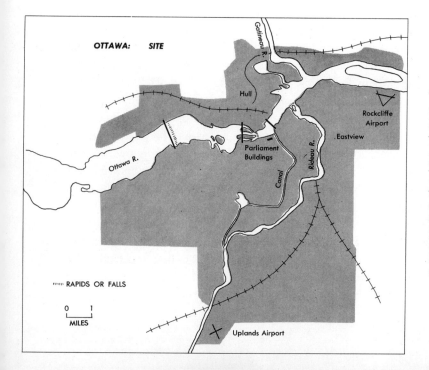

The site of Ottawa is at the confluence of the Rideau and Gatineau with the Ottawa river. Rapids bar navigation beyond this point. The Rideau canal is of little more than scenic interest although the road, rail, and air facilities are important. Prepare a map showing the relationship between Ottawa, Montreal, Toronto and other Canadian cities.

The city is noted for its magnificent parkways and for its fine residential districts. As a capital city it aims at a certain dignity that other cities lack; this dignity is attained, however, at a certain national financial cost. The continued growth of industry in the outskirts of the city and the planned removal of all downtown railway tracks will certainly add to the capital's beauty and importance. In keeping with the two cultures found here, there are also two universities, Ottawa and Carleton.

Canberra in Australia is a younger capital than Ottawa. Unlike Ottawa, which lies within one of the provinces (Ontario), Canberra stands in an independent federal district on the main route between Sydney and Melbourne. The rivalry of these two cities and of their surrounding states prompted the setting up of such an independent city state. This meant, however, that the growth of the city has been slow. Situated in a pleasant, forested, hilly amphitheatre at an altitude of about 2,000 feet, the city enjoys a natural beauty of terrain. An international contest among architects resulted in a plan for the whole city's development and future expansion. As a result, Canberra will grow outwards in the form of a number of radiating cobwebs separated by low hills; this plan, however, poses transportation problems within the city itself. Having a population of just under 50,000, it is still little more than a large town; but the activities of various government departments and of the university have already gained it recognition as an important centre of scientific research.

Note the way this town has been planned as several small units adapted to their setting. What are the advantages and disadvantages of this system?

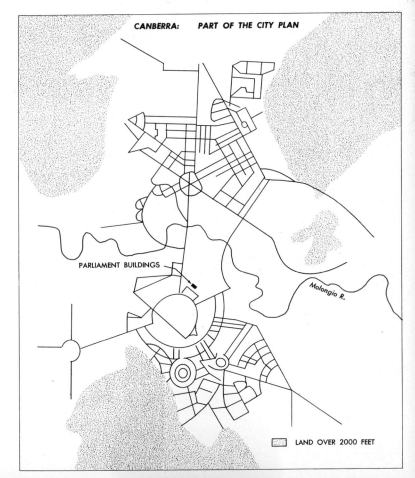

CANBERRA: PART OF THE CITY PLAN

PARLIAMENT BUILDINGS

Molongio R.

LAND OVER 2000 FEET

Pan American Union

Here you see the Legislative Buildings in Brasilia. Suggest a few of the advantages of tall skyscrapers over large lower buildings.

Perhaps the most exciting of the new capitals of the world is **Brasilia,** with its magnificent location and breath-taking architecture. This was a daring and expensive undertaking for the Brazilian government and it is still too early to tell whether it will prove to be a success or an enormous failure.

Resort Centres

The term resort centres can be used to describe a number of types of urban centres, most of which remain rather small. Some, such as the famous spas of central Europe, owe their importance to mineral springs that attract invalids and convalescents. Others, as in New England or Switzerland, are meccas of skiing or other sporting activities. Many are located beside the sea and rely on the attraction of the surging surf or broad beaches to draw the tourists on whom the town depends for economic well-being. A few, such as Niagara, have become famous because of a specific landmark or natural feature. All of these centres require a large mass of population relatively nearby. Indeed, it is the close proximity of this large industrial population which creates the need for such resorts in the first place. Good transportation facilities are essential; in some cases such facilities plus a large population give rise to a certain amount of industrial activity; this condition, however, is seldom prominent in the resort town itself. In examining resort centres we should distinguish between those which have a seasonal traffic and those which are busy throughout the year.

3 GEOGRAPHY AND WORLD AFFAIRS

So far this year we have studied some aspects of several of the *worlds* in which man lives. Earlier, we examined the worlds of the atmosphere and of the sea, worlds which together constitute the world of the physical terrain on which man moves; later we considered the world of climate in relation to the complete natural environment of man in order to note how he has adapted himself to it or has modified it. The world of trade, industry, and agriculture has been touched upon. Beyond and above all of these, is the world of states and governments, of international affairs and world organizations, of international goodwill and traditional national hostilities. The study of these subjects constitutes the field of political geography, which concerns itself with the consequences of the external and internal relationships of states and peoples.

Notice that the word *peoples* is used, not *races*. Throughout the study of political geography, we seldom use the word race, which refers only to broad ethnic groups of mankind with well-developed heritable physical differences. This definition of race excludes such loose usage as reference to a French race, an Italian race, or a Canadian race. On the basis of size and shape of skull, skin colour, and other physical characteristics, we conclude there is a comparatively small number of races. The chief of these are Caucasian, Mongoloid, Negro and Negrito, Mediterranean, Australoid, and Alpine. A detailed study of each of these does not lie in the realm of geography, and further information on each can easily be gained from a good encyclopedia.

Political geographers will often study a particular political state in a detailed manner. Such a study will concern itself with the shape of the physical terrain of the state and of its neighbours, its area and wealth in terms of resources and population, the historical processes that led to the state's present area and boundaries, the standard of living of its people, its trade and transportation facilities, its problems and prospects. Conspicuous in this study is the history of the area concerned, for it is here that the *twins* of history and geography are most closely interrelated.

Another fascinating topic of study in this field is that of international frontiers. In North America, fortunately, international boundaries do not force their way sharply into our lives and certainly they are not today associated with battles and bloodshed and disastrous human rivalries. However, history has taught us how fraught with danger these lines have been in the older countries. High mountains, broad deserts, and wide swamps have often proved to be excellent frontiers. On the other hand, however, forests, rivers, and geometrical lines can often become mere seeds of future discord. Frontiers which have been disputed time after time by adjacent peoples include the Alsace-Lorraine area in France, the Polish-German and Polish-Soviet frontiers, the Trieste borderland between Italy and Yugoslavia, and more recently the Israeli-Arab frontier lines and the Pakistan-Indian lines in Kashmir. A useful and stimulating class project could well be directed towards analyzing one of these situations. Be warned, however, against snap judgments, and bear in mind that usually both sides have a good case. A biased viewpoint often means a continuance of the dispute.

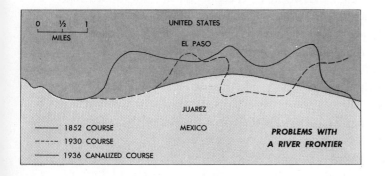

Here you see a frontier that changed repeatedly until the river was canalized. From your atlas, find five other areas where a river is used as a frontier.

A World of International Blocs

A bloc is a combination of nations united by common views, problems, or goals. In a world in which there are so many of these blocs, people can easily become confused as to the constitution and aims of even the more important of them. In the following few pages we will briefly consider an example of each of three different types of bloc. It must be stressed, however, that the proper study of any one of these would probably require a whole year; so here we are only outlining the situation—further study on your part is still required for even a broad understanding of each unit.

Political Blocs

At the present time the world is dominated by two giant super-powers: the U.S.A. and the U.S.S.R. For many years these two mighty states have lived in a condition of unconcealed hostility to each other, and the term *cold war* has been coined to describe such a war that has not yet reached the shooting stage. Generalizations are easy, but dangerous. Yet it is necessary here to point out that the emergence of the U.S.S.R. as a major world power in World War II, coupled with the fact that this power had a vigorous and aggressive ideology, resulted in U.S.S.R.'s threatening to gain world domination. The communist ideology stresses collective ownership by the state of all major industries and of the means of production. However, though it pledges international brotherhood irrespective of colour, race, or creed, it openly aims at world domination and the overthrow of other political and social systems—by force if necessary. Since 1945 the

Soviet Union has by military occupation, treaties, and other devices extended its area of immediate influence, and of at least partial control, to a number of countries that we usually refer to as *satellites*. The strengths of this bloc of communist countries are these:

> a pronounced stress on industrialization, and especially on military or heavy industries;
>
> an apparent lack of personal distinction other than that based upon, or gained by, inherited or acquired ability;
>
> sheer military strength;
>
> the powerful ties binding satellites to the U.S.S.R. (in some cases this is the overt threat of military occupation);
>
> the centralized control of all economic activity as expressed in 5- or 7-year plans;
>
> the contiguity of the communist territories.

The weaknesses of this system and of its bloc (of satellites), are these:

> the stifling of initiative by the stressing of conformity to a party line;

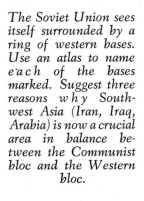

The Soviet Union sees itself surrounded by a ring of western bases. Use an atlas to name each of the bases marked. Suggest three reasons why Southwest Asia (Iran, Iraq, Arabia) is now a crucial area in balance between the Communist bloc and the Western bloc.

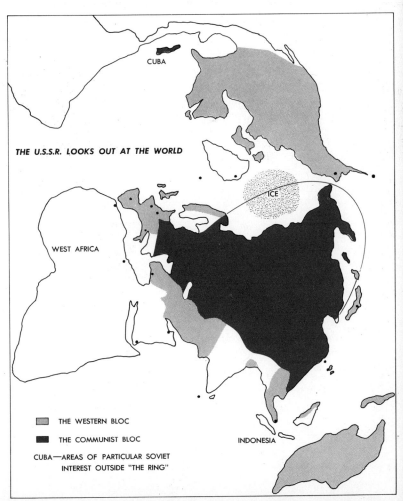

THE U.S.S.R. LOOKS OUT AT THE WORLD

CUBA

WEST AFRICA

ICE

INDONESIA

THE WESTERN BLOC

THE COMMUNIST BLOC

CUBA—AREAS OF PARTICULAR SOVIET INTEREST OUTSIDE "THE RING"

the *absolutism* of a communism that leads to a police state, with its atmosphere of fear and intrigue;

the inconsistency between the professions of idealism and brotherhood in the actual achievements of the system, and the subsequent loss of individual human freedom in the interests of state or party.

It must be borne in mind, however, that to millions of underprivileged, starving human beings the material comforts promised by the communist regime often are made to seem more than sufficient compensation for whatever they can lose. Moreover, we should remember that children brought up under this system will certainly view it in quite a different light from that in which we do who have been reared in democratic traditions. The convinced and dedicated communist is not necessarily a freak.

Against this massive threat, the U.S.A. has built a vast and relatively tenuous *western bloc* which, of necessity, lacks the monolithic rigidity of the communist world. An intricate system of leagues and alliances has been built up on a variety of bases, some of them less sound than others. In most cases these states are held together by a common culture and ideology, a common set of values or traditions. However, economic aid and military assistance constitute the main force that binds together some of the nations of this bloc. With yet others, the tie is a negative one, namely, fear of communism or of the Soviet Union.

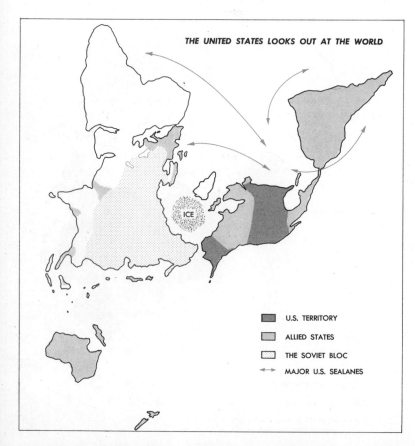

This map shows clearly that the Soviet bloc enjoys internal lines of communication while the Western bloc is widely scattered. Outline two ways in which each bloc can see an advantage in its own position.

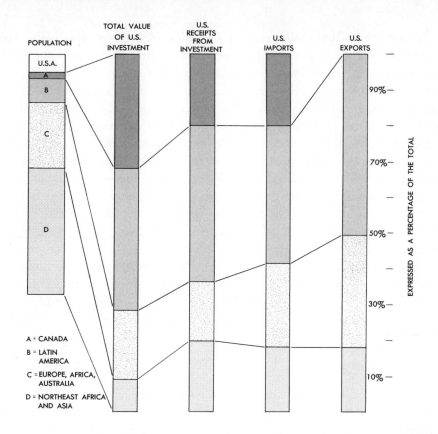

POPULATION

TOTAL VALUE
OF U.S.
INVESTMENT

U.S.
RECEIPTS
FROM
INVESTMENT

U.S.
IMPORTS

U.S.
EXPORTS

U.S.A.

A
B

C

D

A = CANADA
B = LATIN
AMERICA
C = EUROPE, AFRICA,
AUSTRALIA
D = NORTHEAST AFRICA
AND ASIA

EXPRESSED AS A PERCENTAGE OF THE TOTAL

90%—
70%—
50%—
30%—
10%—

The greatest strength is at the same time the chief weakness of the Western bloc, namely, its ideals of freedom and democracy. Democratic methods show greater respect for the rights of the individual and in so doing they are often slower in action and less efficient than more dictatorial methods. The merits of this system in terms of human satisfaction and the full utilizing of human resources are enormous; but it is limited by the fact that it cannot resort to the same violent means that the communist state uses in the pursuit of its aims. If we cherish the ideals of democracy and freedom, we must respect the right of other people to them—even when they decide to join an opposing bloc. To do otherwise would be a contradiction of our beliefs.

Much of the story of modern history is the U.S.S.R.'s attempt to extend its field of authority into hitherto uncommitted territory and of the efforts of the United States to circumvent this by containing the Communist bloc within its present territorial area. The diffuseness of the Western bloc in this great struggle is at once an asset and a drawback. At the present time there are several strongly pro-Soviet states in West Africa—states which could eventually bring the east-west conflict into that vast continent. Indonesia, too, threatens to become a communist tentacle reaching far to the south and giving the communists more immediate access to the Pacific and Indian oceans.

In addition to the wealth, size, and location of the two great blocs, another factor of importance in studying the international situation today is the existence of a third grouping of nations known as the *Neutral bloc*. This consists of states which are not committed to either of the two great powers and which cannot be relied upon by either for support. The past five years have witnessed the birth of many new states in Africa; the accession of most of them to the Neutral bloc has led to its being described in certain circumstances as the Afro-Asian bloc. Many of these countries are as yet underdeveloped; consequently, the Soviet Union and the United States are in rivalry in giving assistance to certain of them. At times this could almost be described as a *war of economic aid*. The importance of the struggle for these nations can be gauged from the fact that more than half of the world's population lives outside the two great blocs. It is in these territories that food shipments, technical aid, cultural exchanges, and even missionary activities, become aspects of the cold war. The contest here is for the minds of people, many of whom have either been ignored or exploited for centuries. To gain any understanding of this global struggle, requires much time and study; but if you follow your newspapers intelligently the main issues will become clear to you.

An Economic Bloc

Almost a century ago, world affairs were dominated and largely controlled by the imperial powers of Europe. The many national states of this smallest of the continents, were wealthy and populous; indeed, they possessed a technological and industrial superiority out of all proportion to their size. With the phenomenal growth of the two super-powers and the weakening of Europe by internal rivalries and bitter wars, these powers have today sunk to a secondary status. After World War II several far-sighted European statesmen realized that the division of their continent into many small national states was a cause of weakness and, more important, a breeding ground for national rivalries and wars. In an age of nuclear destruction war must be avoided. To this end prime ministers De Gasperri in Italy, Adenauer in Germany, and Schuman and Monnet in France advocated the gradual economic union of Europe as a step towards political union into an eventual United States of Europe.

The first step towards this goal was taken in 1951 when the supernational European Coal-Steel Community was established under Jean Monnet with control over the coal and steel industries of France, West Germany, Italy, Belgium, the Netherlands, and Luxembourg. The success of this venture led the six countries to sign a treaty in Rome in 1957 aimed at the complete economic union of all the states. Gradually these countries will eliminate all customs and tariff barriers until by 1970 trade, capital, and labour will be able to move freely throughout all six countries. In effect, this makes them one economic unit, and it makes it necessary that they have a certain degree of administrative and political unity,

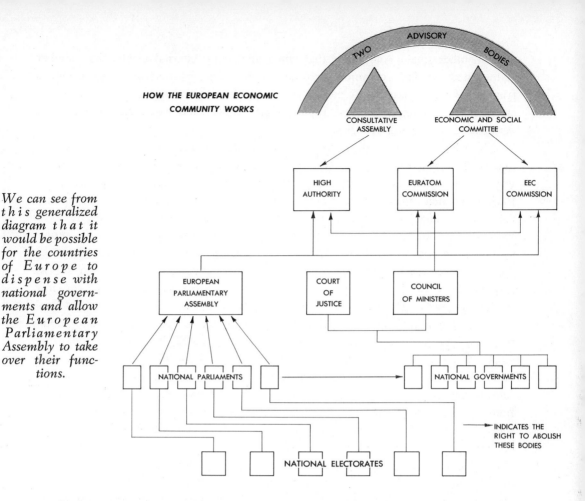

HOW THE EUROPEAN ECONOMIC
COMMUNITY WORKS

We can see from this generalized diagram that it would be possible for the countries of Europe to dispense with national governments and allow the European Parliamentary Assembly to take over their functions.

too. This union has created an enormous labour force and an equally large internal market—two factors which have played a major role in the colossal industrial growth of the two super-powers. Economists and politicians alike have been amazed at the rapidity of the growth of this new economic bloc.

One immediate result of the function of the European Economic Community, as the union of the six is called, was the establishment of a rival European Free Trade Association (E.F.T.A.) by Britain and several other states. This differed from E.E.C. in that it excluded agriculture, it did not affect overseas trade such as Britain's Commonwealth preferences, and it studiously avoided all political implications. It was at best a half-hearted union and consequently failed. With Britain at present engaged in negotiating entry to E.E.C., it can be expected that for some time to come there will be a continued growth in number of states attracted to the Common Market bloc.

One might reasonably raise the question, why don't more countries join the Common Market and thus share in its economic growth and prosperity. The answer is that this organization, like most similar clubs, has a number of entrance requirements. One of these is the loss of a certain amount of independence by

405

each member state. Another is that while abolishing internal tariffs, the member states must impose common external trade policies—regardless of previous friendships and alliances. A certain exception has been made for less developed states in Africa and the West Indies, which have been extended the status of Associated Overseas Territories.

The government of the European Economic Community is rather interesting and is illustrated by a chart. At present the voters in each state elect their own Parliament, which in turn provides the state's own national government. Each Parliament then elects a number of its members to sit on a European Parliamentary Assembly, which, it is hoped, will eventually become the real government of Europe. At the same time each government appoints one person to be its representative on the Council of Ministers as well as a member of the Court of Justice. Once appointed, the members of these two councils are no longer responsible to their own national governments but are now expected to act only in the interests of Europe as a whole. The Council of Ministers determines final policy of the E.E.C. and supervises the work of the E.E.C.'s three major commissions—Euratom (in charge of nuclear energy), the High Authority (coal and steel), and the E.E.C. Commission, which is a completely supernational civil service. The Court of Justice which sits in Luxembourg is responsible for interpreting the Treaty of Rome and resolving internal disputes. Two advisory bodies composed of industrialists, trade unionists, and consumers exist to assist the three commissions. In practice the system works well, although disagreements sometimes arise between the three commissions and the council of ministers. While the European Economic Community is essentially an economic bloc, it is already clear that it is also in part a political one, too. This is inevitable with such economic groupings of nations, although in this case the political implications and developments are not unintentional.

PART OF THE COMMON MARKET "PICTURE OF PROSPERITY"

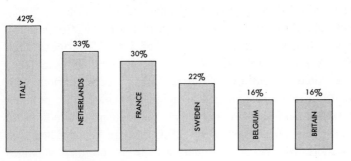

INCREASE IN INDUSTRIAL OUTPUT, 1954-1960

It should be borne in mind that these bars do not represent actual industrial output, but only proportional increase. Suggest reasons for the slower growth of Belgian industry relative to that of West Germany.

Physical Blocs

The first simple alliances of nations in history were generally between adjoining territories and even today in the United Nations and other gatherings

406

there are many examples of nations which vote together on most issues because of their neighbourliness. This is understandable, since neighbours very often face the same problems and have common interests. A good example of a bloc of nations in which the linking factor is their contiguity is the South American or Latin American bloc.

The importance of South America in world affairs has been increasing steadily since World War II and any true understanding of international politics demands a consideration of this vast and complex area. Here we have 20 republics, each with a vote in the U.N., extending through some 7,000 miles of latitude. On a sixth of the world's land area there is a fifteenth of the world's population, but the rate of population increase is far in excess of that of most of the other continents. Latin America's only land contact is with the United States. However, its frontage on the Pacific and Atlantic oceans provides it with 'easy access to all the world's major sea-lanes.

Certain broad generalizations in the fields of economic and social geography can be made about most of the Latin American republics. Homegeneity in their historical background and language is expressed in the term Latin: Portuguese is the language of Brazil, while Spanish, a similar language, is the tongue of all the other states. Nearly 80% of the people in these states live within the tropics, the great majority of them around the coastal fringe. The peoples in each state are a vast mixture of the original American Indians, of descendants of Portuguese and Spanish settlers, of former Negro slaves, and of other Europeans and also Orientals who have arrived in increasing numbers in the twentieth century. The social structure of the states is simple—a division into small, wealthy groups of landowners and industrialists and a large mass of poor, often illiterate, workers. There is no strong middle class as in North America. In spite of dire poverty over large areas, there is still much undeveloped land, particularly in Brazil, Bolivia, Colombia, Ecuador, and Venezuela; but difficulties of terrain are serious barriers to land development. The economic status of the republics is largely that of suppliers of raw materials for U.S. industry. Lack of coal (only Colombia, Chile, Brazil, and Mexico have any sizeable coal deposits) has seriously handicapped industrial growth, as have the poor communication systems in existence. In the world's oil industry the names of Mexico (by virtue of oil discovered in the 1930's) and Venezuela today stand among the three top producers; furthermore, in the metallic minerals, especially bauxite, tin, iron, lead, copper, and manganese, the South American continent produces a large part of the world's total output.

In this graph, the population, agriculture, and i n d u s t r y of 1950 are taken as 100. Notice the fluctuations in agricultural output compared to the steady increase in population. Sufficient investment makes for easier c o n t r o l of industrial output. What countries are providing most of the money for investments in South America?

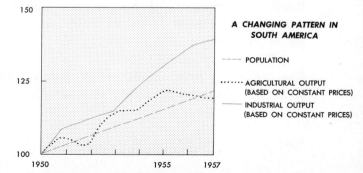

A CHANGING PATTERN IN
SOUTH AMERICA

---- POPULATION

.... AGRICULTURAL OUTPUT
(BASED ON CONSTANT PRICES)

——— INDUSTRIAL OUTPUT
(BASED ON CONSTANT PRICES)

About 45% of all South America's exports go to the United States and the economic ties between the two areas are very close. Indeed, most of the mining industries, and also most of the principal industrial concerns of all types, are owned, financed, and organized by U.S. companies; the firms concerned merely employ local labour and materials. Of course, they usually pay handsome royalties to the government of the country whose deposits they are working, and they also generally pay far higher wages to their workers than do other local industries. However, the fact remains that most of the natural wealth is flowing out of the country without returning any adequate benefit to the people who live there. Such a situation is known as *economic colonialism*, and several South American governments, already aware of this situation, have shown a desire to remedy it.

The links between the United States and these southern republics are based on more than just trade and investment. Since the time of the Monroe Doctrine in 1823 the United States has shown a friendly interest in the South American republics and has even played an important role in their securing of independence. Politically in recent years, these states have, with the exception of Cuba, been strongly opposed to Communism. The problem of mutual defence, too, has drawn the two continents together now more than ever before.

Eventually the community of interests of these nations led them to establish at Bogota in 1948 the Organization of American States, its aim being to maintain peace in the hemisphere, settle disputes, and promote economic, social, and cultural co-operation. Accordingly, it is a remarkable fact that many frontiers of South American states have been settled without any conflict or recourse to arms. Brazil, for example, though fronting on all but two of the other South American states, has established all its thousands of miles of frontier without a single military engagement.

The weaknesses of Latin America are these: its political instability, its limited economic development, and the poverty and illiteracy of the great masses of its 200 million people. Riots and civil disturbances are more easily aroused in areas of poor living conditions and these can lead easily to revolutions. It is ironic that in several Latin American countries, a disproportionate part of the annual budget is spent in military forces in an effort to maintain stability, whereas the expenditure of similar sums on improving farming conditions or transport services would probably go further towards this goal, and would certainly have a more lasting effect.

World Population and Food Supply

One of the most important and distressing lessons that the student of geography learns when he studies such areas as South America, is that millions of people feel the pangs of hunger every day. The hunger and poverty of millions of people undoubtedly merits our deep sympathy and concern, but it also merits our close study, since the history of the world may depend upon the action taken by great masses of these hungry people.

The population of the world is probably increasing by about 150,000 people every day and the rate of increase is constantly rising. Economists have pointed out that the land surface of the earth capable of producing our food is strictly limited and that continued population increase could reach the point where famine and disease would become inevitable. Therefore, we must consider the problem of overpopulation, a condition depending on a large number of variables. A glance at a map showing the distribution of the world's population, will reveal wide desert areas having fewer than 3 people per square mile; yet these people live perhaps in small, vastly overpopulated oases. A map showing the relationship between population and the acreage of adjoining farmland might seem to be useful; yet it would prove inadequate to explain the reason for such densely populated industrial areas as Toronto or New York, or indeed any other of the world's larger cities where many people enjoy a very high standard of living and where no farm land is immediately available. Overpopulation, then, depends on the possible food supply, on industrial development, and on the standard of living as well as on the simple facts of population and area.

How can man find food for his increasing numbers? First of all, it is important to note that the population increase is often most rapid in areas of primitive agricultural and industrial conditions. Furthermore, in many parts of the world, the increased prosperity has resulted in a slowing down of the rate of natural increase. Moreover, governments in certain countries in the world actively encourage a reduction in the normal birth rate as a part of their solution to the problem. Some countries try to solve the problem by large-scale emigration of their young people to more favoured parts of the world. This does not really solve the problem, and already several countries have had to impose restrictions on immigration. Perhaps a more constructive policy towards meeting our growing food requirements is that of increasing agricultural and industrial output.

It has been calculated that about 11,000 million acres of the world's surface are climatically suited to agriculture; of this less than 4,000 million are actually farmed. Not all of the remainder is economically worth farming, but much of it is. One barrier to the opening up of fresh agricultural land in many parts of the world is the lack of funds for special equipment, fertilizer, roads, etc., all of which are needed before new farming settlements can be launched. Moreover, labour is one of these necessities lacking in some areas; however, international agreement could overcome this problem by bringing in people from some already over-populated area. In addition to increasing the area of farmed land, increasing the yield from existing land would also help relieve the food shortage. The development of *Marquis* and other varieties of wheat in Canada, the development of good hybrid corn in the United States, and many other developments sparked by research have progressively led to bigger crops. Areas in India where fertilizer and modern equipment have been provided, have usually shown remarkable increases in yield, and there are many other densely populated regions of Asia and Africa that could profit in the same way.

There is, of course, a definite limit to what can be produced on one acre of land. Nevertheless, further food supply can be derived from sources which man has as yet hardly even tapped. Chlorella, a form of alga, can be produced with a yield of 55,000 pounds per acre compared to 800 pounds per acre for the very prolific soybean. Seaweed, snails, and a multitude of other naturally occurring organisms are also edible, although certain prejudices may have to be overcome before they become widely used.

Certain parts of India and Africa are solving their lack of food supply and of limited development by exploiting local resources in new industries. Industrial plants are usually accompanied by the building of new roads and by a rise in the level of education of the local people. This is especially true where the acquisition of capital has resulted in improvements in agricultural methods and techniques.

One often reads and hears about the *have* and *have-not* countries; such terminology reminds us that one of the basic problems in the study of the world's food supply is in the inequality of its distribution. Many of the Western countries do produce much more food than they can consume; many could certainly produce even more than they already do. This production even reaches the point where farmers in some areas are encouraged, or even paid, not to produce more food.

SOME INTERESTING COMPARISONS

	AREA (in thousands of square miles)	POPULATION (in millions)	NO. OF PEOPLE PER DOCTOR	NEWSPAPERS*
NIGERIA	340	30	57,000	5
GHANA	80	4	18,000	18
TANGANYIKA	360	8	20,000	1
INDIA	1,265	400	7,100	7
INDONESIA	575	82	71,000	7
JAPAN	143	89	1,000	397
BRITAIN	94	51	1,100	570

*Number of daily newspapers in circulation per 1,000 inhabitants

Comparisons are frequently made between the industrial and agricultural outputs of different countries. This table suggests another basis of comparison. For the sake of uniformity, these statistics have been taken from the middle 1950's. Using a good reference work, prepare similar information on Canada and the United States.

While regretting this situation, before condemning it we should pause to consider the effect on world trade if such negative policies were abandoned. The fact remains that much of the world's suffering could be averted by a redistribution of the food production of our bountiful earth.

Colonialism

When people discuss the subject of food supply and population and the associated topic of the development of the Asian and African states, they often find themselves discussing colonialism. Colonization is the term used for the establishment of organized settlement on a large scale in some area beyond the homeland. During the past two centuries particularly, permanent settlements of colonies were established by European peoples throughout Africa and Asia; some of these are now the chief, though not the only, regions of colonial problems. The colonial territories, with few exceptions, lay in the tropical regions of the earth, and this fact is an indication that each such area formed a complement to the mother country; it provided goods that the older state required. Economically the colonies in most cases were tied very closely to the motherland, which completely dominated their import and export trade. Indeed, in many cases, the colony's economic development benefited the colonizing power more than it did the colony itself.

A characteristic of early colonial development is the extensive use of hand labour. Why is this usually so?

France and Britain in recent centuries have probably been the two greatest colonial powers; in fact, their territories in Africa alone at one time occupied an enormous area. In West Africa an interesting contrast existed between the colonial methods of these two countries. The French in many areas administered their colonies well and encouraged the native colonial rulers to absorb French culture with the ultimate aim that these colonies should become overseas parts of France. This actually occurred in some cases; Algeria, for example, did send some native Algerian colonials to be members of the French government in Paris. The British in Nigeria and elsewhere, however, helped the local chiefs to maintain their authority and to rule more efficiently while raising the general economic and educational standards of their people. At the same time, they initiated them into democratic principles. Both the French and British methods have now resulted in the emergence of newly independent states capable of administering their own affairs.

One of the fundamental aspects of colonialism is the frequent contrast between the colonial and the native tribesman in political and economic status. The settler who went to these territories often did so at some risk, if not to life, at least to his health, and certainly to his fortune if his investment were a large one. In most cases his approach resembled that of a businessman's opening a new plant. The important difference between the settler and the businessman is that the former usually found the natives so poor and ill-educated that they were at times completely dependent on him as their employer; hence his power and responsibility became enormous. As time progressed the natives in many areas acquired the necessary education and skills to manage their own affairs and their own countries; the settlers' descendants then became a barrier to the natives' progress towards complete control of their own affairs. This is the dilemma of many lands today. A fair judgment in this situation is not easy. A settler in Rhodesia argues that he came to a semi-arid land where the natives previously scratched the most meagre existence from the soil. By dint of his money (in this case a large fortune), his education, his skill, and thirty years of work, he has been able to plan and build dams and ditches, roads and buildings so that now over 400 natives on his estate live in a luxury they never previously dreamt of. He feels, therefore, that his interest in the land is not that of someone who merely went there for a job. This has become his land and his country. At the other extreme is the African nationalist who would say that this settler has received his reward in his lifetime in Africa and that now he should step aside to allow the natives to manage affairs. It requires only a little sympathetic understanding to appreciate the problem and to see that both sides are partly right. Hasty one-sided judgments are seldom the mark of the person who really understands problems such as this one.

World Organizations

Another characteristic of our modern world in addition to the existence of international blocs is the existence of a number of world organizations. Without doubt the most important of these is the United Nations Organization, which has its headquarters in New York and now has a membership of 111 countries. There is probably a club in your school which studies the work of the U.N.; if not, you will have no difficulty in preparing an outline of its work from the newspapers and magazines. It is sufficient here to point out the purposes of the U.N. as stated in Article 1 of its charter:

> to maintain international peace and security;
>
> to develop friendly relations among nations, based on respect for the principle of equal rights and self-determination of peoples;
>
> to achieve international co-operation in solving international problems of an economic, social, cultural, or humanitarian character, and in promoting and encouraging respect for human rights and fundamental freedoms for all;
>
> to be a centre for harmonizing the actions of nations in the attainment of these common ends.

The International Ice Patrol fulfils a very important function in the North Atlantic in view of the great number of ships regularly using these sea lanes. This is an example of nations co-operating effectively with one another to secure an improvement in conditions. Name three other bodies providing similar examples of co-operation.

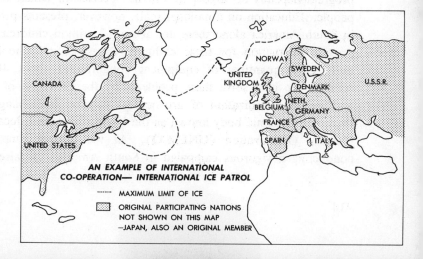

AN EXAMPLE OF INTERNATIONAL
CO-OPERATION— INTERNATIONAL ICE PATROL

------ MAXIMUM LIMIT OF ICE

▨ ORIGINAL PARTICIPATING NATIONS
NOT SHOWN ON THIS MAP
—JAPAN, ALSO AN ORIGINAL MEMBER

It would be a rewarding project in political geography to take one of these aims and prepare a report outlining the activities of the U.N. towards its achievement and suggesting areas in which much more still remains to be done.

As an international forum, the U.N. fulfils a very important function; but many see it as a step towards some form of world government. This idea is still little more than a dream; nonetheless, already there are many people actively working towards its achievement. What would be the advantages of a mighty federal world government?

In addition to the U.N. there are several world organizations devoted to one major purpose, many of them working as subsidiary bodies of the U.N. The World Health Organization (WHO) is devoted to the attainment of the highest possible level of health by all the peoples of the world. Of this group, now numbering 111 nations, the Director General from 1948 to 1953 was Dr. Brock Chisholm, a very distinguished Canadian. Having a budget of less than $24 million, this organization was necessarily limited in its work, but its achievements in co-ordinating the health work of separate governments and in providing technical assistance on problems associated with water supply, mental health, and child care, have been of supreme importance. A major project was begun in 1955, namely, the eradication of malaria. This disease strikes about 250 million people every year, killing approximately 1½ million of them. To remove this scourge WHO is spraying millions of buildings and draining millions of acres of swampland. In 1955 nearly half the world's population lived in danger of malaria, but already areas inhabited by 300 million people have been freed from this threat and current programmes will provide safety for twice as many more. The incidence of malaria and the death rate have both been cut in half. Problems on as vast a scale as those presented by malaria, tuberculosis, leprosy, and others, can be tackled only by a vast international organization such as WHO.

In many areas of the world one of the most serious barriers to any significant improvement in levels of health is the illiteracy of the people themselves. It has been estimated that five out of every ten children in the world never have the opportunity to attend school. Of these five only one has an opportunity to enter high school. Most of the newly developing nations are fully aware that their progress depends in large part on the speed with which they can educate their people. Education on a national scale, however, presents problems. For example, in South America alone there are about 17 million children without schools. To provide instruction for these children, thousands of schools would have to be built, great quantities of equipment bought, and about 400,000 new teachers trained. To help solve these problems by the provision of experts and teachers and by the organization of artistic and cultural interchange between countries, there is a dynamic body known as the United Nations Educational, Scientific, and Cultural Organization (UNESCO). At the present time this organization is conducting a vigorous campaign in South America to raise the general level of literacy and provide at least elementary education for South American children. One may obtain further details on the work of UNESCO and of other U.N. groups by writing to United Nations headquarters in New York City.

The Global Outlook

In our age of jet aircraft, telstar, and interplanetary research, it becomes even more important that people think in terms of the world as a whole. The existence of such worldwide organizations as those sponsored by the United Nations, and the global strategies of the major powers, are themselves evidence of this new way of thinking. At another level, the international conventions of professional and business people, of religious and charitable organizations, and even of boy scouts and similar movements, amply attest this same international outlook. To live intelligently, and especially to understand our environment, it has become necessary for us to be aware of the lives of others in far-off sectors of the world. Donne's *No Man is an Island* is true today in a way that he never envisaged.

Under present circumstances everyone in our society has a responsibility to be in part a geographer. The banker must understand the world monetary system;

Nearly 50 years ago, Mackinder divided the world into a Heartland and two crescents. He stressed the great strategic importance of the heartland as a major centre of continental power: Later, he suggested that the union of the heartland with any one of the densely populated adjacent regions would be a very powerful combination. In an age of transpolar flight, the old heartland has acquired new importance. The Soviet-Chinese alliance would fit in with the second warning he gave.

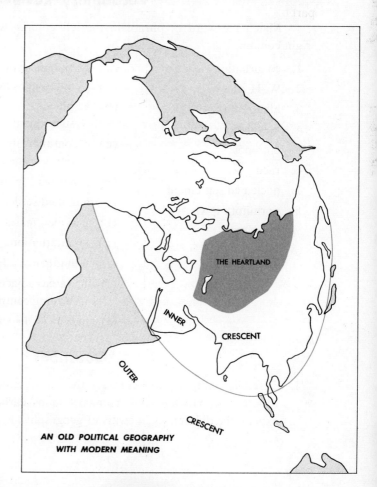

AN OLD POLITICAL GEOGRAPHY
WITH MODERN MEANING

the business man, world markets and trade patterns; the professional man and woman, the research and conditions to be found in other lands and continents; the trade unionist, what his fellow workers are doing elsewhere. Regardless of the field in which your career may lie, geography will still be of value to you.

During this course, you have studied man and his environment in an approach different from that employed in former years. In earlier years you studied regional geography, taking the world area by area in contrast to the general or topic approach which has been used this year. Having studied some of the basic principles of geography, you are now in a position to understand more clearly those subtle relationships that exist between man and his environment—relationships that lie at the heart of all detailed regional studies. It is important now that you continue to build on the geographical base you have laid, by regular critical reading of reliable newspapers and magazines. Such reading will be an important part of your future education.

UNIT REVIEW

Vocabulary Review

Match the word or phrase in the left column with the correct words in the right column.

1. conurbation
2. W. H. O.
3. hinterland
4. megalopolis
5. entrepot
6. race
7. nucleated settlement
8. dormitory town

(a) a human grouping with heritable physical differences from other groups

(b) a place to which goods are brought for subsequent redistribution

(c) a continuously urban area around one large city

(d) a national grouping of people

(e) a unified settlement around one centre

(f) a residential settlement

(g) an international organization

(h) a number of adjoining metropolitan areas

(i) the area adjacent to and focussing on one trading centre

(j) an area of dispersed settlement

Questions

1. Carefully compare and contrast the rural settlement pattern shown on the Moose Jaw, Guelph, and Yamaska maps earlier in this book. Attempt to explain the differences in terms of geographical and historical factors.

2. The map of Vancouver reveals some of this city's advantages and disadvantages as a major port. By reference to the map prepare a report on these.

3. Using the topographical maps, describe the site and situation of St. Catharines, Summerside, and Moose Jaw.

4. What qualities should we look for in a political capital? Illustrate your answer with reference to Canberra and Berlin or Washington and Peking.

5. In what ways are conflicting ideologies a handicap to the progress of many peoples?

6. What geographical, economic, and historical factors are important in the discussion on the close political union of the whole of Europe?

7. Why did the Brazilian government spend such vast sums of money to build its new capital? What is the significance of their choice of location?

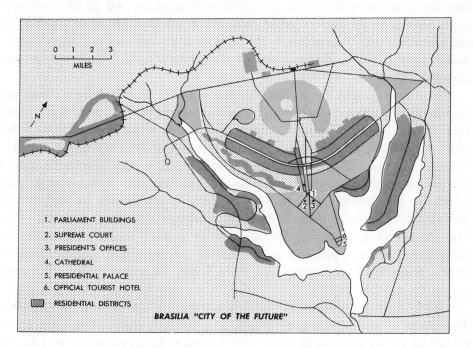

0 1 2 3
MILES

N

1. PARLIAMENT BUILDINGS
2. SUPREME COURT
3. PRESIDENT'S OFFICES
4. CATHEDRAL
5. PRESIDENTIAL PALACE
6. OFFICIAL TOURIST HOTEL
RESIDENTIAL DISTRICTS

BRASILIA "CITY OF THE FUTURE"

Research Assignments

1. Carefully examine the site, situation, and chief functions of either the town in which you live or the one nearest your school.

2. What are the main problems that arise when white labour has to compete with coloured native labour in the tropics?

3. On what evidence would you decide whether a country is overpopulated?

4. Prepare a report showing the various aspects of United Nations' work in Africa.

CAREERS IN GEOGRAPHY

This book might have opened with a chapter entitled "What is Geography?" It didn't because that is not an easy question to answer in simple terms. Instead, it is easier at this point to pause and look back over our year's work and say, "What does a geographer study?" This year you have learned something about the surface of the earth; about the atmosphere and the weather associated with it; about people in different parts of the world, their problems and their way of life; about how all such knowledge can be recorded on maps, graphs, or charts, and how we can use these to work out many of the happenings in the past, and even to foresee certain elements of the future; and, finally, about the world organizations into which nations and peoples are grouping themselves. All of this, and much more, belongs to the field of geography. What is it that ties it all together into one integrated study? In the simplest possible terms, we can say that geography studies people and those things around them that constitute what we call their environment.

In your geography classes this year you will have used at different times your knowledge of mathematics, chemistry, physics, history, biology, and other subjects. Of necessity, geography must call upon all the other sciences in order to build a true understanding of man and his environment. This synthesis of other subjects is one of the characteristics of geography that makes it such a valuable study in our modern, complex world. Geography is a training that provides an excellent foundation for many diverse activities and forms a springboard for further study in a variety of subjects. Because of this fact, we now find many men and women who specialized in geography, participating in a wide variety of activities and occupations. Some of you may enjoy studying geography and may be wondering what a professional geographer does for a living. These two pages will provide part of the answer.

The Canadian government was one of the first to establish a permanent department of professional geographers as a full-time body. The Geographical Branch of the Department of Mines and Technical Surveys consists of a number of trained geographers doing research into such things as population problems in Canada, the development of the arctic Northland, and the mapping of our enormous area. Some governments employ geographers on large-scale development schemes to co-ordinate the work of specialists in other fields or to direct overall planning. In the Department of External Affairs and in other diplomatic fields, geographers can play a significant role by using their training and qualifications.

Many geographers enter the teaching profession at all levels from public school through to university. Most of the universities in North America and

Europe now have departments of geography, and the demand for geographers at this and at the high-school level is still far in excess of the supply.

This year you have studied many maps of different types and have analyzed and drawn others. Geographer-cartographers are sometimes employed drawing maps in an accurate and artistic manner. Others are engaged in cataloguing information and then developing an adequate mapping system to portray their material. Closely associated with those who prepare maps are the geographers who enter the field of city planning. In all the large cities of Canada you can find several geographers involved in the fascinating work of examining housing and traffic, and in drawing up plans for the great highways, buildings, and cities of the future. In this work the geographer provides an essential link between the engineer and the architect on the one hand, and the social worker on the other.

The analyzing of the present in order to provide a key to the future is one of the tasks for which the geographer is eminently qualified; for planning in a diversity of fields is a task which he is often called upon to undertake. Some geographers are employed by large companies such as Shell Oil and Imperial Oil to provide expert advice in the economic problems associated with transport, raw materials, labour, and markets. A highly specialized geographer may become the marketing adviser to a large firm, and, in fact, at least one major Canadian chain store has a professional geographer in just such a post. Before building a large new store or supermarket, a large firm will want to know the best location as determined by the distribution of population, the amount these people are likely to spend, the existing or projected transport facilities, the possible costs, and the prospective profits involved in alternative sites. To answer these questions the market geographer must first amass, and then assess, an enormous body of information; but the value of this information to a large company can easily run into hundreds of thousands of dollars. Several legal firms in Canada also save money by employing geographers in disputes involving land other than those concerned with mere boundary lines.

One of the great advantages in taking a geography course in a high school and later in a university, lies in the diversity of the fields into which such training can lead. Many people who are now town planners, economic consultants, market research analysts, cartographers, diplomats, or government political advisers entered the career in which they found happiness only as the result of a geography course which was wide enough to touch on all of these varied fields. Finally, the main aim of this year's geography course has been to give you a sympathetic understanding of other peoples and their problems, for in the world in which we live there is nothing of greater importance than international understanding.

BIBLIOGRAPHY

ANDERSON, M. S., *The Geography of Living Things*, English Universities Press.

BARANSKY, N., *Economic Geography of the U.S.S.R.*, Foreign Languages Publishing House, Moscow.

BARNETT, L. *Canopy of Air*, Time Inc., 1953.

BIGELOW AND EDMONSON, *Wind Waves at Sea*, Superintendent of Documents, Washington, D.C., 1947.

BIRCH, T. W., *Maps, Topographical & Statistical*, Oxford University Press.

BLAIR, T. A., *Climatology*, Prentice-Hall, 1942.

BLAIR, T. A., *Pilot's Weather Handbook*, Superintendent of Documents, Washington, D.C.

BLAIR, T. A., *Weather Elements*, Prentice-Hall, 1957.

BLAIR, T. A., *Weather Glossary*, Superintendent of Documents, Washington, D.C.

BYGOTT, J., *An Introduction to Mapwork and Practical Geography*, The Copp Clark Publishing Co.

CARSON, R. L., *The Sea Around Us*, Oxford University Press, 1951.

CHAPMAN, L. J. AND PUTNAM, D. F., *Physiography of Southern Ontario*, University of Toronto Press.

COUSTEAU, J. Y., *The Silent World*, Harper and Brothers, 1953.

DICKEN, S. N., *Economic Geography*, The Copp Clark Publishing Company.

DUMONT, R., *Types of Rural Economy*, Methuen & Company, Ltd.

EAST, W. G., *The Geography Behind History*, Thos. Nelson & Sons, Ltd.

FENTON, C. L., *Prehistoric Worlds: Animal Life In Past Ages*, John Day Company, Inc., 1954.

FOLSOM, FRANKLIN, *Exploring American Caves*, Crown Publishers, 1956.

FORDE, C. D., *Habitat, Society and Economy*, E. P. Dutton and Company.

GOUROU, P., *The Tropical World*, Longmans Green.

HADLOW, L., *Climate, Vegetation and Man*, Philosophical Library, 1953.

HAVILAND, M. D., *Forest, Steppe and Tundra*, Cambridge University Press.

HARE, F. K., *The Restless Atmosphere*, Hutchinson University Library.

HOLMES, ARTHUR, *Principles of Physical Geology*, Thos. Nelson and Sons, Ltd.

HOOD, P., *The Atmosphere*, Oxford University Press.

HOOD, P., *How The Earth Is Made*, Oxford University Press.

JAMES, P. E., *The Geography of Man*, Ginn and Company.

KELLOGG, C. E., *The Soils That Support Us*, Macmillan Co.

KENDREW, W. G., *The Climates of the Continents*, The Clarendon Press.

LANE, F. C., *Story of Mountains*, Doubleday & Company, Inc., 1950.

LANE, F. C., *The World's Greatest Lakes*, Doubleday & Company, Inc., 1948.

LEY, W., *Rockets, Missiles and Space Travel*, The Viking Press, Inc., 1957.

MARSHALL, R. K., *Sun, Moon and Planets*, Holt, Rinehart and Winston, Inc., 1952.

MOORE, E. S., *Elementary Geology for Canada*, J. M. Dent and Sons, Ltd.

MOORE, R. C., *Man, Time and Fossils*, Alfred A. Knopf, Inc., 1953.

MOORE, W. G., *Ice-Cap and Tundra*, House of Grant.

MOORE, W. G., *The Northern Forests*, House of Grant.

MOORE, W. G., *Rivers and Their Work*, House of Grant.

MOORE, W. G., *The Sea and the Coast*, House of Grant.

PEARL, R. M., *How to Know the Rocks and Minerals*, McGraw-Hill Book Co. Inc., 1955.

PEARL, R. M., *Rocks and Minerals*, Barnes and Noble, Inc., 1956.

PEEL, R. F., *Physical Geography*, English Universities Press.

PICKLES, T., *Physical Geography*, J. M. Dent and Sons, Ltd.

PICKWELL, G. B., *Deserts*, McGraw-Hill Book Co. Inc., 1939.

POUGH, F. G., *Field Guide to Rocks and Minerals*, Houghton Mifflin Co., 1953.

POUGH, F. G., *All About Volcanoes and Earthquakes*, Random House, Inc., 1953.

RAPPORT, S. B., & WRIGHT, H., *The Crust of the Earth*, New American Library of World Literature, 1955.

RAMSEY, WILLIAM L., AND BURCKLEY, RAYMOND E., *Modern Earth Science*, Holt, Rinehart and Winston, Inc.

ROBINSON, HARRY, *The Mediterranean Lands*, The Copp Clark Publishing Company.

SCHNEIDER, HERMAN, AND NINA, *Rocks, Rivers and the Changing Earth*, Scott, Foresman & Co., 1951.

SHIMER, J. A., *This Sculptured Earth: The Landscape of America*, Columbia University Press, 1959.

SKILLING, W. T., AND RICHARDSON, ROBERT S., *A Brief Text in Astronomy*, Holt, Rinehart and Winston, Inc., 1959.

SMAILES, A. E., *The Geography of Towns*, Hutchinson University Library.

STRAHLER, A. N., *Physical Geography*, J. Wiley and Sons Ltd.

TAYLOR, G., *Environment, Race and Migration*, University of Toronto Press.

TOIT, A. L. DU, *Our Wandering Continents*, Oliver and Boyd Ltd.

The "Life" Nature Library—the volumes entitled
    The Desert
    The Forest
    The Mountains
    The Poles
    The Sea
  are of particular value in this course.

INDEX OF PROPER NAMES

KEY TO PRONUNCIATION

a *cat*	o *top*	ng si*ng*	(3) ksh or sh, an is a*nx*ious
ā *ape*	ō *no*	sh *she*	(4) zh, as in lu*x*urious
ä *jar, car*	ô *dog, all, or*	ch *chin*	(5) z, as in *x*ylophone
à *ask, mast*	u *up*	th *thin*	(initial *x*)
â *care*	ū *mute*	th *this*	ö Fr. *feu*, Ger. sch*ö*n
e *ten*	û *cur, her*	hw *why*	ô Fr. *coq*, Ger. d*o*ch
ē *eve*	ōō *fool*	zh *azure*	ü Fr. *lüne*, Ger. f*ür*
ė *writer*	oo *book, full*	qu kw, as in *qu*it	kh Sc. lo*ch*, Ger. a*ch*
i *if, pity, begin, rely*	oi *oil*	x (1) ks, as in a*x*	ṅ Fr. e*n*fant, no*n*
ī *bite*	ou *out*	(2) gz, as in e*x*it	y' Fr. Versa*ille*s (vàr'say'')

(In pronunciation a dot is used to separate syllables. The secondary accents are marked thus (').)

A

Acadia Coal Co., 359
Adenauer [ad'in·our'], 404
Adirondacks [ad'i·ron'daks], 128, 148
Africa, 8, 80, 85, 101, 102, 152, 166, 211, 212, 226, 229, 243, 261, 308, 313, 315, 325, 362, 364, 375, 378, 380, 382, 392, 403, 406, 410, 411, 412, 417
African Plateau, 340, 395
Agadir [ä'ga·dir'; ag'], 169
Agassiz [ag'a·si], L., 79, 82, 153
Agnes, L., 176
Agricultural Bank of Greece, 258
Aguathana [ä'gwä·tha'na], 358
Alabama, 206
Alaska, 98, 127, 128, 159, 279, 292, 296, 330
Alaska Hwy., 365
Alexander the Great, 364
Alexandria, 2
Algeria, 412
Alpine Mts., 133, 177, 340, 354, 368
Alpine race, 399
Alsace, 372, 400
Amayran Indian, 364
Amazon Basin, 309, 337, 340
Amazonia, 383
Amberley, N.Z., 284
America, 256, 374
American Indians, 407
Amsterdam, 379
Andean [an·dē'an; an'di·an] Plateau, 340
Andes, 363
Antarctica [ant·ärk'ti·ka], 89, 172, 177, 183, 296, 297, 298, 299
Anticosti, 69
Antwerp, 369
Apennines, 368
Appalachian [ap'a·lā'chi·an; lach']: Coalfield, 350, 367; Mountain Chain, 132, 147, 197, 327; Piedmont, 187, Plateau, 150, 350

Arabia, 313
Arabian Desert, 242
Arabian Sea, 337
Aral [ar'al] Sea, 316
Arctic [ärk'tik], 89, 133, 183, 279, 292, 296, 298, 301, 322, 363; Archipelago, 296; Bay, 295; Sea, 92, 95
Argentina, 266, 327, 330, 352, 374
Argentine pampas, 153
Arkell, 23
Artois [àr'twà'), 83
Asia, 90, 101, 122, 133, 169, 192, 199, 206, 211, 225, 229, 262, 267, 287, 300, 306, 311, 313, 315, 325, 326, 332, 351, 363, 375, 376, 378, 410, 411
Assiniboine Mt., 145
Associated Overseas Territories, 406
Association of American Geographers, 419
Aswan [às·won'] Dam, 211
Atacama]ä'tä·kä'mä] Desert, 212, 242, 306, 346
Athabaska, 342
Athapaskin [ath'a·pas'kin) Indians, 294
Athens, 253, 259
Atlantic: Ocean, 93, 94, 95, 101, 131, 183, 208, 262, 320, 355, 368, 371, 374, 407; floor of, 93; Plain, 263
Atlantis, 93
Australasia, 375
Australia, 83, 95, 152, 169, 226, 231, 238, 240, 242, 245, 251, 261, 262, 316, 319, 352, 364, 369, 378, 397
Australoid race, 399
Austria, 212, 225
Avdat experimental farm, 410
Azores [a·zōrz'; ã'zorz), 101
Azov, Sea of, 357

B

Badlands (S. Dakota), 211
Baffin Island, 302
Bahama [ba·hä'ma; hā'] Islands, 101
Baikal [bī·kàl'], L., 80
Balkans, 368
Baltic Sea, 91, 337, 356
Baltimore, 355
Banff, 174
Basle [bäl; same place as Basel, bä'zl], 372
Bear Butte, 157
Bedeque Bay, 40
Bedouins [bed'ōō·inz], 314, 383
Beira [bā'ē·ra], 395
Belgium, 353, 404
Belleville, 181
Bell Island (Nfld.), 345, 358
Benares [bi·nä'riz], 390
Bengazi [ben·gä'zi], 237
Benguela [ben·gel'a; beng·] Current, 101
Benguela Railway, 395
Berber, 315
Berg Lake, 20
Bering Sea, 300
Bering Strait, 90
Berlin, 184, 369, 417
Bindibu [bin'di·bōō'], 245-249
Bingham, 161
Birmingham, 345
Bjerknes [byerk'nes], 71
Blackhead Persian Sheep, 235
Black Hills, 148
Black Sea, 357, 372
Blue Creek, 20
Blue Ridge Pkway., 147
Bogota [bō'go·tä'], 408
Bolivia, 407
Bombay, 376
Bonn, 8
Bonneville Lake, 153
Borneo, 383
Boston, 368
Bowen Island, 44
Brahman [brä'mun] cattle, 264

L

Labrador, 66, 182, 296, 345, 371, 393
Labrador Current, 101
LaFlèche Cave, 200
Lapps, 300, 322
Latin America, 386, 407, 408
Latin American bloc, 407
Laurentian-Algoman region, 128
Leamington, 319
Le Havre [lu ä'vr'; hä'vr'), 369
Leningrad, 356
Levadhia [lå·vä'thyä], 259
Lever Lake, 41
Lhasa [lä'su; las'u], 390
Libya, 237
Liege [li·äzh; lyezh], 353
Lille [lēl], 353
Little Harbor Lake, 44
Liverpool, 375
Lobito [loō·vē'toō], 395
London, 20, 48, 369, 375, 382, 390
Lorraine, 342, 352, 399
Los Angeles [los an'ju·lus; ang'gu·lus; lēz], 84, 299, 317
Low Countries, 385
Lusk Cave, 200
Luxembourg, 404, 406
Lyons, 354

M

MacKay Lake, 248
Magellan Strait, 375
Magdalen [mag'da·len] Island, 213
Makinder, 415
Malaya, 193, 309, 323, 343
Malayan Peninsula, 325
Mammoth Cave, 195
Manchester, 353
Manhattan Island, 389
Manitoba, 153, 167, 269
Manitoba, Lake, 153, 270
Mannheim, 372
Marianas [mä'rē·a'näs] trench, 89, 145
Marie Byrd Land, 89
Maritime Provinces, 167
Marmora, 161, 343
Marseilles [mär·sālz; mår'se'y'], 354
Maryland, 345
Masai [mä·sī'], 314
Massachusetts Institute of Technology, 184
Mazinaw Lake fault, 165
McMaster University, 394
McMurdo Sound, 299
Mecca, 390
Mediterranean race, 399
Mediterranean region, 122, 123, 250-259, 267, 277, 279, 306, 316, 332, 354
Mediterranean Sea, 253, 317, 337, 363, 375, 376
Mekong [mä'kong'] River, 193

Melbourne, 369, 397
Merino sheep, 235
Merriton, 32
Mesabi [mu·sä'bi], 343
Mexico, 150, 161, 195, 206, 231, 242, 316, 407
Mexico, Gulf of, 75, 101, 167, 319, 374
Michigan, Lake, 194, 208, 355
Mid-Atlantic Ridge, 95
Middle East, 348, 363, 364
Milan [mi·lan'], 369
Mile Creek, 32
Milwaukee, 355
Mines and Technical Surveys, Dept. of, 5, 13, 14, 48
Minnesota, 153, 273, 343
Mississippi, 206
Mississippi R., 80, 85, 189, 371
Missouri, 211
Moho project, 87, 89, 140
Mohs [mōz], Fredrick, 112
Monashee Range, 146
Moncton, 358
Mongol, 383
Mongolia, 266, 313
Mongoloid [mong'gu·loid'], 399
Monnet [mon'ä'], Jean, 404
Monroe Doctrine, 408
Monteregian Hills, 150
Montreal, 355, 358, 360, 368, 371, 389, 390, 391, 396
Moose Jaw, 35-37, 40, 41, 416
Moose Jaw Creek, 36, 37, 40
Morocco, 169
Moscow [mos'kou; ·kō], 356, 357, 365
Mural Glacier, 20
Murray River, 316
Murrumbidgee [mûr'um·bij'i] R:, 316
Mozambique [mōz'um·bēk'], 235

N

Nairobi [nī·rō'bi], 231
Namur [nä·moōr'; na'mür'], 353
Nancy [nan'si; nän'sē'], 353
Naples, 159
National Research Council, 396
Negrito [ni·grē'tō], 323, 399
Negro, 323, 399
Netherlands, 85, 279, 404
Neva River, 356
Nevada, 80, 265
New Brunswick, 151
Newcastle, 353
New England, 129, 352, 355, 398
Newfoundland, 66, 94, 128, 130, 358, 374
New Mexico, 167, 195
New Orleans, 371, 375
New Waterford, 358
New York, 55, 82, 148, 266, 286, 355, 368, 375, 389, 390, 391, 409, 413
New York Barge Canal System, 371

New York Central R.R., 355
New Zealand, 82, 124, 266, 277, 279, 280, 281, 282, 321, 330, 332, 352
Niagara Escarpment, 130, 199, 393
Niagara Falls, 339, 352, 355, 398
Niagara Gorge, 32, 339
Niagara Peninsula, 319, 352
Niagara region, 355
Niagara River, 339, 360
Nigeria, 309, 382, 411, 412
Nigerian, 229
Nile River, 166, 193, 364
Nile Valley, 315
Nome, 164
North Africa, 84, 167, 313, 378
North America, 2, 8, 69, 74, 79, 84, 90, 99, 128, 129, 132, 133, 193, 231, 244, 262, 277, 279, 287, 292, 318, 321, 326, 332, 340, 348, 352, 363, 364, 365, 368, 371, 373, 375, 376, 378, 384, 387, 389, 399, 407, 418
North Atlantic, 374, 375
North Atlantic Drift, 101, 278
North Atlantic Fishing Banks, 332
Norman, 383
North Dakota, 153, 273
Northern Hemisphere, 55, 56, 57, 100, 261, 296, 306, 374
North Pole, 12, 55, 89
North Sea, 278, 372
Norway, 71, 102, 365, 376
Nova Scotia, 163, 167, 201, 212, 337, 358
Nova Scotia Iron and Steel Co., 359
Nyasa [nī·as'u; nyä'sä] Lake, 80
Nyasaland, 235

O

Oakville, 355
Ob River, 85
Ocean Falls, 329
Ohio R., 368
Oimekon [oi'myu·kun], 292
Okefenokee [ō'ku·fi·nō'ki] Swamp, 327
Old Sydney Collieries, 359
Ontario, 21, 25, 41, 75, 85, 161, 166, 167, 181, 199, 212, 291, 294, 322, 340, 343, 345, 351, 367, 384, 396, 397
Ontario, Lake, 80, 393
Oregon, 80, 98, 279
Organization of American States, 408
Orient, 123
Oriental Communism, 391
Oshawa, 355
Ottawa, 14, 182, 200, 304, 351, 355, 368, 371, 388, 396, 397
Ottawa R., 166, 360, 391
Owen Sound, 199
Oxford, 390

425

GENERAL INDEX AND GLOSSARY

fissures, 157, 159, 165
flame test, for minerals, 114
flax, 319, 353, 356, 357
flint, 108
flip ship, 102
floes, ice, 302, 333
flood level, 23
flood plain, 85, 187, 311, 317, 318
floods and flood control, 85, 86, 189, 192, 254, 311
flood, spring, 85
flows, lava, 151
fluorescence, of minerals, 114
fluted surfaces, 209
fodder, 316, 320, 322
fog, 101, 278, 373; advection, 66; conditions producing, 66; ground, 66; radiation, 66
fold: axis of the, 164; pitching, 164
folding, 109, 125, 146, 147, 152, 163, 164, 165, 167, 168
fold mountains, 146-148, 164
foot wall, 166
force of gravity, 138
forests, 323-331; equatorial, 323-324; monsoon, 325-326; of China climate, 326-327; rainforest, 325-326; taiga, 330-331; temperate hardwoods, 327-328; tropical, 326; west-coast marine, 328,330
fossils, 107, 110, 125-127, 129, 130, 133, 167; in plains, 153; in rocks, 107; marine, 163
fraction scale, 13
freshwater lakes, 153
frontal action, 293
frontiers, 399; disputed, 400
fronts: cold, 72, 73; formation of, 72; ice, 173; occluded, 72; on weather maps, 71; stationary, 73; warm, 72, 73
frost, 297, 317, 322
frost-free period, 286
fruits, 309, 312, 313, 316, 319, 320, 322, 326, 374, 375; citrus, 252, 315-318
fuel, 350, 352
fumaroles, 159, 161
fungus, 297
fur-bearing animals, 330
fur industry, 330

G

gabbro, 106
gale, 61
galeria forests, 231
gallery, 197
gamma rays, 48
gangue (waste mineral products of little commercial value), 111, 161
garnet, 168
gases, atmospheric, 50
gases, in soil, 118
Geiger counter, 114
gem minerals, 111
geode, 111, 199

geological background, 125-135
geological time sequence, 128-135
geyser, 160
ghost towns, 395
gill nets, 333
glacial: deposition, 21, 85, 106, 174, 179-181; drift, 117; erosion, 172, 174; lakes, 79; landscape, 148; periods, 182, 183; streams, 181
glaciation: 15, 80, 128, 172-184; alpine, 173, 174; causes of, 182; cirque, 176, 177; continental, 177, 178; deposition, 179-182; mountain, 20; valley, 174, 175
glaciers, 21, 25, 28, 172, 174, 175, 339; alpine, 172-174, 175, 177; cirque, 18, 173, 175, 176, 177; continental, 133, 172, 177, 178; deposits of, 21, 106, 154; erosion by, 172, 174; formation of, 172-173; melting of, 183; movement of, 172-173, 175; tributary, 18, 174; valley, 18, 173, 174, 175
global outlook, 415
globe, 2, 4
gneiss, 109
gnomonic projection, 4
goats, 253, 311, 313, 314, 315, 317, 321
gold, 92, 111, 113, 114, 157, 161, 193, 341, 343, 344, 357, 395
Goode's projection, 8
graben (a trough formed by the sinking of land between roughly parallel fault scarps), 80, 82, 166
gradient, 16, 23, 81, 186, 339
gradient (and isobars), 70
grain, 315, 316, 322, 370, 371, 374; drying of, 274; storage, 274
granite, 106, 109, 111, 119, 167
grapes, 315, 316, 317
graphite, 115, 168, 347
gravel, 24, 95, 107, 108, 193, 343, 347
gravitational force (of earth), 49
gravity, earth's, 50
great circle routes, 374, 377
great circles, 3, 6
green belt, 388
grid, 2
ground fog, 66
ground water, 81, 82, 83, 86, 118
gulf stream, 101
gully, 150
gully erosion, 123
gullying, 186, 192, 193
gum, 326, 327
gusher, 348
guyots (large, flat-topped submarine mountains), 94
gypsum, 114, 131, 167, 347

H

hachure, 15, 16, 213
hachuring, 15, 16
haciendas, 386
hail, 68

hamada, 210
hand lines, 333
hanging valley, 175
hanging wall, 166
harbours, 167, 205, 358, 391
hardness, of minerals, 112
hardpan, 120, 121, 239
hardwoods, 120, 324, 325, 327, 328
harvest, 272
head of navigation, 389
headward erosion, 186
heat energy, 52
heat waves, 53
helium, 46, 162
hematite, 115, 344
hemp, 310, 318
herding, 313, 314, 317, 319
high altitude winds, 56
highland, 305
high-pressure belts, 55, 70, 242, 251, 252
hillock dunes, 210
hill shading, 15, 16
hinterland, 391, 392
hogback ridges, 148, 156, 164
home industry, 349
homes, 382, 383
hook, 202
horizon, 118, 119, 121
horizontal equivalent, 15, 17
horizontal scale, 17
horn, 177
hornblende, 105, 106
horse, 314, 318, 363
horst, 166, 167
hot springs, 82, 160
humidity: in atmosphere, 48, 62, 63; measurement of, 62 (c.f. precipitation)
humus, 117, 118, 119, 120, 121, 122, 123, 222, 252, 309
hurricanes, 59, 60, 61, 86, 262
hydraulicking, 342
hydroelectric dams, 340
hydroelectricity, 338-340, 352, 354-356, 395
hydrogen, 46
hydrologic cycle (the endless process by which water is evaporated from the sea, precipitated over the land and eventually returned to the sea), 78, 79, 85, 185
hydrosphere (the earth's water surface), 91, 104
hydrothermal deposits, 161
hydroxide, 120
hygrometer, 77

I

ice, 95, 127, 172, 174, 339, 382
Ice Age, 133, 153, 182
icebergs, 373
icecap, 177, 183, 216, 298, 305, 306
icefields, 18, 173, 174
ice floes, 302, 333
ice front, 173

431

retsina, 257
rhinoceros, 227
rhumb line, 6, 7
ria coast (c.f. estuarine coast)
ribbon falls, 175
ribbon settlement, 25
rice, 311, 315, 318; planting, 227
ridges, 146, 147
rift valley, 166
rip currents (swift currents running away from the shore through lines of breakers), 98
rivers, 21, 25, 85, 333, 365, 370; basin, 86; canalized, 25; erosion, 174, 192, 193; flood plain, 318; flow, 86; mature, 187; old age, 189
river terraces, 190
river valley, 315
river valley, drowned, 167
road maps, 12, 13, 15
road systems, 365, 366; classification, 365; factors determining routes, 365
roche moutonnée, 178
rockering, 343
rock crystals, 106
rocks, 104-110, 111, 117, 125, 129, 156, 165, 166; acidic, 105, 106; carbonate, 110; classification, 105, 110, 126; definition, 104; density, 141; extrusive rock, 105, 106, 156; folding, 147; formation of, 107; identification, 110; igneous, 81, 105, 106, 109, 111, 147, 152, 155, 157, 161, 164; impermeable, 81, 83; intrusive, 105, 106, 125, 156, 157; metamorphic, 81, 105, 109, 110, 111, 152, 168; metamorphism, 167; of ocean floor, 91; pedestal, 209; permeable, 81, 83, 197, 198; reservoir, 348; sedimentary, 25, 81, 105-109, 110, 111, 125, 146, 147, 148, 152, 153, 156, 157, 164, 167, 348; strata, 107, 163, 164, 168; stratified, 107, 164; texture, 110; weathering of, 47; weight, 141; volcanic, 160
rock sheep, 178
rosewood, 325
rotation of crops, 192, 270, 283, 311, 318
rotation, of the earth, 10, 55
rubber, 221, 310, 326
rubies, 111
run-off, 316, 339
rural depopulation, 387
rural settlement, 37, 384
rust, 271
ruwares, 233

S

saeter, 383
sage, 238
salinity, 91

salmon, 333-335; cycle, 334; method of catching, 334; types of, 334
salt, 91, 92, 118, 131, 148, 167, 211, 212, 316, 344, 346, 357
saltation, 186
salt core, 148
salt domes, 148
salt pan, 120
saltwater seas, 153
sand, 24, 95, 107, 108, 117, 193, 343, 347
sandbanks, 373
sandbar, 202, 206, 213
sand-blast action, 208
sand hills, 208
sandpits, 41
sandstone, 107, 108, 109, 167, 249
sandstorms, 211, 244
Sanson-Flamsteed projection, 8
satellite countries, 401
satellites, artificial, 49
satellite towns, 388
satellite, underwater, 88
saturation point, 62
saturation zone, 82
Saturn, rings of, 139
savanna regions, 120, 217, 228-236, 251, 252, 305, 312, 313
sawmills, 327, 329
scale, fraction, 13
scale, linear, 13
scale, of map, 12, 13
scoria (rough masses of volcanic rock with a honeycomb-like structure), 106, 158
scrolls, 188
sea, 106, 129; heating of, 92; temperature of, 92
sea breeze, 59
sea caves, 201
sea cliffs, 201
seal, 302, 333
sea level, 201
sectile minerals, 114
sedimentary rock, 25, 81, 105-109, 110, 111, 125, 146, 147, 148, 152, 153, 156, 157, 164, 167, 348; chemical, 107; conglomerate, 108; diastrophism, 167; folding, 164; formation of, 107; fragmental, 107; organic, 107, 109; types of, 107, 108
seed, 271, 283
seismic sea wave, 98
seismographic recordings, 140
selenium, 193
selva, 221, 223, 226, 229, 230, 306, 308
semi-deciduous vegetation, 226, 229
semidesert, 120, 322
send, 202
sensible temperature, 262
setting, 14
settlement, 29, 382-386; coastal, 369; dispersed, 21, 384, 385; homes and villages, 382-383; nucleated, 385, 386; pattern, 21, 83, 385; plantation, 386; railway, 33; ribbon, 25; rural, 37,

384, 386; spring-line, 81, 84; tourist centre, 41; urban, 387-399
shadow zone (a region of the earth's surface where a particular earthquake wave cannot easily be detected), 140
shaft mining, 344
shale, 107, 108, 109, 167
sheep, 235, 252, 282, 285, 313, 314, 315, 317, 318, 319, 321, 322
sheep farm, 281-285
sheet erosion, 123
sheetwash, 186, 192
shelter belts, 124
shield areas, 152
shipbuilding, 353, 355, 356, 358
shipping industry, 357, 376, 377, 391
shock waves, 140
shorelines (c.f. coast and coastline); economic aspects, 205-206
sial layer, 140
siderite, 344
siefs, 208
silica, 105, 158, 168, 193
silicious minerals, 111, 115
silicon, 111
silicon dioxide, 127
silk industry, 354, 357
sill, 157
silt, 117, 311
Silurian period, 129, 130
silver, 111, 129, 157, 161, 341, 345, 346
silver iodide crystals, 67
sima layer, 140, 141
sinkholes, 197, 198
sisal, 313
site, 339, 358, 389
situation, 389
slate, 109, 168
sleet, 68
slope, 16, 119, 164; concave, convex, even, 16, 17; of equilibrium, 202
slough (c.f. kettle)
slough, tropical, 239
sluicing, 343
smog, 48, 49
smoke, 48, 64
snow, 68, 173
snowfield, 145
snowline, 173
soapstone, 115
sodium carbonate, 162
sodium chloride, 92
sodium nitrate, 346
soil, 117-124, 160, 308, 310, 316; azonal, 119; brown-forest, 122, 280, 289; brown laterite, 120; brown podzol, 289; brown steppe, 239; chernozem, 121, 122, 267, 321; chestnut laterite, 120; classification, 119-122; components, 117-118; erosion, 120, 122-124, 192, 252, 338; formation, 118, 119; intrazonal, 119; lateritic, 119, 120, 226, 308; leaching, 118-122, 318, 346; loess, 119, 121, 155, 193, 207,

435

436

world organizations, 413-415; U.N.E.S.C.O., 414, 415; U.N.O., 413; W.H.O., 414

world population and food supply, 409-411

world's natural wealth, 308-335; agriculture, 308-322; fisheries, 332-335; forest wealth, 323-331

Y

yaks, 318, 363
yam, 309, 323
yazoo stream, 189
yellow soils, 122, 252
yerba maté, 327
yurts, 314, 383

Z

zenithal gnomonic projection, 4
zinc, 345, 354
zonal soils, 119
zone of fracture, 166
zones of balance, 121